THE GRAMMAR OF SCIENCE

by KARL PEARSON

"La critique est la vie de la science."
COUSIN

GLOUCESTER, MASS.

PETER SMITH

1969

KARL PEARSON

Born in London in 1857, Karl Pearson was Scholar and Fellow of King's College, Cambridge; Professor of Applied Mathematics and Mechanics in 1884 and first Galton Professor of National Eugenics in 1911, both appointments being in the University of London and at University College. The first edition of The Grammar of Science *was published in 1892; revised in 1900; and published in a final edition in 1911. Karl Pearson died in 1936.*

Meridian Library edition first published September 1957

Introduction copyright 1957 by Meridian Books, Inc.

Library of Congress Catalog Card Number: 57-10844
Manufactured in the United States of America
Reprinted, 1969 by Permission of
The World Publishing Company

INTRODUCTION

It is a common-place that the practical fruits of modern natural science have transformed the face of the earth and the lives of men. Nor is it less well-recognized that these fruits are frequently the products of difficult theoretical conceptions and of a disciplined method of inquiry. It is therefore not surprising that although everyone to-day is exposed to the impact of applied science, familiarity with the theoretical and logical foundations of scientific advance is not widespread.

It may nevertheless seem like a paradox that even distinguished men of science often possess no clear ideas concerning the theoretical notions they employ or the logic of inquiry they practice. The paradox is mitigated, however, if one recalls that this fact has parallels in other areas of human activity. A great painter or a great athlete is not always the best expounder of his art, because he may never have felt the need to reflect deeply on what is involved in his achievements or to formulate clearly the principles of his procedure.

There are, indeed, two circumstances which help explain why it is that high competence in special areas of science may go hand in hand with considerable naivete about the character of the scientific enterprise. Men are usually trained for a career of research by acquiring through repeated practice habits of workmanship conforming to implicit standards of excellence, rather than by learning some codified system of rules for the conduct of inquiry. In consequence, a man can be an extraordinarily gifted investigator of nature without being able to articulate the logic he employs; and should he be pressed to describe for some ceremonial occasion the principles of his method, he will most likely reproduce the half-forgotten philosophical credos he may have acquired during his years of intellectual immaturity. As Einstein once advised his readers, if one wishes to learn what are the methods theoretical physicists use, "don't listen to their words, fix your attention on their deeds." It is usually only when their habitual methods are found to be unequal to new problems, that scientists feel impelled to reflect seriously on questions of scientific procedure and to formulate with care the principles of scientific method.

A further point needs to be noted. The language of theoretical physics is notoriously abstract. It can be manipulated with great rigor on a purely technical level; but what is actually asserted by it often seems obscure and remote from the things encountered in every-day experience. Nevertheless, much of the language of physical theory is borrowed from every-day speech. It is therefore natural to suppose that the meanings such terms possess in familiar contexts of daily experience can be appropriately associated with them, even after the terms acquire new technical uses. For example, words like "cause", "force", "energy" and "mass" have been employed for centuries in contexts of human behavior; and though these words have become counters in physical theories, for many scientists the words retain their original anthropomorphic connotations. But while the dubious philosophic interpretations that scientists frequently give to their theories may mislead the layman, such interpretations play no significant role in the normal course of scientific research. Nevertheless, at critical junctures in the history of science, when apparently well-established theories cease to be effective guides in new areas of research, such misleading interpretations can be serious hindrances to further intellectual advance.

In point of fact, despite the general disinterest of most practicing scientists in the methodological foundations of their subject, periods of great scientific progress are also periods of intensive self-criticism. Our own age is such a period, and the 19th century was another. Karl Pearson's *The Grammar of Science* is an influential example of the kind of intellectual house-cleaning that was undertaken by distinguished scientific thinkers in most civilized countries during the latter part of that century. Pearson's book sought to make explicit, for scientific specialists as well as for laymen, the precise meanings of a large number of basic theoretical concepts, to articulate the logic of scientific procedure, and to provide a perspective for viewing modern science in relation to other vital human enterprises. Much of the book was inspired by a vigorous hostility to various forms of philosophical idealism then widely current in England; for

INTRODUCTION

like many others of his generation, Pearson was convinced
that those philosophical ideas were the main obstacle to the
extension of the methods of natural science to important
areas of human concern. Pearson undoubtedly contributed to
changing the prevailing climate of opinion concerning the
nature of science; and the conception of science for which he
argued continues to be professed by many Anglo-American
scientific minds. Some of his discussions have been rendered
obsolete by the progress of science itself. His book has nevertheless not lost its value, not only as a historical document,
but also as an analysis of theoretical notions that are still of
central importance in contemporary thought.

Karl Pearson was born in London, in 1857, the son of an
English barrister. He was a man with varied intellectual
interests and with broadly liberal social sympathies. As an
undergraduate at Cambridge University he showed considerable aptitude for history, anthropology, sociology and
philosophy, as well as for the mathematical sciences; and he
continued to cultivate these disciplines—and eventually to
lecture and write about them—during the years he spent as
a student on the continent of Europe. He was appointed in
1884 to the chair of applied mathematics at University
College, London. In his lectures on mechanics he sought to
present the fundamentals of the subject "freed from the
metaphysics and confused thinking" that in his judgment
characterized the usual expositions of the science. He believed,
moreover, that it is of highest social importance to make the
essentials of scientific method widely known, and he therefore
lectured extensively to popular audiences on the basic concepts of the sciences. *The Grammar of Science*, first published
in 1892, developed systematically the general ideas on science
he tried to communicate to his university classes and the
general public. But Pearson's place in the history of science
is based on his fundamental contributions to theoretical
statistics. His attention was attracted to biological evolution
and biological variation as fields for the application of quantitative methods. With his colleague W.F.R. Weldon, professor zoology at the University of London, he established a

biometric laboratory for the collection and study of numerical data in biology; and he developed basic mathematical tools for analyzing such materials. He eventually founded the periodical *Biometrika*, which he edited personally until his death in 1936.

Pearson ascribed to science the role of the great liberator of mankind. He argued vigorously that the scope of scientific method is not limited to the natural sciences. He also cherished the hope that when the temper of mind essential for the success of science would be widespread, men "are less likely to be led by mere appeal to the passions or by blind emotional excitement to sanction acts which in the end may lead to social disaster." In these convictions he echoed earlier voices, and anticipated later ones. Pearson was, moreover, a thorough-going empiricist in his views on the foundations of knowledge, and sought to show that knowledge of the world is not attainable by purely abstract reasoning. His opposition to the philosophies regnant in his day was indeed directed against their implicit assumption that there are *a priori* truths about the structures of things. Pearson also subscribed to an essentially instrumentalist conception of the function of scientific theory; and he maintained that theories are simply convenient tools for predicting the course of events, and ultimately for achieving success in man's struggle for existence. On the other hand, Pearson's empiricism was controlled by the psychological assumptions he took over uncritically from the major tradition of British philosophy. He thus accepted the view that the ultimate data of knowledge are individual sense impressions, occurring atomistically at the nerve endings of the brain. He was therefore compelled to maintain that science can deal only with the contents of the mind, so that "beyond the sense impressions, beyond the brain terminals of the sensory nerves we cannot go." Similarly, he argued that a scientific law is nothing but an economical description of the sequences of sense-perceptions; and he construed atoms and molecules, not as physical things existing independently of the mind, but as "intellectual conceptions by aid of which physicists classify phenomena and

INTRODUCTION

formulate the relationships between their sequences." Pearson's philosophical preconceptions are certainly debatable, if not entirely discredited. Fortunately, they do not seriously affect his discussion of many special topics, and *The Grammar of Science* continues to be an instructive and challenging essay.

Ernest Nagel

Columbia University

Note: The first edition of *The Grammar of Science* contained ten chapters. A second edition appeared in 1900, and included two additional chapters on evolution. The third edition, of which the present book is a re-issue, was published in 1911, and contained only the first eight chapters of the previous editions. This edition deals exclusively with questions in the physical sciences. Pearson planned to publish a second part which would bring the materials on the life sciences up to date; but for unknown reasons he never carried out this plan.

PREFACE TO THE THIRD EDITION

THIS work has been out of print for some time, and I have long meditated as to whether it was or was not desirable to reissue it. And, if it were desirable, the problem of how it could possibly be done in a manner likely to satisfy the modern reader has raised much doubt in my mind. Reading the book again after many years, it was surprising to find how the heterodoxy of the 'eighties had become the commonplace and accepted doctrine of to-day. Nobody believes now that science *explains* anything; we all look upon it as a shorthand description, as an economy of thought. Yet in 1885, when in issuing Clifford's *Common Sense of the Exact Sciences*, I defined mass as a ratio of accelerations, and said that the current definitions of matter and force were unintelligible, it called forth the most strong protest from more than one distinguished physicist. And, again, the *Grammar of Science* which first saw the light in 1892 belonged to an age when the leader of British mathematical physicists was confidently asserting that there was nothing he was more sure of than the objective reality of the ether. It seems almost unnecessary now to republish a book, the lesson of which is that objective force and matter have nothing whatever to do with science, and that atom and ether are merely intellectual concepts solely useful for the purpose of describing our perceptual routine. Why! the physicists themselves are nowadays almost prepared for each individual observer carrying about his own ether, and are even more certain than the author of the *Grammar* that ether and atom must account for, but need not obey, the Newtonian mechanics! What possible purpose, then, can this *Grammar* serve? Were the author still young and not burdened with many other tasks, a very serviceable function could be performed by showing that the methods of the *Grammar* extend even further than was indicated in 1892. Beyond such discarded fundamentals as "matter" and "force" lies still another fetish amidst the inscrutable arcana of even modern science, namely, the category of cause and effect. Is this category anything but a conceptual limit to experience, and without any basis in perception beyond a statistical approximation? The very idea will be scouted now, as Professor Tait scouted in 1885 the non-reality of force, or Lord Kelvin later the non-reality of the ether. But the real question is, what will men of science be saying twenty years hence? They may then recognise that the distinction between the physical and the biological sciences is really only quantitative, and the physicists who now see only absolute dependence or perfect independence may then smile over the penurious narrowness of mathematical function as they smile now over the insufficiency of the old laws of motion. Or, again, may there not be some danger that the physicist of to-day may treat his electron, as he treated his old unchangeable atom, as a reality of experience, and forget that it is only a construct of his own imagination, just so far useful as it describes his experience, and certain to be replaced by a wider concept as his insight expands? The *Grammar* would find full scope for its methods had its author had the leisure to rewrite it from the standpoint just indicated. All that it has been possible to do has been to add a chapter indicating what the author thinks to be the

PREFACE

expansion taking place in our ideas of causation. He has further, through the kindness of his colleague, Professor E. Cunningham, been able to include a chapter on Modern Physical Ideas. That chapter indicates, not that the physicists are discovering a new perceptual reality, but that they are seeking for a mathematical concept wide enough to describe a much enlarged perceptual experience. It may reasonably be doubted whether they have yet found it.

These two new sections involved dividing the book into two parts, for there is much also to be added to the chapters dealing with living forms, where progress in the last ten years has been as great as in the physical branches of science. I trust this enlarged second part of the *Grammar* may be out this year.

I can only hope that the third edition of my book has not been so far modified as to repel its old friends. For my part, I am compelled to regard it as scarcely renovated as fully as it ought to have been. Still, even in its present form the writers of elementary text-books on dynamics might, if they would favour it with a perusal, learn that the time-honoured three laws of motion are not all that modern science has to say about mechanism, and that even schoolboys must sooner or later rebel against being told that "a body remains at rest or moves in a straight line unless acted upon by a force" or that "mass is the quantity of matter in a body," an absolute constant independent of its motion!

KARL PEARSON.

University College, London,
January 19, 1911.

PREFACE TO THE SECOND EDITION

DURING the eight years which have elapsed since this *Grammar* was first published, the views expounded in it have undoubtedly met with wider acceptance than the author in the least anticipated. There are many signs that a sound idealism is surely replacing, as a basis for natural philosophy, the crude materialism of the older physicists. More than one professor of metaphysics has actually discovered that he can best attack "modern" science by criticising ancient statements as to mechanism from a standpoint remarkably similar to that of the *Grammar*. Step by step men of science are coming to recognise that mechanism is not at the bottom of phenomena, but is only the conceptual shorthand by aid of which they can briefly describe and resume phenomena. That all science is description and not explanation, that the mystery of change in the inorganic world is just as great and just as omnipresent as in the organic world, are statements which will appear platitudes to the next generation. Formerly men had belief as to the super-sensuous, and thought they had knowledge of the sensuous. The science of the future, while agnostic as to the supersensuous, will replace knowledge by belief in the perceptual sphere, and reserve the term knowledge for the conceptual sphere—the region of their own concepts and ideas—of ether, atom, organic corpuscle, and vital force—of physical and plasmic mechanics. That this change of view as to the basis of science cannot take place without misunderstanding,[1] or without giving an opportunity to those who dislike science to decry its weaknesses, is only natural. To change the basis of operations during a campaign always gives a chance to the enemy, but the chance must be risked if thereby we place ourselves permanently in a position of greater strength for offence and defence. If the reader questions whether there is still war between science and dogma, I must reply that there always will be as long as knowledge is opposed to ignorance. To know requires exertion, and it is intellectually easiest to shirk effort altogether by accepting phrases which cloak the unknown in the undefinable.

Meanwhile the need for remodelling the fundamental mechanical principles as we find them stated in elementary text-books of physics and dynamics remains as urgent as ever. Professor A. E. H. Love is, indeed, to be congratulated in having in his *Theoretical Mechanics*[2] ventured a good way in the right direction, but his work will hardly be used for elementary science teaching, and it is through the latter only that we can hope to give the new and sounder scientific conceptions general currency. For the present the *Grammar* may yet be of service. After an eight years' life and an issue of some 4000 copies, it reappears in a revised and enlarged form. The chief additions are the chapters on Evolution, dealing with fundamental conceptions in the field of biological science. The progress in this direction during the last few years enables me to define several of these conceptions much

[1] See, for example, Mr. St. George Mivart's attack on the present work as essentially materialistic !—*Fortnightly Review*, 1896.

[2] Cambridge University Press, 1897. That a well-known Harvard Professor should have used the *Grammar* as a basis for the term's discussions in his post-graduate *Seminar* is another hopeful sign that many minds are being stirred to reconsider the fundamental concepts of science.

more accurately than was possible in 1892, and to indicate, if only in vague outline, what a fascinating field is being here transferred from the synoptic to the precise division of science (see the chapter on the Classification of the Sciences). Many changes have been made in the wording, but few in the substance of the earlier parts of this book. For valuable suggestions in the chapters on Evolution I have to thank Mr. Francis Galton, F.R.S., Professor W. F. R. Weldon, F.R.S., and Mr. G. Udny Yule.

If I have not paid greater attention to my numerous critics, it is not that I have failed to study them ; it is simply that I have remained—obstinately it may be —convinced that the views expressed are, relatively to our present state of knowledge, substantially correct. Such changes in form as I have made have been chiefly suggested by further experience in the difficulties which await both pupil and teacher. I can only conclude by expressing a hope that if old friends meet the *Grammar* in its new form, they will not be displeased by either the superficial changes or the more substantial additions.

KARL PEARSON.

UNIVERSITY COLLEGE, LONDON,
December 1899.

PREFACE TO THE FIRST EDITION

THERE are periods in the growth of science when it is well to turn our attention from its imposing superstructure and to carefully examine its foundations. The present book is primarily intended as a criticism of the fundamental concepts of modern science, and as such finds its justification in the motto placed upon its title-page. At the same time the author is so fully conscious of the ease of criticism and the difficulty of reconstruction, that he has attempted not to stop short at the lighter task. No one who knows the author's views, or who reads, indeed, this book, will believe that he holds the labour of the great scientists or the mission of modern science to be of small account. If the reader finds the opinions of physicists of world-wide reputation, and the current definitions of physical concepts called into question, he must not attribute this to a purely sceptical spirit in the author. He accepts almost without reserve the great results of modern physics; it is the language in which these results are stated that he believes needs reconsideration. This reconsideration is the more urgent because the language of physics is widely used in all branches of biological (including sociological) science. The obscurity which envelops the *principia* of science is not only due to an historical evolution influenced by the authority which attaches even to the phraseology used by great discoverers, but to the fact that science, as long as it had to carry on a difficult warfare with metaphysics and dogma, like a skilful general conceived it best to hide its own deficient organisation. There can be small doubt, however, that this deficient organisation will not only in time be perceived by the enemy, but that it has already had a very discouraging influence both on scientific recruits and on intelligent laymen. Anything more hopelessly illogical than the statements with regard to force and matter current in elementary text-books of science, it is difficult to imagine ; and the author, as a result of some ten years' teaching and examining, has been forced to the conclusion that these works possess little, if any, *educational* value ; they neither encourage the growth of logical clearness nor form any exercise in scientific method. One result of this obscurity we probably find in the ease with which the physicist, as compared with either the pure mathematician or the historian, is entangled in the meshes of such pseudo-sciences as natural theology and spiritualism. If the constructive portion of this work appears to the reader unnecessarily dogmatic or polemical, the author would beg him to remember that it is essentially intended to arouse and stimulate the reader's own thought, rather than to inculcate doctrine : this result is often best achieved by the assertion and contradiction which excite the reader to independent inquiry.

The views expressed in this *Grammar* on the fundamental concepts of science, especially on those of force and matter, have formed part of the author's teaching since he was first called upon (1882) to think how the elements of dynamical science could be presented free from metaphysics to young students. But the endeavour to put them into popular language only dates from the author's appointment, in 1891, to Sir Thomas Gresham's professorship in geometry. The substance of this work

PREFACE

formed the topic of two introductory courses on the *Scope and Concepts of Modern Science*. Gresham College is but the veriest shred of what its founder hoped and dreamt it would become—a great teaching university for London—but the author in writing this volume, whatever its failings, felt that as far as in him lay he was endeavouring to return to the precedent set by the earlier and more distinguished of his predecessors in the chair of geometry. To restore the chair and the college to its pristine importance is work well worth doing, but it lies in the hands of men hardly trained to appreciate the social value of science and general culture.

This *Grammar of Science*, imperfect as it is, would have been still more wanting but for the continual help and sympathy of several kind friends. Mr. W. H. Macaulay of King's College, Cambridge, has given aid in many ways, ever trying to keep the author's scientific radicalism within moderate and reasonable bounds. To his friend, Mr. R. J. Parker of Lincoln's Inn, the author is indebted for a continuation of that careful and suggestive revision which he has for the last ten years given to nearly everything the author has written. Especially, however, his thanks are due to Dr. R. J. Ryle of Barnet, whose logical mind and wide historical reading have produced a " betterment," which gives him almost a tenant-right in these pages. Lastly, the author has to thank his friend and former pupil, Miss Alice Lee, Assistant-Lecturer in Physics at Bedford College, London, for the preparation of the index and for several important corrections.

KARL PEARSON.

GRESHAM COLLEGE, LONDON,
January 1892.

CONTENTS

Introduction by Ernest Nagel   v
Prefaces   xi
CHAPTER I. INTRODUCTORY
1. The Need of the Present   1
2. Science and Citizenship   6
3. The First Claim of Modern Science   8
4. Essentials of Good Science   9
5. The Scope of Science   12
6. Science and Metaphysics   14
7. The Ignorance of Science   19
8. The Wide Domain of Science   24
9. The Second Claim of Science   25
10. The Third Claim of Science   29
11. Science and the Imagination   30
12. The Method of Science Illustrated   32
13. Science and the Aesthetic Judgment   34
14. The Fourth Claim of Science   36
CHAPTER II. THE FACTS OF SCIENCE
1. The Reality of Things   39
2. Sense-Impressions and Consciousness   42
3. The Brain as a Central Telephone Exchange   44
4. The Nature of Thought   46
5. Other-Consciousness as an Eject   48
6. Attitude of Science towards Ejects   51
7. The Scientific Validity of a Conception   53
8. The Scientific Validity of an Inference   55
9. The Limits to Other-Consciousness   57
10. The Canons of Legitimate Inference   59
11. The External Universe   60
12. Outside and Inside Myself   63
13. Sensations as the Ultimate Source of the Materials of Knowledge   66
14. Shadow and Reality   69
15. Individuality   71
16. The Futility of "Things-in-Themselves"   72
17. The Term Knowledge is Meaningless if applied to Unthinkable Things   74
CHAPTER III. THE SCIENTIFIC LAW
1. Résumé and Foreword   77
2. Of the Word Law and its Meanings   79
3. Natural Law relative to Man   82
4. Man as the Maker of Natural Law   85
5. The Two Senses of the Words "Natural Law"   87
6. Confusion between the Two Senses of Natural Law   88
7. The Reason behind Nature   90
8. True Relation of Civil and Natural Law   93
9. Physical and Metaphysical Supersensuousness   95
10. Progress in the Formulating of Natural Law   96

11. The Universality of Scientific Law   100
12. The Routine of Perceptions is possibly a **Product of**
    the Perceptive Faculty   101
13. The Mind as a Sorting-Machine   106
14. Science, Natural Theology, and Metaphysics   107
15. Conclusions   109
CHAPTER IV. CAUSE AND EFFECT—PROBABILITY
 1. Mechanism   113
 2. Force as a Cause   116
 3. Will as a Cause   118
 4. Secondary Causes involve no Enforcement   120
 5. Is Will a First Cause?   122
 6. Will as a Secondary Cause   123
 7. First Causes have no Existence for Science   127
 8. Cause and Effect as the Routine of Experience   128
 9. Width of the Term Cause   131
10. The Universe of Sense-Impressions as a Universe
    of Motions   132
11. Necessity belongs to the World of Conceptions,
    not to that of Perceptions   134
12. Routine in Perception is a necessary Condition of
    Knowledge   136
13. Probable and Provable   139
14. Probability as to Breaches in the Routine of
    Perceptions   142
15. The Basis of Laplace's Theory lies in an
    Experience as to Ignorance   143
16. Nature of Laplace's Investigation   147
17. The Permanency of Routine for the Future   148
CHAPTER V. CONTINGENCY AND CORRELATION—THE
             INSUFFICIENCY OF CAUSATION
 1. The Routine of Perceptions is Relative rather
    than Absolute   152
 2. The Ultimate Elements of the Inorganic as of the
    Organic Universe may be Individual and not Same   155
 3. The Category of Association, as replacing Causation 156
 4. Symbolic Measure of the Intensity of Association
    or Contingency   160
 5. The Universe as governed by Causation and as
    governed by Contingency   165
 6. Classification of A and B by Measurement.
    Mathematical Function   167
 7. On the Multiplicity of "Causes"   171
 8. The Universe as a Complex of Contingent, not
    Causally Linked Phenomena   173
 9. The Measure of Correlation and its Relation to
    Contingency   174
CHAPTER VI. SPACE AND TIME
 1. Space as a Mode of Perception   179
 2. The Infinite Bigness of Space   184

3. The Infinite Divisibility of Space 186
4. The Space of Memory and Thought 189
5. Conceptions and Perceptions 191
6. Sameness and Continuity 194
7. Conceptual Space. Geometrical Boundaries 197
8. Surfaces as Boundaries 199
9. Conceptual Discontinuity of Bodies. The Atom 201
10. Conceptual Continuity. Ether 205
11. On the General Nature of Scientific Conceptions 206
12. Time as a Mode of Perception 208
13. Conceptual Time and its Measurement 213
14. Concluding Remarks on Space and Time 217

CHAPTER VII. THE GEOMETRY OF MOTION
1. Motion as the Mixed Mode of Perception 220
2. Conceptual Analysis of a Case of Perceptual
      Motion. Point-Motion 222
3. Rigid Bodies as Geometrical Ideals 225
4. On Change of Aspect, or Rotation 227
5. On Change of Form, or Strain 229
6. Factors of Conceptual Motion 232
7. Point-Motion. Relative Character of Position
      and Motion 233
8. Position. The Map of the Path 236
9. The Time-Chart 239
10. Steepness and Slope 242
11. Speed as a Slope. Velocity 244
12. The Velocity Diagram or Hodograph. Acceleration 246
13. Acceleration as a Spurt and a Shunt 249
14. Curvature 251
15. The Relation between Curvature and Normal
      Acceleration 255
16. Fundamental Propositions in the Geometry of
      Motion 258
17. The Relativity of Motion. Its Synthesis from
      Simple Components 260

CHAPTER VIII. MATTER
1. "All things move"—but only in Conception 266
2. The Three Problems 269
3. How the Physicists define Matter 271
4. Does Matter occupy Space? 275
5. The "Common-sense" View of Matter as
      Impenetrable and Hard 279
6. Individuality does not denote Sameness in
      Substratum 281
7. Hardness not Characteristic of Matter 285
8. Matter as non-Matter in Motion 286
9. The Ether as "Perfect Fluid" and "Perfect Jelly" 289
10. The Vortex-Ring Atom and the Ether-Squirt Atom 292
11. A Material Loophole into the Supersensuous 294
12. The Difficulties of a Perceptual Ether 297

13. Why do Bodies move?   299

CHAPTER IX. THE LAWS OF MOTION

1. Corpuscles and their Structure   305
2. The Limits to Mechanism   309
3. The First Law of Motion   311
4. The Second Law of Motion, or the Principle of Inertia   313
5. The Third Law of Motion. Mutual Acceleration is determined by Relative Position   317
6. Velocity as an Epitome of Past History. Mechanism and Materialism   322
7. The Fourth Law of Motion   326
8. The Scientific Conception of Mass   329
9. The Fifth Law of Motion. The Definition of Force   330
10. Equality of Masses tested by Weighing   333
11. How far does the Mechanism of the Fourth and Fifth Laws of Motion extend?   337
12. Density as the Basis of the Kinetic Scale   339
13. The Influence of Aspect on the Corpuscular Dance   343
14. The Hypothesis of Modified Action and the Synthesis of Motion   344
15. Criticism of the Newtonian Laws of Motion   348

CHAPTER X. MODERN PHYSICAL IDEAS

1. The Present Crisis in Physical Science and its Sources   355
2. The Origin of the Atomic View of Electricity   358
3. On the Electro-magnetic Constitution of the Atom   361
4. Electro-magnetic Mass   364
5. A Mechanical Ether Irrational   367
6. On Current Definitions of Electric Charge and Intensity at a Point   370
7. The Possibility of a Logical Definition of the Fundamental Quantities of the Electron Theory   371
8. On Fluid or Space Distribution of Electricity   374
9. On Motion Relative to the Ether in Relation to Experience   377
10. Theory of Relativity   379
11. Electro-magnetic Inertia according to the Theory of Relativity   383
12. The Present Value of Newtonian Dynamics   385

APPENDIX

Note I   On the Principle of Inertia and "Absolute Rotation"   389
Note II   On Newton's Third Law of Motion   392
Note III   William of Occam's Razor   392
Note IV   A. R. Wallace on Matter   393
Note V   On the Reversibility of Natural Processes   394

THE GRAMMAR OF SCIENCE

CHAPTER I

INTRODUCTORY—THE SCOPE AND METHOD OF SCIENCE

§ 1.—*The Need of the Present*

WITHIN the past forty years so revolutionary a change
has taken place in our appreciation of the essential facts
in the growth of human society, that it has become
necessary not only to rewrite history, but to profoundly
modify our theory of life and gradually, but none the less
certainly, to adapt our conduct to the novel theory.   The
insight which the investigations of Darwin, seconded by
the suggestive but far less permanent work of Spencer,
have given us into the development of both individual and
social life, has compelled us to remodel our historical ideas
and is slowly widening and consolidating our moral
standards.   This slowness ought not to dishearten us, for
one of the strongest factors of social stability is the inertness, nay, rather active hostility, with which human
societies receive all new ideas.   It is the crucible in which
the dross is separated from the genuine metal, and which
saves the body-social from a succession of unprofitable
and possibly injurious experimental variations.   That the
reformer should often be also the martyr is, perhaps, a not
over-great price to pay for the caution with which society
as a whole must move ; it may require years to replace a
great leader of men, but a stable and efficient society can
only be the outcome of centuries of development.

If we have learnt, it may be indirectly, from the writings of Darwin that the methods of production, the mode of holding property, the forms of marriage, the organisations of the family and of the commune are the essential factors which the historian has to trace in the growth of human society ; if in our history books we are ceasing to head periods with the names of monarchs and to devote whole paragraphs to their mistresses, still we are far indeed from clearly grasping the exact interaction of the various factors of social evolution, or from understanding why one becomes predominant at this or that epoch. We can indeed note periods of great social activity and others of apparent quiescence, but it is probably only our ignorance of the exact course of social evolution which leads us to assign fundamental changes in social institutions either to individual men or to reformations and revolutions. We associate, it is true, the German Reformation with a replacement of collectivist by individualist standards, not only in religion but also in handicraft, art, and politics. The French Revolution in like manner is the epoch from which many are inclined to date the rebirth of those social ideas which have largely remoulded the mediaeval relations of class and caste, relations little affected by the sixteenth-century Reformation. Coming somewhat nearer to our own time, we can indeed measure with some degree of accuracy the social influence of the great changes in the methods of production, the transition from home to capitalistic industry, which transformed English life in the first half of last century, and has since made its way throughout the civilised world. But when we actually reach our own age, an age one of the most marked features of which is the startlingly rapid growth of the natural sciences and their far-reaching influence on the standards of both the comfort and the conduct of human life, we find it impossible to compress its social history into the bald phrases by which we attempt to connote the characteristics of more distant historical epochs.

It is very difficult for us who live in the first years of the twentieth century to rightly measure the relative

importance of what our age is doing in the history of civilisation. In the first place, we can look at it only from one
standpoint—that of the *past*. It needed at least an
Erasmus to predict the outcome of the Reformation from
all that *preceded* the Diet of Worms. Or to adopt a
metaphor, a blind man climbing a hill might have a considerable appreciation of the various degrees of steepness
in the parts he had traversed, and he might even have a
reasonable amount of certainty as to the slope whereon
he was standing for the time being, but whether that slope
led immediately to a steeper ascent, or was practically the
top, it would be impossible for him to say. In the next
place, we are too close to our age, both in position and feeling, to appreciate without foreshortening and personal
prejudice the magnitude of the changes which are undoubtedly taking place.

The contest of opinion in nearly every field of thought
—the struggle of old and new standards in every sphere
of activity, in religion, in commerce, in social life—touch
the spiritual and physical needs of the individual far too
nearly for him to be a dispassionate judge of the age in
which he lives. That we play our parts in an era of
rapid social change can scarcely be doubted by any one
who regards attentively the marked contrasts presented
by our modern society. It is an era alike of great self-
assertion and of excessive altruism ; we see the highest intellectual power accompanied by the strangest recrudescence
of superstition ; there is a strong socialist drift and yet
not a few remarkable individualist teachers ; the extremes
of religious faith and of unequivocal freethought are found
jostling each other. Nor do these opposing traits exist
only in close social juxtaposition. The same individual
mind, unconscious of its own want of logical consistency,
will often exhibit our age in microcosm.

It is little wonder that we have hitherto made small
advance towards a common estimate of what our time is
really contributing to the history of human progress. The
one man finds in our age a restlessness, a distrust of
authority, a questioning of the basis of all social institutions

and long-established methods—characteristics which mark for him a decadence of social unity, a collapse of the time-honoured principles which he conceives to be the sole possible guides of conduct. A second man with a different temperament pictures for us a golden age in the near future, when the new knowledge shall be diffused through the people, and when those modern notions of human relations, which he finds everywhere taking root, shall finally have supplanted worn-out customs.

One teacher propounds what is flatly contradicted by a second. " We want more piety," cries one ; " We must have less," retorts another. " State interference in the hours of labour is absolutely needful," declares a third ; " It will destroy all individual initiation and self-depend-ence," rejoins a fourth. " The salvation of the country depends upon the technical education of its workpeople," is the shout of one party ; " Technical education is merely a trick by which the employer of labour thrusts upon the nation the expense of providing himself with better human machines," is the prompt answer of its opponents. " We need more private charity," say some ; " All private charity is an anomaly, a waste of the nation's resources and a pauperising of its members," reply others. " Endow scientific research and we shall know the truth, when and where it is possible to ascertain it " ; but the counterblast is at hand : " To endow research is merely to encourage the research for endowment ; the true man of science will not be held back by poverty, and if science is of use to us, it will pay for itself." Such are but a few samples of the conflict of opinion which we find raging around us. The prick of conscience and the spur of highly wrought sympathy have succeeded in arousing a wonderful restless-ness in our generation—and this at a time when the advance of positive knowledge has called in question many old customs and old authorities. It is true that there are but few remedies which have not a fair chance to-day of being put upon their trial. Vast sums of money are raised for every sort of charitable scheme, for popular entertainment, for technical instruction, and even for higher education—in short, for religious, semi-religious, and non-religious movements of all types. Out of this chaos ought at least to come some good ; but how shall we set the good against the evil which too often arises from ill-defined, or even undefined, appropriation of those resources which the nation has spared by the hard labour of the past, or can obtain by drawing on the future's credit ?

The responsibility of individuals, especially with regard to wealth, is great, so great that we see a growing tendency of the state to interfere in the administration of private charities and to regulate the great educational institutions endowed by private or semi-public benefactions in the past. But this tendency to throw back the responsibility from the individual upon the state is really only throwing it back on the social conscience of the citizens as a body —the " tribal conscience," as Professor Clifford was wont to call it. The wide extension of the franchise for both local and central representation has cast a greatly in-creased responsibility on the individual citizen. He is brought face to face with the most conflicting opinions and with the most diverse party cries. The state has become in our day the largest employer of labour, the greatest dispenser of charity, and, above all, the school-master with the biggest school in the community. Directly or indirectly the individual citizen has to find some reply to the innumerable social and educational problems of the day. He requires some guide in the determination of his own action or in the choice of fitting representatives. He is thrust into an appalling maze of social and educational problems ; and if his tribal conscience has any stuff in it, he feels that these problems ought not to be settled, so far as he has the power of settling them, by his own personal interests, by his individual prospects of profit or loss. He is called upon to form a judgment apart, if it possibly may be, from his own feelings and emotions—a judgment in what he conceives to be the interests of society at large. It may be a difficult thing for the large employer of labour to form a right judgment in matters of

factory legislation, or for the private schoolmaster to see
clearly in questions of state-aided education. None the
less we should probably all agree that the tribal conscience
ought for the sake of social welfare to be stronger than
private interest, and that the *ideal* citizen, if he existed,
would form a judgment free from personal bias.

§ 2.—*Science and Citizenship*

How is such a judgment—so necessary in our time
with its hot conflict of individual opinions and its increased responsibility for the individual citizen—how is
such a judgment to be formed? In the first place, it is
obvious that it can only be based on a clear knowledge of
facts, an appreciation of their sequence and relative
significance. The facts once classified, once understood,
the judgment based upon them ought to be independent
of the individual mind which examines them. Is there
any other sphere, outside that of ideal citizenship, in which
there is habitual use of this method of classifying facts and
forming judgments upon them? For if there be, it cannot
fail to be suggestive as to methods of eliminating individual bias; it ought to be one of the best training
grounds for citizenship. The classification of facts and
the formation of absolute judgments upon the basis of
this classification—judgments independent of the idiosyncrasies of the individual mind—essentially sum up the
aim and method of modern science. The scientific man
has above all things to strive at self-elimination in his
judgments, to provide an argument which is as true for
each individual mind as for his own. *The classification of
facts, the recognition of their sequence and relative significance
is the function of science*, and the habit of forming a judgment upon these facts unbiassed by personal feeling is
characteristic of what may be termed the scientific frame
of mind. The scientific method of examining facts is not
peculiar to one class of phenomena and to one class of
workers; it is applicable to social as well as to physical
problems, and we must carefully guard ourselves against

supposing that the scientific frame of mind is a peculiarity of the professional scientist.

Now this frame of mind seems to me an essential of good citizenship, and of the several ways in which it can be acquired few surpass the careful study of some one branch of natural science. The insight into method and the habit of dispassionate investigation which follow from acquaintance with the scientific classification of even some small range of natural facts, give the mind an invaluable power of dealing with other classes of facts as the occasion arises.[1] The patient and persistent study of some one branch of natural science is even at the present time within the reach of many. In some branches a few hours' study a week, if carried on earnestly for two or three years, would be not only sufficient to give a thorough insight into scientific method, but would also enable the student to become a careful observer and possibly an original investigator in his chosen field, thus adding a new delight and a new enthusiasm to his life. The importance of a just appreciation of scientific method is so great, that I think the state may be reasonably called upon to place instruction in pure science within the reach of all its citizens. Indeed, we ought to look with extreme distrust on the large expenditure of public money on polytechnics and similar institutions, if the manual instruction which it is proposed to give at these places be not accompanied by efficient teaching in pure science. The scientific habit of mind is one which may be acquired by all, and the readiest means of attaining to it ought to be placed within the reach of all.

The reader must be careful to note that I am only praising the scientific habit of mind, and suggesting one

[1] To decry specialisation in education is to misinterpret the purpose of education. The true aim of the teacher must be to impart an appreciation of method and not a knowledge of facts. This is far more readily achieved by concentrating the student's attention on a small range of phenomena, than by leading him in rapid and superficial survey over wide fields of knowledge. Personally I have no recollection of at least 90 per cent of the *facts* that were taught to me at school, but the notions of *method* which I derived from my instructor in Greek Grammar (the contents of which I have long since forgotten) remain in my mind as the really valuable part of my school equipment for life.

of several methods by which it may be cultivated. No assertion has been made that the man of science is necessarily a good citizen, or that his judgment upon social or political questions will certainly be of weight. It by no means follows that, because a man has won a name for himself in the field of natural science, his judgments on such problems as Socialism, Home Rule, or Biblical Criticism will necessarily be sound. They will be sound or not according as he has carried his scientific method into these fields. He must properly have classified and appreciated his facts, and have been guided by them, and not by personal feeling or class bias in his judgments. It is the scientific habit of mind as an essential for good citizenship and not the scientist as a sound politician that I wish to emphasise.

§ 3.—*The First Claim of Modern Science*

I have gone a rather roundabout way to reach my definition of science and scientific method. But it has been of purpose, for in the spirit—and it is a healthy spirit—of our age we are accustomed to question all things and to demand a reason for their existence. The sole reason that can be given for any social institution or form of human activity—I mean not how they came to exist, which is a matter of history, but why we continue to encourage their existence—lies in this : their existence tends to promote the welfare of human society, to increase social happiness, or to strengthen social stability. In the spirit of our age we are bound to question the value of science ; to ask in what way it increases the happiness of mankind or promotes social efficiency. We must justify the existence of modern science, or at least the large and growing demands which it makes upon the national exchequer. Apart from the increased physical comfort, apart from the intellectual enjoyment which modern science provides for the community—points often and loudly insisted upon and to which I shall briefly refer later—there is another and more fundamental justification for the time and energy spent in scientific work. From the standpoint of morality, or from the relation of the individual unit to other members of the same social group, we have to judge each human activity by its outcome in *conduct*. How, then, does science justify itself in its influence on the conduct of men as citizens? I assert that the encouragement of scientific investigation and the spread of scientific knowledge by largely inculcating scientific habits of mind will lead to more efficient citizenship and so to increased social stability. Minds trained to scientific methods are less likely to be led by mere appeal to the passions or by blind emotional excitement to sanction acts which in the end may lead to social disaster. In the first and foremost place, therefore, I lay stress upon the educational side of modern science, and state my position in some such words as these :—

Modern Science, as training the mind to an exact and impartial analysis of facts, is an education specially fitted to promote sound citizenship.

Our first conclusion, then, as to the value of science for practical life turns upon the efficient training it provides in *method*. The man who has accustomed himself to marshal facts, to examine their complex mutual relations, and predict upon the result of this examination their inevitable sequences—sequences which we term natural laws and which are as valid for every normal mind as for that of the individual investigator—such a man, we may hope, will carry his scientific method into the field of social problems. He will scarcely be content with merely superficial statement, with vague appeal to the imagination, to the emotions, to individual prejudices. He will demand a high standard of reasoning, a clear insight into facts and their results, and his demand cannot fail to be beneficial to the community at large.

§ 4.—*Essentials of Good Science*

I want the reader to appreciate clearly that science justifies itself in its methods, quite apart from any serviceable knowledge it may convey. We are too apt to forget this purely educational side of science in the great value of its practical applications. We see too often the plea raised for science that it is *useful knowledge*, while philology and philosophy are supposed to have small utilitarian or commercial value. Science, indeed, often teaches us facts of primary importance for practical life ; yet not on this account, but because it leads us to classifications and systems independent of the individual thinker, to sequences and laws admitting of no play-room for individual fancy, must we rate the training of science and its social value higher than those of philology and philosophy. Herein lies the first, but of course not the sole, ground for the popularisation of science. That form of popular science which merely recites the results of investigations, which merely communicates *useful knowledge*, is from this standpoint bad science, or no science at all. Let me recommend the reader to apply this test to every work professing to give a popular account of any branch of science. If any such work gives a description of phenomena that appeals to his imagination rather than to his reason, then it is bad science. The first aim of any genuine work of science, however popular, ought to be the presentation of such a classification of facts that the reader's mind is irresistibly led to acknowledge a logical sequence—a law which appeals to the reason before it captivates the imagination. Let us be quite sure that whenever we come across a conclusion in a scientific work which does not flow from the classification of facts, or which is not directly stated by the author to be an assumption, then we are dealing with bad science. Good science will always be intelligible to the logically trained mind, if that mind can read and translate the language in which science is written. The scientific method is one and the same in all branches, and that method is the method of all logically trained minds. In this respect the great classics of science are often the most intelligible of books, and if so, are far better worth reading than popularisations of them written by men with

less insight into scientific method. Works like Darwin's
Origin of Species and *Descent of Man*, Lyell's *Principles of
Geology*, Helmholtz's *Sensations of Tone*, or Galton's *Natural
Inheritance*, can be profitably read and largely understood by those who are not specially trained in the several
branches of science with which these works deal.[1] It may
need some patience in the interpretation of scientific terms,
in learning the language of science, but like most cases in
which a new language has to be learnt, the comparison of
passages in which the same word or term recurs, will soon
lead to a just appreciation of its true meaning. In the
matter of language the descriptive natural sciences such as
geology or biology are more easily accessible to the layman than the exact sciences such as algebra or mechanics,
where the reasoning process must often be clothed in
mathematical symbols, the right interpretation of which
may require months, if not years, of study. To this distinction between the descriptive and exact sciences I
propose to return later, when we are dealing with the
classification of the sciences.

I would not have the reader suppose that the mere
perusal of some standard scientific work will, in my opinion,
produce a scientific habit of mind. I only suggest that it
will give some insight into scientific method and some
appreciation of its value. Those who can devote persist-
ently some four or five hours a week to the conscientious
study of any *one* limited branch of science will achieve in
the space of a year or two much more than this. The
busy layman is not bound to seek about for some branch
which will give him useful facts for his profession or occupation in life. It does not indeed matter for the purpose
we have now in view whether he seek to make himself
proficient in geology, or biology, or geometry, or mechanics,
or even history or folklore, if these be studied scientifically.
What is necessary is the *thorough* knowledge of some
small group of facts, the recognition of their relationship

---

[1] The list might be easily increased, for example by W. Harvey's *Ana-
tomical Dissertation on the Motion of the Heart and Blood*, and by Faraday's
Experimental Researches.

to each other, and of the formulae or laws which express scientifically their sequences. It is in this manner that the mind becomes imbued with the scientific method and freed from individual bias in the formation of its judgments—one of the conditions, as we have seen, for ideally good citizenship. This first claim of scientific training, its education in method, is to my mind the most powerful claim it has to state support. I believe more will be achieved by placing instruction in pure science within the reach of all our citizens, than by any number of polytechnics devoting themselves to technical education, which does not rise above the level of manual instruction.

§ 5.—*The Scope of Science*

The reader may perhaps feel that I am laying stress upon *method* at the expense of material content. Now this is the peculiarity of scientific method, that when once it has become a habit of mind, that mind converts *all* facts whatsoever into science. The field of science is unlimited ; its material is endless, every group of natural phenomena, every phase of social life, every stage of past or present development is material for science. *The unity of all science consists alone in its method, not in its material.* The man who classifies facts of any kind whatever, who sees their mutual relation and describes their sequences, is applying the scientific method and is a man of science. The facts may belong to the past history of mankind, to the social statistics of our great cities, to the atmosphere of the most distant stars, to the digestive organs of a worm, or to the life of a scarcely visible bacillus. It is not facts themselves which make science, but the method by which they are dealt with. The material of science is co-extensive with the whole physical universe, not only that universe as it now exists, but with its past history and the past history of all life therein. When every fact, every present or past phenomenon of that universe, every phase of present or past life therein, has been examined, classified, and co-ordinated with the rest, then the mission of science will be completed. What is this but saying that the task of science can never end till man ceases to be, till history is no longer made, and development itself ceases ?

It might be supposed that science has made such strides in the last two centuries, and notably in the last fifty years, that we might look forward to a day when its work would be practically accomplished. At the beginning of this century it was possible for an Alexander von Humboldt to take a survey of the entire domain of then extant science. Such a survey would be impossible for any scientist now, even if gifted with more than Humboldt's powers. Scarcely any specialist of to-day is really master of all the work which has been done in his own comparatively small field. Facts and their classification have been accumulating at such a rate, that nobody seems to have leisure to recognise the relations of sub-groups to the whole. It is as if individual workers in both Europe and America were bringing their stones to one great building and piling them on and cementing them together without regard to any general plan or to their individual neighbour's work ; only where some one has placed a great corner-stone is it regarded, and the building then rises on this firmer foundation more rapidly than at other points, till it reaches a height at which it is stopped for want of side support. Yet this great structure, the proportions of which are beyond the ken of any individual man, possesses a symmetry and unity of its own, notwithstanding its haphazard mode of construction. This symmetry and unity lie in scientific method. The smallest group of facts, if properly classified and logically dealt with, will form a stone which has its proper place in the great building of knowledge, wholly independent of the individual workman who has shaped it. Even when two men work unwittingly at the same stone they will but modify and correct each other's angles. In the face of all this enormous progress of modern science, when in all civilised lands men are applying the scientific method to natural, historical, and mental facts, we have yet to admit that the goal of science is and must be infinitely distant.

For we must note that when from a sufficient if partial classification of facts a simple principle has been discovered which describes the relationship and sequences of any group, then this principle or law itself generally leads to the discovery of a still wider range of hitherto unregarded phenomena in the same or associated fields.[1]   Every great advance of science opens our eyes to facts which we had failed before to observe, and makes new demands on our powers of interpretation.   This extension of the material of science into regions where our great-grandfathers could see nothing at all, or where they would have declared human knowledge impossible, is one of the most remarkable features of modern progress.   Where they interpreted the motion of the planets of our own system, we discuss the chemical constitution of stars, many of which did not exist for them, for their telescopes could not reach them. Where they discovered the circulation of the blood, we see the physical conflict of living poisons within the blood, whose battles would have been absurdities for them. Where they found void and probably demonstrated to their own satisfaction that there was void, we conceive great systems in rapid motion capable of carrying energy through brick walls as light passes through glass.   Great as the advance of scientific knowledge has been, it has not been greater than the growth of the material to be dealt with.   The goal of science is clear—it is nothing short of the complete interpretation of the universe.   But the goal is an ideal one—it marks the *direction* in which we move and strive, but never a stage we shall actually reach.   The universe grows ever larger as we learn to understand more of our own corner of it.

§ 6.—*Science and Metaphysics*

Now I want to draw the reader's attention to two results which flow from the above considerations, namely :

---

[1] For example, while in the last two decades our theory of light and magnetism has advanced by leaps and bounds, we have at the same time discovered wide ranges of novel phenomena, of which we had previously no cognisance.

that the material of science is coextensive with the whole life, physical and mental, of the universe, and furthermore that the limits to our perception of the universe are only apparent, not real. It is no exaggeration to say that the universe was not the same for our great-grandfathers as it is for us, and that in all probability it will be utterly different for our great-grandchildren. The universe is a variable quantity, which depends upon the keenness and structure of our organs of sense, and upon the fineness of our powers and instruments of observation. We shall see more clearly the important bearing of this latter remark when we come to discuss more closely in another chapter how the universe is largely the construction of each individual mind. For the present we must briefly consider the former remark, which defines the unlimited scope of science. To say that there are certain fields—for example, *metaphysics*—from which science is excluded, wherein its methods have no application, is merely to say that the rules of methodical observation and the laws of logical thought do not apply to the facts, if any, which lie within such fields. These fields, if indeed such exist, must lie outside any intelligible definition which can be given of the word *knowledge*. If there are facts, and sequences to be observed among those facts, then we have all the requisites of scientific classification and knowledge. If there are no facts, or no sequences to be observed among them, then the possibility of *all* knowledge disappears. The greatest assumption of everyday life—the inference which the metaphysicians tell us is wholly beyond science —namely, that other beings have consciousness as well as ourselves, seems to have just as much or as little *scientific* validity as the statement that an earth-grown apple would fall to the ground if carried to the planet of another star. Both are beyond the range of experimental demonstration, but to assume uniformity in the characteristics of brain " matter " under certain conditions seems as scientific as to assume uniformity in the characteristics of stellar " matter." Both are only working hypotheses and valuable in so far as they simplify our description of the

universe. Yet the distinction between science and metaphysics is often insisted upon, and not unadvisedly, by
the devotees of both. If we take any group of physical
or biological facts—say, for example, electrical phenomena
or the development of the ovum—we shall find that,
though physicists or biologists may differ to some extent
in their measurements or in their hypotheses, yet in the
fundamental principles and sequences the professors of
each individual science are in practical agreement among
themselves. A similar if not yet so complete agreement
is rapidly springing up in both mental and social science,
where the facts are more difficult to classify and the bias
of individual opinion is much stronger. Our more
thorough classification, however, of the facts of human
development, our more accurate knowledge of the early
history of human societies, of primitive customs, laws,
and religions, our application of the principle of natural
selection to man and his communities, are converting
anthropology, folklore, sociology, and psychology into
true sciences. We begin to see indisputable sequences
in groups of both mental and social facts. The causes
which favour the growth or decay of human societies
become more obvious and more the subject of scientific
investigation. Mental and social facts are thus not
beyond the range of scientific treatment, but their
classification has not been so complete, nor for obvious
reasons so unprejudiced, as those of physical or biological
phenomena.

The case is quite different with metaphysics and those
other supposed branches of human knowledge which claim
exemption from scientific control.[1] Either they are based
on an accurate classification of facts, or they are not. But
if their classification of facts were accurate, the application

[1] It is perhaps impossible to satisfactorily define the metaphysician, but
the meaning attached by the present writer to the term will become clearer in
the sequel. It is here used to denote a class of writers, of whom well-known
examples are : Kant, in his later uncritical period (when he discovered that
the universe was created in order that man might have a sphere for moral
action !) ; the post-Kantians (notably Hegel and Schopenhauer), and their
numerous English disciples, who "explain" the universe without having even
an elementary knowledge of physical science.

of the scientific method ought to lead their professors to a practically identical system. Now one of the idiosyncrasies of metaphysicians lies in this : that each metaphysician has his own system, which to a large extent excludes that of his predecessors and colleagues. Hence we must conclude that metaphysics are built either on air or on quicksands—either they start from no foundation in facts at all, or the superstructure has been raised before a basis has been found in the accurate classification of facts. I want to lay special stress on this point. There is no short cut to truth, no way to gain a knowledge of the universe except through the gateway of scientific method. The hard and stony path of classifying facts and reasoning upon them is the only way to ascertain truth. It is the reason and not the imagination which must ultimately be appealed to. The poet may give us in sublime language an account of the origin and purport of the universe, but in the end it will not satisfy our aesthetic judgment, our idea of harmony and beauty, like the few facts which the scientist may venture to tell us in the same field. The one will agree with all our experiences past and present, the other is sure, sooner or later, to contradict our observation because it propounds a dogma, where we are yet far from knowing the whole truth. Our aesthetic judgment demands harmony between the representation and the represented, and in this sense science is often more artistic than modern art.

The poet is a valued member of the community, for he is known to be a poet ; his value will increase as he grows to recognise the deeper insight into nature with which modern science provides him. The metaphysician is a poet, often a very great one, but unfortunately he is not known to be a poet, because he strives to clothe his poetry in the language of reason, and hence it follows that he is liable to be a dangerous member of the community. The danger at the present time that metaphysical dogmas may check scientific research is, perhaps, not very great. The day has gone by when the Hegelian philosophy threatened to strangle infant science in Germany ;

—that it begins to languish at Oxford is a proof that it is practically dead in the country of its birth. The day has gone by when philosophical or theological dogmas of any kind can throw back for generations the progress of scientific investigation. There is no restriction now on research in any field, or on the publication of the truth when it has been reached. But there is nevertheless a danger which we cannot afford to disregard, a danger which retards the spread of scientific knowledge among the unenlightened, and which flatters obscurantism by discrediting the scientific method. There is a certain school of thought which finds the laborious process by which science reaches truth too irksome ; the temperament of this school is such that it demands a short and easy cut to knowledge, where knowledge can only be gained, if at all, by the long and patient toiling of many groups of workers, perhaps through several centuries. There are various fields at the present day wherein mankind is ignorant, and the honest course for us is simply to confess our ignorance. This ignorance may arise from the want of any proper classification of facts, or because supposed facts are themselves inconsistent, unreal creations of untrained minds. But because this ignorance is frankly admitted by science, an attempt is made to fence off these fields as ground which science cannot profitably till, to shut them up as a preserve whereon science has no business to trespass. Wherever science has succeeded in ascertaining the truth, there, according to the school we have referred to, are the " legitimate problems of science." Wherever science is yet ignorant, there, we are told, its method is inapplicable ; there some other relation than cause and effect (than the same sequence recurring with the like grouping of phenomena), some new but undefined relationship rules. In these fields, we are told, problems become philosophical and can only be treated by the method of philosophy. The philosophical method is opposed to the scientific method ; and here, I think, the danger I have referred to arises. We have defined the scientific method to consist in the orderly classification of facts followed by the recognition of their relationship and recurring sequences. The scientific judgment is the judgment based upon this recognition and free from personal bias. If this were the philosophical method there would be no need of further discussion, but as we are told the subject-matter of philosophy is not the " legitimate problem of science," the two methods are presumably not identical. Indeed the philosophical method seems based upon an analysis which does not start with the classification of facts, but reaches its judgments by some obscure process of internal cogitation. It is therefore dangerously liable to the influence of individual bias; it results, as experience shows us, in an endless number of competing and contradictory systems. It is because the so-called philosophical method does not, when different individuals approach the same range of facts,[1] lead, like the scientific, to practical unanimity of judgment, that science, rather than philosophy, offers the better training for modern citizenship.

§ 7.—*The Ignorance of Science*

It must not be supposed that science for a moment denies the existence of some of the problems which have hitherto been classed as philosophical or metaphysical. On the contrary, it recognises that a great variety of physical and biological phenomena lead directly to these problems. But it asserts that the methods hitherto applied to these problems have been futile, because they have been unscientific. The classifications of facts hitherto made by the system-mongers have been hopelessly inadequate or hopelessly prejudiced. Until the scientific study of psychology, both by observation and experiment, has advanced immensely beyond its present limits—and this may take generations of work—science can only answer to the great majority of " metaphysical " problems,

[1] This statement by no means denies the existence of many moot points, unsettled problems in science ; but the genuine scientist *admits* that they are unsolved. As a rule they lie just on the frontier line between knowledge and ignorance, where the pioneers of science are pushing forward into unoccupied and difficult country.

" I am ignorant." Meanwhile it is idle to be impatient or to indulge in system-making. The cautious and laborious classification of facts must have proceeded much further than at present before the time will be ripe for drawing conclusions.

Science stands now with regard to the problems of life and mind in much the same position as it stood with regard to cosmical problems in the seventeenth century. Then the system-mongers were the theologians, who declared that cosmical problems were not the " legitimate problems of science." It was vain for Galilei to assert that the theologians' classification of facts was hopelessly inadequate. In solemn congregation assembled they settled that :—

" *The doctrine that the earth is neither the centre of the universe nor immovable, but moves even with a daily rotation, is absurd, and both philosophically and theologically false, and at the least an error of faith.*" [1]

It took nearly two hundred years to convince the whole theological world that cosmical problems were the legitimate problems of science and science alone, for in 1819 the books of Galilei, Copernicus, and Keppler were still upon the index of forbidden books, and not till 1822 was a decree issued allowing books teaching the motion of the earth about the sun to be printed and published in Rome !

I have cited this memorable example of the absurdity which arises from trying to pen science into a limited field of thought, because it seems to me exceedingly suggestive of what must follow again, if any attempt, philosophical or theological, be made to define the " legitimate problems of science." Wherever there is the slightest possibility for the human mind to *know*, there is a legitimate problem of science. Outside the field of actual knowledge can only lie a region of the vaguest opinion

---

[1] " *Terram non esse centrum Mundi, nec immobilem, sed moveri motu etiam diurno, est item propositio absurda, et falsa in Philosophia, et Theologice considerata ad minus erronea in fide*" (Congregation of Prelates and Cardinals, June 22, 1633).

and imagination, to which unfortunately men too often, but still with decreasing prevalence, pay higher respect than to knowledge.

We must here investigate a little more closely what the man of science means when he says, "*Here I am ignorant.*" In the first place, he does not mean that the method of science is necessarily inapplicable, and accordingly that some other method is to be sought for. In the next place, if the ignorance really arises from the inadequacy of the scientific method, then we may be quite sure that no other method whatsoever will reach the truth. The ignorance of science means the enforced ignorance of mankind. I should be sorry myself to assert that there is any field of either mental or physical perceptions which science may not in the long course of centuries enlighten. Who can give us the assurance that the fields already occupied by science are alone those in which knowledge is possible? Who, in the words of Galilei, is willing to set limits to the human intellect? It is true that this view is not held by several leading scientists, both in this country and Germany. They are not content with saying, "We *are* ignorant," but they add, with regard to certain classes of facts, "Mankind must *always* be ignorant." Thus in England Professor Huxley has invented the term *Agnostic*, not so much for those who are ignorant as for those who limit the possibility of knowledge in certain fields. In Germany Professor E. du Bois-Reymond has raised the cry, "*Ignorabimus*" ("We shall be ignorant"), and both his brother and he have undertaken the difficult task of demonstrating that with regard to certain problems human knowledge is impossible.[1] We must, however, note that in these cases we are not concerned with the limitation of the scientific method, but with the denial of the possibility that any method whatever can lead to knowledge. Now I venture to think that there is great danger in this cry, "We *shall* be ignorant." To cry "We are ignorant" is safe and

---

[1] See especially Paul du Bois-Reymond : *Über die Grundlagen der Erkenntnis in den exacten Wissenschaften.* Tübingen, 1890.

healthy, but the attempt to demonstrate an endless futurity of ignorance appears a modesty which approaches despair. Conscious of the past great achievements and the present restless activity of science, may we not do better to accept as our watchword that sentence of Galilei: "Who is willing to set limits to the human intellect?"—interpreting it by what evolution has taught us of the continual growth of man's intellectual powers.

Scientific ignorance may, as I have remarked (p. 18), either arise from an insufficient classification of facts, or be due to the unreality of the facts with which science has been called upon to deal. Let us take, for example, fields of thought which were very prominent in mediaeval times, such as alchemy, astrology, witchcraft. In the fifteenth century nobody doubted the "facts" of astrology and witchcraft. Men were ignorant as to how the stars exerted their influence for good or ill; they did not know the exact mechanical process by which all the milk in a village was turned blue by a witch. But for them it was nevertheless a fact that the stars did influence human lives, and a fact that the witch had the power of turning the milk blue. Have we solved the problems of astrology and witchcraft to-day?

Do we now know how the stars influence human lives, or how witches turn milk blue? Not in the least. We have learnt to look upon the facts themselves as unreal, as vain imaginings of the untrained human mind; we have learnt that they could not be described scientifically because they involved notions which were in themselves contradictory and absurd. With alchemy the case was somewhat different. Here a false classification of real facts was combined with inconsistent sequences—that is, sequences not deduced by a rational method. So soon as science entered the field of alchemy with a true classification and a true method, alchemy was converted into chemistry and became an important branch of human knowledge. Now it will, I think, be found that the fields of inquiry, where science has not yet penetrated and where the scientist still confesses ignorance, are very like the

alchemy, astrology, and witchcraft of the Middle Ages.
Either they involve facts which are in themselves unreal
—conceptions which are self-contradictory and absurd, and
therefore incapable of analysis by the scientific or any
other method,—or, on the other hand, our ignorance arises
from an inadequate classification and a neglect of scientific
method.

This is the actual state of the case with those mental
and spiritual phenomena which are said to lie outside the
proper scope of science, or which appear to be disregarded
by scientific men. No better example can be taken than
the range of phenomena which are entitled Spiritualism.
Here science is asked to analyse a series of facts which
are to a great extent unreal, which arise from the vain
imaginings of untrained minds and from atavistic tendencies
to superstition. So far as the facts are of this character,
no account can be given of them, because, like the witch's
supernatural capacity, their unreality will be found at
bottom to make them self-contradictory. Combined,
however, with the unreal series of facts are probably
others, connected with hypnotic and other conditions,
which are real and only incomprehensible because there
is as yet scarcely any intelligent classification or true
application of scientific method. The former class of facts
will, like astrology, never be reduced to law, but will one
day be recognised as absurd ; the other, like alchemy,
may grow step by step into an important branch of
science. Whenever, therefore, we are tempted to desert
the scientific method of seeking truth, whenever the silence
of science suggests that some other gateway must be
sought to knowledge, let us inquire first whether the
elements of the problem, of whose solution we are ignorant,
may not after all, like the facts of witchcraft, arise from
a superstition, and be self-contradictory and incomprehensible because they are unreal.

If on inquiry we ascertain that the facts cannot
possibly be of this class, we must then remember that it
may require long ages of increasing toil and investigation
before the classification of the facts can be so complete

that science can express a definite judgment on their relationship. Let us suppose that the Emperor Karl V. had said to the learned of his day : " I want a method by which I can send a message in a few seconds to that new world, which my mariners take weeks in reaching. Put your heads together and solve the problem." Would they not undoubtedly have replied that the problem was impossible ? To propose it would have seemed as ridiculous to them as the suggestion that science should straightway solve many problems of life and mind seems to the learned of to-day. It required centuries spent in the discovery and classification of new facts before the Atlantic cable became a possibility. It may require the like or even a longer time to unriddle those psychical and biological enigmas to which I have referred ; but he who declares that they can never be solved by the scientific method is to my mind as rash as the man of the early sixteenth century would have been had he declared it utterly impossible that the problem of talking across the Atlantic Ocean should ever be solved.

§ 8.—*The Wide Domain of Science*

If I have put the case of science at all correctly, the reader will have recognised that modern science does much more than demand that it shall be left in undisturbed possession of what the theologian and metaphysician please to term its " legitimate field." It claims that the whole range of phenomena, mental as well as physical— the entire universe—is its field. It asserts that the scientific method is the sole gateway to the whole region of knowledge. The word science is here used in no narrow sense, but applies to all reasoning about facts which proceeds, from their accurate classification, to the appreciation of their relationship and sequence. The touchstone of science is the universal validity of its results for all normally constituted and duly instructed minds. Because the glitter of the great metaphysical systems becomes as dross when tried by this touchstone, we are compelled to classify them as interesting works of the imagination, and not as solid contributions to human knowledge.

Although science claims the whole universe as its field, it must not be supposed that it has reached, or ever can reach, complete knowledge in every department. Far from this, it confesses that its ignorance is more widely extended than its knowledge. In this very confession of ignorance, however, it finds a safeguard for future progress. Science cannot give its consent to man's development being some day again checked by the barriers which dogma and myth are ever erecting round territory that science has not yet effectually occupied. It cannot allow theologian or metaphysician, those Portuguese of the intellect, to establish a right to the foreshore of our present ignorance, and so hinder the settlement in due time of vast and yet unknown continents of thought. In the like barriers erected in the past science finds some of the greatest difficulties in the way of intellectual progress and social advance at the present. It is the want of impersonal judgment, of scientific method, and of accurate insight into facts, a want largely due to a non-scientific training, which renders clear thinking so rare, and random and irresponsible judgments so common, in the mass of our citizens to-day. Yet these citizens, owing to the growth of democracy, have graver problems to settle than probably any which have confronted their forefathers since the days of the Revolution.

§ 9.—*The Second Claim of Science*

Hitherto the sole ground on which we have considered the appeal of modern science to the citizen is the *indirect* influence it has upon conduct owing to the more efficient mental training which it provides. But we have further to recognise that science can on occasion adduce facts having far more *direct* bearing on social problems than any theory of the state propounded by the philosophers from the days of Plato to those of Hegel. I cannot bring home to the reader the possibility of this better than by citing some of the conclusions to which the theory of heredity elaborated by the German biologist Weismann introduces us. Weismann's theory lies on the borderland of scientific knowledge ; his results are still open to discussion, his conclusions to modification.[1]   But to indicate the manner in which science can directly influence conduct, we will assume for the time being Weismann's main conclusion to be correct.   One of the chief features of his theory is the non-inheritance by the offspring of characteristics acquired by the parents in the course of life.   Thus good or bad habits acquired by the father or mother in their lifetime are not inherited by their children.   The effects of special training or of education on the parents have no direct influence on the child before birth.   The parents are merely trustees who hand down their commingled stocks to their offspring.   From a bad stock can come only bad offspring, and if a member of such a stock is, owing to special training and education, an exception to his family, his offspring will still be born with the old taint.[2]   Now this conclusion of Weismann's—if it be valid, and all we can say at present is that the arguments in favour of it are remarkably strong—radically affects our judgment on the moral conduct of the individual, and on the duties of the state and society towards their degenerate members.   No degenerate and feeble stock will ever be converted into healthy and sound stock by the accumulated effects of education, good laws, and

---

[1] His theory of the "continuity of the germ plasm" is in many respects open to question, but his conclusion as to acquired characteristics being uninherited stands on firmer ground.   See Weismann, *Essays on Heredity and Kindred Biological Problems*, Oxford, 1889.   A good criticism will be found in C. Ll. Morgan's *Animal Life and Intelligence*, chap. v. ; a summary in W. P. Ball's *Are the Effects of Use and Disuse Inherited?*   The reader should also consult P. Geddes and J. A. Thomsom, *The Evolution of Sex*, and a long discussion in *Nature*, vols. xl. and xli. (*sub indice*, Weismann, *Heredity*).

[2] Class, poverty, localisation do much to approximately isolate stock, to aggregate the unfit even in modern civilisation.   The mingling of good and bad stock due to dispersion is not to be commended, for it degenerates the good as much as it improves the bad.   What we need is a check to the fertility of the inferior stocks, and this can only arise with new social habits and new conceptions of the social and the anti-social in conduct.

sanitary surroundings. Such means may render the individual members of the stock passable if not strong members of society, but the same process will have to be gone through again and again with their offspring, and this in ever-widening circles, if the stock, owing to the conditions in which society has placed it, is able to increase in numbers. The suspension of that process of natural selection which in an earlier struggle for existence crushed out feeble and degenerate stocks, may be a real danger to society, if society relies solely on changed environment for converting its inherited bad into an inheritable good. If society is to shape its own future—if we are to replace the stern processes of natural law, which have raised us to our present high standard of civilisation, by milder methods of eliminating the unfit—then we must be peculiarly cautious that in following our strong social instincts we do not at the same time weaken society by rendering the propagation of bad stock more and more easy.

If the views of Weismann be correct—if the bad man can by the influence of education and surroundings be made good, but the bad stock can never be converted into good stock—then we see how grave a responsibility is cast at the present day upon every citizen, who directly or indirectly has to consider problems relating to the state endowment of education, the revision and administration of the Poor Law, and, above all, the conduct of public and private charities annually disposing of immense resources. In all problems of this kind the blind social instinct and the individual bias at present form extremely strong factors of our judgment. Yet these very problems are just those which, affecting the whole future of our society, its stability and its efficiency, require us, as good citizens, above all to understand and obey the laws of healthy social development.

The example we have considered will not be futile, nor its lessons worthless, should Weismann's views after all be inaccurate. It is clear that in social problems of the kind I have referred to, the laws of heredity, whatever

they may be, must profoundly influence our judgment.
The conduct of parent to child, and of society to its anti-
social members, can never be placed on sound and permanent bases unless regard be paid to what science has to
tell us as to the fundamental problems of inheritance. The
" philosophical" method can never lead to a real theory
of morals. Strange as it may seem, the laboratory
experiments of a biologist may have greater weight than
all the theories of the state from Plato to Hegel! The
scientific classification of facts, biological or historical, the
observation of their correlation and sequence, the resulting
absolute, as opposed to the individual judgment—these
are the sole means by which we can reach truth in such a
vital social question as that of heredity. In these considerations alone there appears to be sufficient justification
for the national endowment of science, and for the universal
training of our citizens in scientific methods of thought.
Each one of us is now called upon to give a judgment
upon an immense variety of problems, crucial for our
social existence. If that judgment confirms measures and
conduct tending to the increased welfare of society, then
it may be termed a moral, or, what is the same thing, a
social judgment. It follows, then, that to ensure a judgment's being moral, method and knowledge are essential
to its formation. It cannot be too often insisted upon
that the formation of a moral judgment—that is, one
which the individual is reasonably certain will tend to
social welfare—does not depend solely on the readiness
to sacrifice individual gain or comfort, or on the impulse
to act unselfishly : it depends in the first place on knowledge and method. The first demand of the state upon
the individual is not for self-sacrifice, but for self-develop-
ment. The man who gives a thousand pounds to a vast
and vague scheme of charity may or may not be acting
socially ; his self-sacrifice, if it be such, proves nothing ;
but the man who gives a vote, either directly or even
indirectly, in the choice of a representative, after forming
a judgment based upon *knowledge*, is undoubtedly acting
socially, and is fulfilling a higher standard of citizenship.

§ 10.—*The Third Claim of Science*

Thus far I have been more particularly examining the influence of science on our treatment of social problems. I have endeavoured to point out that science cannot legitimately be excluded from any field of investigation after truth, and that, further, not only is its *method* essential to good citizenship, but that its *results* bear closely on the practical treatment of many social difficulties. In this I have endeavoured to justify the state endowment and teaching of pure science as apart from its technical applications. If in this justification I have laid most stress on the advantages of scientific method—on the training which science gives us in the appreciation of evidence, in the classification of facts, and in the elimination of personal bias, in all that may be termed exactness of mind—we must still remember that ultimately the *direct* influence of pure science on practical life is enormous. The observations of Newton on the relation between the motions of a falling stone and the moon, of Galvani on the convulsive movements of frogs' legs in contact with iron and copper, of Darwin on the adaptation of woodpeckers, of tree-frogs, and of seeds to their surroundings, of Kirchhoff on certain lines which occur in the spectrum of sunlight, of other investigators on the life-history of bacteria—these and kindred observations have not only revolutionised our conception of the universe, but they have revolutionised, or are revolutionising, our practical life, our means of transit, our social conduct, our treatment of disease. What at the instant of its discovery appears to be only a sequence of purely theoretical interest, becomes the basis of discoveries which in the end profoundly modify the conditions of human life. It is impossible to say of any result of pure science that it will not some day be the starting-point of wide-reaching technical applications. The frogs' legs of Galvani and the Atlantic cable seem wide enough apart, but the former was the starting-point of the series of investigations which ended in the latter. In the recent discovery of Hertz that the action of electro-magnetism is propagated in waves like light—in his confirmation of Maxwell's theory that light is only a special phase of electro-magnetic action—we have a result which, if of striking interest to pure science, seems yet to have no immediate practical application.[1]   But that man would indeed be a bold dogmatist who would venture to assert that the results which may ultimately flow from this discovery of Hertz's will not, in a generation or two, do more to revolutionise life than the frogs' legs of Galvani achieved when they led to the perfection of the electric telegraph.

§ 11.—*Science and the Imagination*

There is another aspect from which it is right that we should regard pure science—one that makes no appeal to its utility in practical life, but touches a side of our nature which the reader may have thought that I have entirely neglected.   There is an element in our being which is not satisfied by the formal processes of reasoning ; it is the imaginative or aesthetic side, the side to which the poets and philosophers appeal, and one which science cannot, to be scientific, disregard.   We have seen that the imagination must not replace the reason in the deduction of relation and law from classified facts.   But, none the less, disciplined imagination has been at the bottom of all great scientific discoveries.   All great scientists have, in a certain sense, been great artists ; the man with no imagination may collect facts, but he cannot make great discoveries.   If I were compelled to name the Englishmen who during our generation have had the widest imaginations and exercised them most beneficially, I think I should put the novelists and poets on one side and say Michael Faraday and Charles Darwin.   Now it is very needful to understand the exact part imagination plays in pure science.   We can, perhaps, best achieve this result by considering the following proposition : Pure science has a further strong claim upon us on

---

[1] Even since this sentence was written a first and initially quite unexpected application to practical life has arisen in wireless telegraphy !

account of the exercise it gives to the imaginative faculties
and the gratification it provides for the aesthetic judgment.
The exact meaning of the terms "scientific fact" and
"scientific law" will be considered in later chapters, but
for the present let us suppose an elaborate classification
of such facts has been made, and their relationships and
sequences carefully traced. What is the next stage in
the process of scientific investigation? Undoubtedly it
is the use of the imagination The discovery of some
single statement, some brief *formula* from which the
whole group of facts is seen to flow, is the work, not of
the mere cataloguer, but of the man endowed with creative
imagination. The single statement, the brief formula,
the few words of which replace in our minds a wide
range of relationships between isolated phenomena, is
what we term a scientific *law*. Such a law, relieving our
memory from the burden of individual sequences, enables
us, with the minimum of intellectual fatigue, to grasp a
vast complexity of natural or social phenomena. The
discovery of law is therefore the peculiar function of the
creative imagination. But this imagination has to be a
disciplined one. It has in the first place to appreciate the
whole range of facts, which require to be resumed in a
single statement; and then when the law is reached—
often by what seems solely the inspired imagination of
genius—it must be tested and criticised by its discoverer
in every conceivable way, till he is certain that the
imagination has not played him false, and that his law
is in real agreement with the whole group of phenomena
which it resumes. Herein lies the key-note to the
scientific use of the imagination. Hundreds of men have
allowed their imagination to solve the universe, but the
men who have contributed to our real understanding of
natural phenomena have been those who were unstinting
in their application of criticism to the product of their
imaginations. It is such criticism which is the essence
of the scientific use of the imagination, which is, indeed,
the very life-blood of science.[1]

[1] *La critique est la vie de la science*, says Victor Cousin.

No less an authority than Faraday writes :—

"The world little knows how many of the thoughts and theories which have passed through the mind of a scientific investigator have been crushed in silence and secrecy by his own severe criticism and adverse examination ; that in the most successful instances not a tenth of the suggestions, the hopes, the wishes, the preliminary conclusions have been realised."

§ 12.—*The Method of Science Illustrated*

The reader must not think that I am painting any ideal or purely theoretical method of scientific discovery. He will find the process described above accurately depicted by Darwin himself in the account he gives us of his discovery of the law of natural selection. After his return to England in 1837, he tells us,[1] it appeared to him that :—

"By collecting all facts which bore in any way on the variation of animals and plants under domestication and nature, some light might perhaps be thrown on the whole subject. My first note-book was opened in July 1837. I worked on true Baconian principles,[2] and, without any theory, collected facts on a wholesale scale, more especially with respect to domesticated productions, by printed inquiries, by conversation with skilful breeders and

---

[1] *The Life and Letters of Charles Darwin*, vol. i. p. 83.

[2] It is from men like Laplace and Darwin, who have devoted their lives to natural science, rather than from workers in the pure field of conception, like Mill and Stanley Jevons, that we must seek for a true estimate of the Baconian method. Beside Darwin's words we may place those of Laplace on Bacon :—

"Il a donné pour la recherche de la vérité, le précepte et non l'exemple. Mais en insistant avec toute la force de la raison et de l'éloquence, sur la nécessité d'abandonner les subtilités insignifiantes de l'école, pour se livrer aux observations et aux expériences, et en indiquant la vraie méthode de s'élever aux causes générales des phénomènes, ce grand philosophe a contribué aux progrès immenses que l'esprit humain a faits dans le beau siècle où il a terminé sa carrière " ("Théorie analytique des Probabilités," *Œuvres*, t. vii. p. clvi.). The carpenter who uses a tool is a better judge of its efficiency than the smith who forges it. For a good sketch of the estimation in which Bacon was held by his *scientific* contemporaries see the introduction to Prof. Fowler's edition of the *Novum Organum*.

gardeners, and by extensive reading. When I see the list of books of all kinds which I read and abstracted, including whole series of Journals and Transactions, I am surprised at my own industry. I soon perceived that selection was the keystone of man's success in making useful races of animals and plants. But how selection could be applied to organisms living in a state of nature remained for some time a mystery to me."

Here we have Darwin's scientific classification of facts, what he himself terms his "systematic inquiry." Upon the basis of this systematic inquiry comes the search for a law. This is the work of the imagination ; the inspiration in Darwin's case being apparently due to a perusal of Malthus' *Essay on Population*. But Darwin's imagination was of the disciplined scientific sort. Like Turgot, he knew that if the first thing is to invent a system, then the second is to be disgusted with it. Accordingly there followed the period of self-criticism, which lasted four or five years, and it was no less than *nineteen* years before he gave the world his discovery in its final form. Speaking of his inspiration that natural selection was the key to the mystery of the origin of species, he says :—

" Here, then, I had at last got a theory by which to work ; but I was so anxious to avoid prejudice, that I determined not for some time to write even the briefest sketch of it. In June 1842 (*i.e.* four years after the inspiration), I first allowed myself the satisfaction of writing a very brief abstract of my theory in pencil in 35 pages ; and this was enlarged during the summer of 1844 into one of 230 pages, which I had fairly copied out and still possess."

Finally an abstract from Darwin's manuscript was published with Wallace's Essay in 1858, and the *Origin of Species* appeared in 1859.

In like manner, Newton's imagination was only paralleled by that power of self-criticism which led him to lay aside a demonstration touching the gravitation of the moon for nearly eighteen years, until he had supplied a missing link in his reasoning. But our details of Newton's life and discoveries are too meagre for us to see his method as closely as we can Darwin's, and the account I have given of the latter is amply sufficient to show the actual application of scientific method, and the real part played in science by the disciplined use of the imagination.[1]

§ 13.—*Science and the Aesthetic Judgment*

We are justified, I think, in concluding that science does not cripple the imagination, but rather tends to exercise and discipline its functions. We have still, however, to consider another phase of the relationship of the imaginative faculty to pure science. When we see a great work of the creative imagination, a striking picture or a powerful drama, what is the essence of the fascination it exercises over us? Why does our aesthetic judgment pronounce it a true work of art? Is it not because we

---

[1] That the classification of facts is often largely guided by the imagination as well as the reason must be fully admitted. At the same time, an accurate classification, either due to the scientist himself or to previous workers, must exist in the scientist's mind before he can proceed to the discovery of law. Here, as elsewhere, the reader will find that I differ very widely from Stanley Jevons' views as developed in his *Principles of Science*. I cannot but feel that chapter xxvi. of that work would have been recast had the author been acquainted with Darwin's method of procedure. The account given by Jevons of the Newtonian method seems to me to lay insufficient stress upon the fact that Newton had a wide acquaintance with physics *before* he proceeded to use his imagination and test his theories by experiment—that is, to a period of self-criticism. The reason that pseudo-scientists cumber the reviewer's table with idle theories, often showing great imaginative power and ingenuity, is not solely want of self-criticism. Their theories, as a rule, are not such as the scientist himself would ever propound and criticise. Their impossibility is obvious, because their propounders have neither formed for themselves, nor been acquainted with others' classifications of the groups of facts which their theories are intended to summarise. Newton and Faraday *started* with full knowledge of the classifications of physical facts which had been formed in their own days, and proceeded to further conjoint theorising and classifying. Bacon, of whom Stanley Jevons is, I think, unreasonably contemptuous, lived at a time when but little had been done by way of classification, and he was wanting in the scientific imagination of a Newton or a Faraday. Hence the barrenness of his method in his own hands. The early history of the Royal Society's meetings shows how essentially the period of collection and classification of facts preceded that of valuable theory.

With Stanley Jevons' last chapter on *The Limits of Scientific Method* the present writer can only express his complete disagreement; many of its arguments appear to him unscientific, if it were not better to term them anti-scientific.

find concentrated into a brief statement, into a simple formula or a few symbols, a wide range of human emotions and feelings? Is it not because the poet or the artist has expressed for us in his representation the true relationship between a variety of emotions, which we, in a long course of experience, have been consciously or unconsciously classifying? Does not the beauty of the artist's work lie for us in the accuracy with which his symbols resume innumerable facts of our past emotional experience? The aesthetic judgment pronounces for or against the interpretation of the creative imagination according as that interpretation embodies or contradicts the phenomena of life, which we ourselves have observed.[1] It is only satisfied when the artist's formula contradicts none of the emotional phenomena which it is intended to resume. If this account of the aesthetic judgment be at all a true one, the reader will have remarked how exactly parallel it is to the scientific judgment.[2] But there is really more than mere parallelism between the two. The laws of science are, as we have seen, products of the creative imagination. They are the mental interpretations—the formulae under which we resume wide ranges of phenomena, the results of observation on the part of ourselves or of our fellow-men. The scientific interpretation of phenomena, the scientific account of the universe, is therefore the only one which can permanently satisfy the aesthetic judgment, for it is the only one which can never be entirely contradicted by our observation and experience. It is necessary to strongly emphasise this side of science, for we are frequently told that the growth of science is destroying the beauty and poetry of life. It is undoubtedly rendering many of the old interpretations of life meaningless, because it demonstrates that they are false to the facts which they profess to describe. It does not follow from this, however,

[1] How important a part length and variety of emotional experience play in the determination of the aesthetic judgment is easily noted by investigating the favourite authors and pictures of a few friends of diverse ages and conditions.

[2] The curious reader may be referred to Wordsworth's " General View of Poetry " in his preface to the *Lyrical Ballads*, 1815.

that the aesthetic and scientific judgments are opposed ; the fact is, that with the growth of our scientific knowledge the basis of the aesthetic judgment is changing and must change. There is more real beauty in what science has to tell us of the chemistry of a distant star, or in the life-history of a protozoon, than in any cosmogony produced by the creative imagination of a pre-scientific age. By "more real beauty" we are to understand that the aesthetic judgment will find more satisfaction, more permanent delight, in the former than in the latter. It is this continual gratification of the aesthetic judgment which is one of the chief delights of the pursuit of pure science.

§ 14.—*The Fourth Claim of Science*

There is an insatiable desire in the human breast to resume in some short formula, some brief statement, the facts of human experience. It leads the savage to "account" for all natural phenomena by deifying the wind and the stream and the tree. It leads civilised man, on the other hand, to express his emotional experience in works of art, and his physical and mental experience in the formulae or so-called laws of science. Both works of art and laws of science are the product of the creative imagination, both afford material for the gratification of the aesthetic judgment. It may seem at first sight strange to the reader that the laws of science should thus be associated with the creative imagination in man rather than with the physical world outside him. But, as we shall see in the course of the following chapters, the laws of science are products of the human mind rather than factors of the external world. Science endeavours to provide a mental *résumé* of the universe, and its last great claim to our support is the capacity it has for satisfying our cravings for a brief description of the history of the world. Such a brief description, a formula resuming all things, science has not yet found and may probably never find, but of this we may feel sure, that its method of seeking for one is the sole possible method, and that the truth it has reached is the only form of truth which can permanently satisfy the aesthetic judgment. For the present, then, it is better to be content with the fraction of a right solution than to beguile ourselves with the whole of a wrong solution. The former is at least a step towards the truth, and shows us the direction in which other steps may be taken. The latter cannot be in entire accordance with our past or future experience, and will therefore ultimately fail to satisfy the aesthetic judgment. Step by step that judgment, restless under the growth of positive knowledge, has discarded creed after creed, and philosophic system after philosophic system. Surely we might now be content to learn from the pages of history that only little by little, slowly line upon line, man, by the aid of organised observation and careful reasoning, can hope to reach knowledge of the truth, that science, in the broadest sense of the word, is the sole gateway to a knowledge which can harmonise with our past as well as with our possible future experience. As Clifford puts it, "Scientific thought is not an accompaniment or condition of human progress, but human progress itself."

SUMMARY

1. The scope of science is to ascertain truth in every possible branch of knowledge. There is no sphere of inquiry which lies outside the legitimate field of science. To draw a distinction between the scientific and philosophical fields is obscurantism.

2. The scientific method is marked by the following features :— (a) Careful and accurate classification of facts and observation of their correlation and sequence ; (b) the discovery of scientific laws by aid of the creative imagination ; (c) self-criticism and the final touchstone of equal validity for all normally constituted minds.

3. The claims of science to our support depend on : (a) The efficient mental training it provides for the citizen ; (b) the light it brings to bear on many important social problems ; (c) the increased comfort it adds to practical life ; (d) the permanent gratification it yields to the aesthetic judgment.

LITERATURE

BACON, FRANCIS.—Novum Organum, London, 1620. A good edition by
    T. Fowler. Clarendon Press, 1878.

BOIS-REYMOND, E. DU.—Über die Grenzen des Naturerkennens. Veit and Co., Leipzig, 1876.

BOIS-REYMOND, P. DU. — Über die Grundlagen der Erkenntnis in den exacten Wissenschaften. H. Laupp, Tübingen, 1890.

CLIFFORD, W. K.—Lectures and Essays. Macmillan, 1879. ("Aims and Instruments of Scientific Thought," "The Ethics of Belief," and "Virchow on the Teaching of Science.")

HAECKEL, E.—Freie Wissenschaft und freie Lehre. E. Schweizerbart, Stuttgart, 1878.

HALDANE, J. S.—"Life and Mechanism," Mind, ix. pp. 27-47; also Nature, vol. xxvii., 1883, p. 561, vol. xxiv., 1886, p. 73; and also Haldane, R. B., Proceedings of the Aristotelean Society, 1891, vol. i. No. 4, part i. pp. 22-27.

HELMHOLTZ, H.—On the Relation of the Natural Sciences to the Totality of the Sciences, translated by C. H. Schaible. London, 1869.

This occurs also in the Popular Lectures, translated by Atkinson and others, First Series, p. 1. Longmans, 1881.

HERSCHEL, Sir JOHN.—A Preliminary Dissertation on Natural Philosophy. London, 1830.

JEVONS, W. STANLEY.—The Principles of Science : A Treatise on Logic and Scientific Method, 2nd ed. Macmillan, 1877.

PEARSON, K.—The Ethic of Freethought : A Selection of Essays and Lectures ("The Enthusiasm of the Market-place and of the Study"). A. and C. Black, 2nd ed., 1901. The Chances of Death and other Studies in Evolution, vol. i. ("Science and Politics" and "Reaction"). Edward Arnold, 1897.

VIRCHOW, R.—Die Freiheit der Wissenschaft im modernen Staat (Versammlung deutscher Naturforscher). München, 1877.

CHAPTER II

THE FACTS OF SCIENCE

§ 1.—*The Reality of Things*

IN our first chapter we have frequently spoken of the classification of *facts* as the basis of the scientific method ; we have also had occasion to use the words *real* and *unreal, universe* and *phenomenon*. It is proper, therefore, that before proceeding further we should endeavour to clear up our ideas as to what these terms signify. We must strive to define a little more closely in what the material of science consists. We have seen that the legitimate field of science embraces all the mental and physical facts of the universe. But what are these facts in themselves, and what is for us the criterion of their reality ?

Let us start our investigation with some "external object," and as apparent simplicity will be satisfied by taking a familiar requisite of the author's calling, namely, a blackboard, let us take it.[1] We find an outer rectangular frame of brownish-yellow colour, which on closer inspection we presume to be wood, surrounding an inner fairly smooth surface painted black. We can measure a certain height, thickness, and breadth, we notice a certain degree of hardness, weight, resistance to breaking, and, if we examine further, a certain temperature, for the board feels to us cold or warm. Now although the blackboard at first sight appears a very simple object, we see

---

[1] The blackboard as an "object-lesson" is such a favourite instance with the writer, that the reader will perhaps pardon him the use of it here. *Seine Mundart klebt iedem an.*

that it at once leads us up to a very complex group of properties. In common talk we attribute all these properties to the blackboard, but when we begin to think over the matter carefully we shall find that the real link between them is by no means so simple as it seems to be. To begin with, I receive certain impressions of size and shape and colour by means of my organs of sight, and these enable me to pronounce with very considerable certainty that the object is a blackboard made of wood and coated with paint, even before I have touched or measured it. I *infer* that I shall find it hard and heavy, that I could if I pleased saw it up, and that I should find it to possess various other properties which I have learnt to *associate* with wood and paint. These inferences and associations are something which I *add* to the sight-impressions, and which I myself contribute from my past experience and put into the object—blackboard. I might have reached my conception of the blackboard by impressions of touch and not by those of sight. Blindfolded I might have judged of its size and shape, of its hardness and surface texture, and then have inferred its probable use and appearance, and associated with it all blackboard characteristics. In both cases it must be noted that a *sine qua non* of the existence of an *actual* blackboard is some immediate sense-impression to start with. The sense-impressions which determine the reality of the external object may be very few indeed, the object may be largely constructed by inferences and associations, but *some* sense-impressions there must be if I am to term the object real, and not a product merely of my imagination. The existence of a certain number of sense-impressions leads me to infer the possibility of my receiving others, and this possibility I can, if I please, put to the test.

I have heard of the Capitol at Washington, and although I have never been to America, I am convinced of the reality of America and the Capitol—that is, I believe certain sense-impressions would be experienced by me if I put myself in the proper circumstances. In this case I have had indirect sense-impressions, contact with

Americans, and with ships and chattels coming from America, which lead me to believe in the "reality" of America and of what my eyes or ears have told me of its contents. In constructing the Capitol it is clear that past experience of a variety of kinds is largely drawn upon. But it must be noted that this past experience is itself based upon sense-impressions of one kind or another. These sense-impressions have been as it were stored in the memory. A sense-impression, if sufficiently strong, leaves in our brain some more or less permanent trace of itself, which is rendered manifest in the form of association whenever an immediate sense-impression of a like kind recurs. The stored effects of past sense-impressions form to a great extent what we are accustomed to speak of as an "external object." On this account such an object must be recognised as largely constructed by ourselves; we add to a greater or less number of immediate sense-impressions an associated group of stored sense-impressions. The proportion of the two contributions will depend largely on the keenness of our organs of sense and on the length and variety of our experience. Owing to the large amount we ourselves contribute to most external objects, Professor Lloyd Morgan, in the able discussion of this matter in his *Animal Life and Intelligence* (p. 312), proposes to use the term *construct* for the external object. For our present purpose, it is very needful to bear in mind that an external object is in general a construct—that is, a combination of immediate with past or stored sense-impressions. The reality of a thing depends upon the possibility of its occurring in whole or part as a group of immediate sense-impressions.[1]

---

[1] The division between the real and unreal, and again between the real and ideal, is less distinct than many may think. For example, the planet Neptune passed from the ideal to the real, but the atom is still ideal. The ideal passes into the real when its perceptual equivalent is found, but the unreal can never become real. Thus the concepts of the metaphysicians, Kant's *thing in itself* or Clifford's *mind stuff*, are in my sense of the words unreal (not ideal), they cannot become immediate sense-impressions, but the physical hypotheses as to the nature of matter are ideal (not unreal), for they do not lie absolutely outside the field of possible sense-impressions.

§ 2.—*Sense-Impressions and Consciousness*

This conception of reality as based upon sense-impressions requires careful consideration and some reservations and modifications. Let us examine a little more closely what we are to understand by the word sense-impression. In turning round quickly in my chair, I knock my knee against a sharp edge of the table. Without any thought of what I am doing, my hand moves down and rubs the bruised part, or the knee may cause me so much discomfort that I get up, think of what I shall do, and settle to apply some arnica. Now the two actions on my part appear of totally different character—at least on first examination. In both cases physiologists tell us that as a primary stage a message is carried from the affected part by what is termed a *sensory nerve* to the brain. The manner in which this nerve conveys its message is without doubt physical, although its exact *modus operandi* is still unknown. At the brain what we term the sense-impression is formed, and there most probably some physical change takes place which remains with a greater or less degree of persistence in the case of those stored sense-impressions which we term memories. Everything up to the receipt of the sense-impression by the brain is what we are accustomed to term physical or mechanical; it is a legitimate inference to suppose that what from the psychical aspect we term memory has also a physical side, that the brain takes for every memory a permanent physical impress, whether by change in the molecular constitution or in the elementary motions of the brain-substance, and that such physical impress is the source of our stored sense-impression.[1] These physical impresses play an important part in the manner in which future sense-impressions of a like character are received. If these immediate sense-impressions be of sufficient strength, or amplitude as we might perhaps venture to say,

---

[1] The closest physical analogies to the "permanent impresses" termed memory are the *set* and *after-strain* of the elastician. To assert that they are more than analogies would be to usurp the function of the physiologist.

they will call into some sort of activity a number of physical impresses due to past sense-impressions allied, or, to use a more suggestive word, *attuned* to the immediate sense-impression. The immediate sense-impression is conditioned by the physical impresses of the past, and the general result is that complex of present and stored sense-impressions which we have termed a "construct."

Besides the *sensory* nerves which convey the messages to the brain, there are other nerves which proceed from the brain and control the muscles, termed *motor nerves*. Through these motor nerves a message is sent to my hand bidding it rub my bruised knee. This message may be sent immediately or after my fingers have been dipped in arnica. In the latter case a very complex process has been gone through. I have realised that the sense-impression corresponds to a bruised knee, that arnica is good for a bruise, that a bottle of arnica is to be found in a certain cupboard, and so forth. Clearly the sense-impression has been conditioned by a number of past impresses before the motor nerve of the arm is called into play to rub the knee. The process is described as think-ing, and as a variety of past experiences may come into play, the ultimate message to the motor nerves appears to us voluntary, and we call it an act of *will*, however much it is really conditioned by the stored sense-impressions of the past. On the other hand, when, without apparently exciting any past sense-impressions, the message from the sensory nerve no sooner reaches the brain than a command is sent along the motor nerve for the hand to rub the knee, I am said to act involuntarily, from instinct or habit. The whole process may be so rapid, I may be so absorbed in my work, that I never realised the message from the sensory nerve at all. I do not even say to myself, " I have knocked my knee and rubbed it." Only a spectator, perhaps, has been conscious of the whole process of knee-knocking and rubbing. Now this is in many respects an important result. I can receive a sense-impression without recognising it, or a sense-impression does not involve consciousness. In this case there is no exciting of a group of stored sense-impressions, no chain of what we term thoughts intervening between the immediate sense-impression and the message to the motor nerve. Thus what we term consciousness is largely, if not wholly, due to the stock of stored impresses, and to the manner in which these condition the messages given to the motor nerves when a sensory nerve has conveyed a message to the brain. The measure of consciousness will thus largely depend on (1) the extent and variety of past sense-impressions, and (2) the degree to which the brain can permanently preserve the impress of these sense-impressions, or what might be termed the complexity and plasticity of the brain.

§ 3.—*The Brain as a Central Telephone Exchange*

The view of brain activity here discussed may perhaps be elucidated by comparing the brain to the central office of a telephone exchange, from which wires radiate to the subscribers A, B, C, D, E, F, etc., who are senders, and to W, X, Y, Z, etc., who are receivers of messages. A, having notified to the company that he never intends to correspond with anybody but W, his wire is joined to W's, and the clerk remains unconscious of the arrival of the message from A and its despatch to W, although it passes through his office.[1] There is indeed no call-bell. This corresponds to an instinctive exertion following unconsciously on a sense-impression. Next the clerk finds by experience that B invariably desires to correspond with X, and consequently whenever he hears B's call-bell he links him mechanically to X, without stopping for a moment his perusal of *Tit-Bits*. This corresponds to any habitual exertion following unconsciously on a sense-impression. Lastly, C, D, E, and F may set their bells ringing for a variety of purposes; the clerk has in each

---

[1] If these wires were connected *outside* the office, we should have an analogy to certain possibilities of reflex action, which arise from sensory and motor nerves being linked before reaching the brain—*e.g.* a frog's leg will be moved so as to rub an irritated point on its back even after the removal of the brain

case to answer their demands, but this may require him to listen to the special communications of these subscribers, to examine his lists, his post-office directory, or any other source of information stored in his office. Finally, he shunts their wires so as to bring them in circuit with those of Y and Z, which seem to best suit the nature of the demands. This corresponds to an exertion following consciously on the receipt of a sense-impression. In all cases the activity of the exchange arises from the receipt of a message from one of a possibly great but still finite number of senders, A, B, C, D, etc. ; the originality of the clerk is confined to immediately following their behests or to satisfying their demands to the best of his ability by the information stored in his office. The analogy, of course, must not be pressed too far—in particular, senders and receivers must be considered distinct, for sensory and motor nerves do not appear to interchange functions. But the conception of the brain as a central exchange certainly casts considerable light not only on the action of sensory and motor nerves, but also on thought and consciousness. Without sense-impressions there would be nothing to store ; without the faculty of receiving permanent impress, without memory, there would be no possibility of thought ; and without this thought, this period of hesitation between sense-impression and exertion, there would be no consciousness. When an exertion follows immediately on a sense-impression we speak of the exertion as involuntary, our action as subject to the mechanical control of the " external object " to which we attribute the sense-impression. On the other hand, when the exertion is conditioned by stored sense-impresses we term our action voluntary. We speak of it as determined from " within ourselves," and assert the " freedom of our will." In the former case the exertion is conditioned solely by the immediate sense-impression ; in the latter it is conditioned by a complex of impressions partly im- mediate and partly stored. The past training, the past history and experience which mould character and de- termine the will, are really based on sense-impressions received at one time or another, and hence we may say that exertion, whether immediate or deferred, is to a large extent the product, directly or indirectly, of sense-impressions.

§ 4.—*The Nature of Thought*

There are still one or two points to be noted here. In the first place, the immediate sense-impression is to be looked upon as the spark which kindles thought, which brings into play the still remaining impresses of past sense-impressions. But the complexity of the human brain is such, its stored sense-impressions are linked together in so many and diverse ways—partly by continual thinking, partly by immediate sense-impressions occurring in proximity and so linking together apparently discordant groups of past impressions—that we are not always able to recognise the relation between an immediate sense-impression and the resulting train of thought. Nor, on the other hand, can we always trace back a train of thought to the immediate sense-impression from which it started. Yet we may take it for certain that elements of thought are ultimately the permanent impresses of past sense-impressions, and that thought itself is started by immediate sense-impressions.[1]

This statement must not be in any way supposed to narrow the material of thought to those combinations of "external objects" which we associate with immediate sense-impressions. Thought once excited, the mind passes with wonderful activity from one stored impression to another, it classifies these impressions, analyses or simplifies their characteristics, and forms general notions of properties and modes. It proceeds from the direct—what might perhaps be termed the physical—association of memory, to the indirect or mental association ; it passes from

[1] The exact train of thought which follows an immediate sense-impression depends largely on the physical condition of the brain at the time of its receipt, and is further largely conditioned by the mode in which stored sense-impressions have been previously excited, *i.e.* the extent to which memory has been exercised in the past.

perceiving to *conceiving*. The mental association or recognition of relation between the impresses of past sense-impressions has probably, if we could follow it, as definite a physical side as the physical association of immedate sense-impressions with past impresses. But the physical side of the impress is only a reaonable inference from the physical nature of the immediate sense-impression, and we must therefore content ourselves at present by considering it highly probable that every process of thought has a physical aspect, even if we are very far as yet from being able to trace it out.

This process of mental association we can only recognise as certainly occurring in our individual selves. The reason why we infer it in others we shall consider later. The amount of it, however, in our individual selves must largely depend on the variety and extent of our store of impresses, and further on the individual capacity for thinking, or on the form and development of the physical organ wherein the process of thinking takes place, *i.e.* on the brain. The brain in the individual man is probably considerably influenced by heredity, by health, by exercise, and by other factors, but speaking generally the physical instruments of thought in two normal human beings are machines of the same type, varying indeed in efficiency, but not in kind or function. For the same two normal human beings the organs of sense are also machines of the same type and thus within limits only capable of conveying the same sense - impressions to the brain. Herein consists the similarity of the universe for all normal human beings. The same type of physical organ receives the same sense-impressions and forms the same "constructs." Two normal perceptive faculties construct practically the same universe. Were this not true, the results of thinking in one mind would have no validity for a second mind. The universal validity of science depends upon the similarity of the perceptive and reasoning faculties in normal civilised men.

The above discussion of the nature of thought is ot course incomplete ; it offers no real explanation of the psychical side of thought. It is merely intended to suggest the manner in which we may consider thought to be associated with its physical accompaniments. What the actual relations between the psychical and physical aspects of thought are, we do not know, and, as in all such cases, it is best to directly confess our ignorance. It is no use, indeed only dangerous, in the present state of our knowledge with regard to psychology and the physics of the brain, to fill the void of ignorance by hypotheses which can neither be proven nor refuted. Thus if we say that thought and motion are the same thing seen from different sides, we make no real progress in our analysis, for we can form no conception whatever as to what the nature in itself of this thing may be. Indeed, if we go further and compare thought and motion to the concave and convex sides of the same surface, we may do positive harm rather than good ; for convexity and concavity when accurately defined by the mathematician are not different qualities, but only degrees of the same quantity, curvature, passing the one into the other through zero-curvature or flatness, On the other hand, the distinction between the psychical and physical aspects of brain activity seems to be essentially one of quality, not of degree. It is better to content ourselves in the present state of our knowledge by remarking that in all probability sense-impressions lead to certain physical (including under this term possible chemical) activities of the brain, and that these activities are recognised by each individual *for himself only* under the form of thought. Each individual recognises his own consciousness, perceives that the interval between sensation and exertion is occupied by a certain psychical process. We recognise consciousness in our individual selves, we *assume* it to exist in others.

§ 5.—*Other-Consciousness as an Eject*

The assumption just referred to is by no means of the same nature as that which we make every moment in the formation of what we have termed constructs from a limited group of immediate sense-impressions. I see the shape, size, and colour of the blackboard, and I *assume* that I shall find it hard and heavy. But here the assumed properties are capable of being put to the direct test of immediate sense-impression. I can touch and lift the blackboard and complete my analysis of its properties. Even the Capitol in Washington, of which I have had no direct sense-impression, is capable of being put to the same sort of direct test. Another man's consciousness, however, can never, it is said, be directly perceived by sense-impression, I can only *infer* its existence from the apparent similarity of our nervous systems, from observing the same hesitation in his case as in my own between sense-impression and exertion, and from the similarity between his activities and my own. The inference is really not so great as the metaphysicians would wish us to believe. It is an inference ultimately based on the physical fact of the interval between sense-impression and exertion ; and though we cannot as yet physically demonstrate another person's consciousness, neither can we demonstrate physically that earth-grown apples would fall at the surface of the planet of a fixed star, nor that atoms really are component parts in the structure of matter. It may be suggested that if our organs of sense were finer, or our means of locomotion more complete, we might be able to see atoms or to carry earth-grown apples to a fixed star—in other words, to test physically, or by immediate sense-impression, these inferences. But :—

"When I come to the conclusion that *you* are conscious, and that there are objects in your consciousness similar to those in mine, I am not inferring any actual or possible feelings of my own, but *your* feelings, which are not, and cannot by any possibility become, objects in my consciousness." [1]

To this it may be replied, that, were our physiological knowledge and surgical manipulation sufficiently complete, it is conceivable that it would be possible for me to be

[1] W. K. Clifford, "On the Nature of Things-in-Themselves," *Lectures and Essays*, vol. ii. p. 72.

conscious of your feelings, to recongise your consciousness as a direct sense-impression ; let us say, for example, by connecting the *cortex* of your brain with that of mine through a suitable commissure of nerve-substance. The possibility of this physical verification of other-consciousness does not seem more remote than that of a journey to a fixed star. Indeed, there are some who think that without this hypothetical nerve-connection the processes popularly termed " anticipating another person's wishes," " reading his thoughts," etc., have in them the elements of a sense-impression of other-consciousness, and are not entirely indirect inferences from practical experience.

Clifford has given the name *eject* to existences which, like other-consciousness, are only inferred, and the name is a convenient one. At the same time it seems to me doubtful whether the distinction between *object* (what might possibly come to my consciousness as a direct sense-impression) and *eject* is so marked as he would have us to believe. The complicated physical motions of another person's brain, it is admitted, might possibly be objective realities to me ; but, on the other hand, might not the hypothetical brain commissure render me just as certain of the workings of another person's consciousness as I am of my own ? In this respect, therefore, it does not seem necessary to assert that consciousness lies outside the field of science, or must perforce escape the methods of physical experiment and research. We may be far enough removed from knowledge at the present time, but I see no logical hindrance to our asserting that in the dim future we might possibly obtain objective acquaintance with what at present appears merely as an eject. We may say this indeed without any dogmatic assumption that psychical effects can all be *reduced* to physical motion. Psychical effects are without doubt excited by and accompanied by physical action, and our only assumption is the not unreasonable one, that a suitable physical link might transfer an appreciation of psychical activity from one psychical centre to another.

§ 6.—*Attitude of Science towards Ejects*

Indeed in some respects other-consciousness appears less beyond our reach than many inferred existences. Some physicists infer the existence of atoms, although they have had no experience of any individual atom, because the hypothesis of their existence enables them to briefly resume a number of sense-impressions. We infer the existence of other-consciousness for a precisely similar reason ; but in this case we have the advantage of knowing at least one individual consciousness, namely, our own. We see in ourselves how it links sense-impression and deferred exertion. While the atom, like other-consciousness, might possibly some day attain to objective reality, there are certain conceptions dealt with by science for which, as we shall see in the sequel, this is impossible. For example, our geometrical ideas of curves and surfaces are of this character. None the less, although they might with greater logic be termed *ejects* than, perhaps, other-consciousness, there are few who would deny that they have their ultimate origin in sense-impressions, from which they have been extracted or isolated by the process of mental generalisation, to which we have previously referred (p. 46). A still more marked class of conceptions, which we are incapable of verifying directly by any form of immediate sense-impression, is that of historical facts. We believe that King John really signed *Magna Charta*, and that there was a period when snow-fields and glaciers covered the greater part of England, yet these conceptions can never have come to our consciousness as direct sense-impressions, nor can they be verified in like manner. They are conclusions we have reached by a long chain of inferences, starting in direct sense-impressions and ending in that which, unlike atom and other-consciousness, can by no possibility be verified directly by immediate sense-impression. When, therefore, we state that all the contents of our mind are ultimately based on sense-impressions, we must be careful to recognise that the mind has by classification and isolation proceeded to conceptions which are widely removed from sense-impressions capable of immediate verification.   The contents of the mind at any instant are very far from being identical with the range of actual or possible sense-impressions at that instant.   We are perpetually drawing inferences from our immediate and stored sense-impressions as to things which lie beyond immediate verification by sense ;—that is, we infer the existence of things which do not belong to the objective world, or which at any rate cannot be directly verified by immediate sense-impression as belonging to it at the present moment.   Strange as it may seem, science is largely based upon inferences of this kind ; its hypotheses lie to a great extent beyond the region of the immediately sensible, and it chiefly deals with conceptions drawn from sense-impressions, and not with sense-impressions themselves.

This point needs to be specially emphasised, for we are often told that the scientific method applies only to the external world of phenomena, and that the legitimate field of science lies solely among immediate sense-impressions.   The object of the present work is to insist on a directly contrary proposition, namely, that science is in reality a classification and analysis of the contents of the mind ; and the scientific method consists in drawing just comparisons and inferences from the stored impresses of past sense-impressions, and from the conceptions based upon them.   Not till the immediate sense-impression has reached the level of a conception, or at least a perception, does it become material for science.   In truth, the field of science is much more consciousness than an external world. In thus vindicating for science its mission as interpreter of conceptions rather than as investigator of a " natural law " ruling an " external world of material," I must remind the reader that science still considers the whole contents of the mind to be ultimately based on sense-impressions. Without sense-impressions there would be no consciousness, no conceptions for science to deal with.   In the next place we must be careful to note that not every conception, still less every inference, has scientific validity.

§ 7.—*The Scientific Validity of a Conception*

In order that a conception may have scientific validity, it must be self-consistent, and deducible from the perceptions of the normal human being. For instance, a centaur is not a self-consistent conception ; as soon as our knowledge of human and equine anatomy became sufficiently developed, the centaur became an unthinkable thing—a self-negating idea. As the man-horse is seen to be a compound of sense-impressions, which are irreconcilable anatomically, so the man-god, whose cruder type is Hercules, is also seen to be a chimera, a self-contradictory conception, as soon as we have clearly defined the physical and mental characteristics of man. But even if an individual mind has reached a conception, which at any rate for that mind is perfectly self-consistent, it does not follow that such a conception must have scientific validity, except as far as science may be concerned with the analysis of that individual mind. When a person conceives that one colour—green—suffices to describe the flowers and leaves of a rose-tree in my garden, I know that his conception may, after all, be self-consistent, it may be in perfect harmony with his sense-impressions. I merely assert that his perceptive faculty is *abnormal*, and hold him to be colour-blind. I may study the individual abnormality scientifically, but his conception has no scientific validity, for it is not deducible from the perceptions of the normal human being. Here indeed we have to proceed very cautiously if we are to determine what self-consistent conceptions have scientific validity. Above all, we must note that a conception does not cease to be valid because it has not been deduced by the majority of normal human beings from their perceptions. The conception that a new individual will originate from the union of a male and female cell may never have actually been deduced by a majority of normal human beings from their perceptions. But if any normal human being be trained in the proper methods of observation, and be placed in the right circumstances for investigating, he will draw from his perceptions this conception and not its negation. It is in this sense, therefore, that we are to understand the assertion that a conception to have scientific validity must be *deducible* from the perceptions of the normal human being.

The preceding paragraph shows us how important it is that the observations and experiments of science should be repeated as often and by as many observers as possible, in order to ensure that we are dealing with what has validity for all normal human beings, and not with the results of an abnormal perceptive faculty. It is not only, however, in experiments or observations which can be repeated easily, but still more in those which it is very difficult or impossible to repeat, that a great weight of responsibility lies upon the recorder and the public which is called upon to accept his results. An event may have occurred in the presence of a limited number of observers. That the event itself cannot recur, and that it is totally out of accord with our customary experience, are not in themselves sufficient grounds for disregarding it from the scientific standpoint. Yet what an onus is laid on the individual observers to test whether their perceptive faculties were normal on the occasion, and whether their conceptions of what took place were justified by their perceptions! Still greater onus is laid on men at large to criticise and probe the evidence given by such observers, to question whether they were men trained to observe, and calm and collected at the time of the reported event. Were they not, perhaps, in an exalted state of mind, biassed by pre-conceptions or hindered by the physical surroundings from clear perception? In short, were or were not their perceptive faculties in a normal condition, and were or were not the circumstances such that normal perception was possible? It can scarcely be questioned that when the truth or falsehood of an event or observation may have important bearings on conduct, over-doubt is more socially valuable than over-credulity.[1] In an age like our

---

[1] A good example of another class of experiment, that which it is difficult or unadvisable to repeat frequently, may be drawn from Brown-Séquard's

own, which is essentially an age of scientific inquiry, the prevalence of doubt and criticism ought not to be regarded with despair or as a sign of decadence. It is one of the safeguards of progress ;—*la critique est la vie de la science*, I must again repeat. One of the most fatal (and not so impossible) futures for science would be the institution of a scientific hierarchy which would brand as heretical all doubt as to its conclusions, all criticism of its results.

§ 8.—*The Scientific Validity of an Inference*

Much of what we have just said with regard to the scientific validity of conceptions holds with regard to the scientific validity of inferences, for conceptions pass imperceptibly into inferences. The scope of the present work will only permit us to discuss briefly the limits of legitimate inference and induction. For a fuller discussion the reader must be referred to treatises on logic, in particular to the chapters on inference and induction in Stanley Jevons' *Principles of Science* (chapters iv.-vii., x.-xii., especially). In the first place, the inference which is scientifically valid is that which could be drawn by every logically trained normal mind, if it were in possession of the conceptions upon which the inference has been based. Stress must here be laid on the distinction between " *could* be drawn " and " actually *would* be drawn." There are many minds which have clearly defined con-

researches on the inheritance by guinea-pigs of diseases acquired by their parents during life. These researches were conducted on a large scale and with great expenditure of time and animal life. (Brown-Séquard kept upwards of five hundred guinea-pigs at once.) Yet we must confess that if these experiments were conducted with every precaution that self-criticism might suggest, the " degrading effect" of inflicting disease and pain on this large amount of animal life would have been more than compensated by the light which the experiments might have cast on the socially important problem of the inheritance of acquired characters. Unfortunately, Brown-Séquard's conceptions and inferences do not appear valid to many scientists, and there rested upon this investigator the onus of proving that (1) all possible precautions for the accuracy of the results were actually taken, and (2), being taken, that the experiments were such as could reasonably have been supposed capable of solving the problems proposed.

ceptions, but refuse either from inertia or emotional bias to draw the inferences from them which can be drawn. A scientific inference—witness Darwin's as to the validity of natural selection —however logical, often takes years to overcome the inertia of the scientific world itself, and longer still may be the period before it forms an essential factor of the thought of the majority of normal-minded human beings. Yet, while logically trained minds which are able to draw inferences frequently neglect to do so, the illogically trained, on the other hand, unfortunately devote a large part of their ill-regulated energies to the production of every kind of cobweb of rash inference ; and this with such rapidity that the logical broom fails to keep pace with their activity. The mediaeval superstitions as to ghosts and necromancy are scarcely discredited before they reappear as theosophy and spiritualism.

The assumption which lies at the bottom of most popular fallacious inference might pass without reference, for it is obviously absurd, were it not, alas! so widely current. The assumption is simply this : that the strongest argument in favour of the truth of a statement is the absence or impossibility of a demonstration of its falsehood. Let us note some of its products :—All the constituents of material bodies are to be found in the atmosphere ; it is impossible to assert that these constituents could not be brought together.[1] *Ergo*, the Mahatmas of Thibet can take upon themselves material forms in St. John's Wood.——Science cannot demonstrate that the uniform action of material causes precludes the hypothesis of a benevolent Creator. *Ergo*, the primitive impulses and hopes of men receive confirmation from science.——Consciousness is found associated with matter ; we cannot demonstrate that consciousness is not found with *all* forms of matter. *Ergo*, all matter is conscious, or matter and mind are never found except in conjunction,

---

[1] " That is a noteworthy fact which I have not fully appreciated before," remarks the untrained mind, and is already more than half converted to theosophy.

and we may legitimately speak of the "consciousness of society" and the "consciousness of the universe." These are but a few actual samples of the current method of fallacious inference—usually, be it remarked, screened beneath an unlimited flow of words, and not thus exhibited in its naked absurdity. When we recognise how widely inferences of this character affect conduct in life, and yet grasp how unstable must be the basis of such conduct, how liable to be shaken to the foundations by the first stout logical breeze, then we understand how honest doubt is far healthier for the community, is more social, than unthinking inference, light-hearted and over-ready belief. Doubt is at least the first stage towards scientific inquiry; and it is better by far to have reached that stage than to have made no intellectual progress whatever.

§ 9.—*The Limits to Other-Consciousness*

We cannot better illustrate the limits of legitimate inference than by considering the example we have dealt with in § 5, and asking how far we may infer the existence of consciousness and of thought. We have seen (p. 52) that consciousness is associated with the process which *may* intervene in the brain between the receipt of a sense-impression from a sensory nerve and the despatch of a stimulus to action through a motor nerve. Consciousness is thus associated with physiological machinery of a certain character, which we sum up under brain and nerves. Further, it depends upon the lapse of an interval between sense-impression and exertion, this interval being filled, as it were, with the mutual resonance and cling-clang of stored sense-impressions and the conceptions drawn from them. Where no like machinery, no like interval can be observed, there we have no right to infer any consciousness. In our fellow-men we observe this same machinery and the like interval, and we infer consciousness, it may be as an eject, but as an eject which, as we have seen (p. 50), might not inconceivably, however improbably, become some day an object. In the lower forms of life we observe machinery approximately like our own, and a shorter and shorter interval between sense-impression and exertion ; we may reasonably infer consciousness, if in reduced intensity. We cannot, indeed, put our finger on a definite type of life and say here consciousness ends, but it is completely illogical to infer its existence where we can find no interval between sense-impression and exertion, or where we can find no nervous system. Because we cannot point to the exact form of material life at which consciousness ceases, we have no more right to infer that consciousness is associated with all life, still less with all forms of matter, than we have to infer that there must always be wine mixed with water, because so little wine can be mixed with water that we are unable to detect its presence. Will, too, as we have seen, is closely connected with consciousness ; it is the feeling in our individual selves when exertion flows from the store of past self-impresses " within us," and not from the immediate sense-impression which we term " without us." We are justified, therefore, in inferring the feeling of will as well as consciousness in nervous systems more or less akin to our own ; we may throw them out from ourselves, *eject* them into certain forms of material life. But those who eject them into matter, where no nervous system can be found, or even into existences which they postulate as immaterial, are not only exceeding enormously the bounds of scientific inference, but forming conceptions which, like that of the centaur, are inconsistent in themselves. From will and consciousness associated with material machinery we can infer nothing whatever as to will and consciousness without that machinery. We are passing by the trick of a common-name to things of which we can postulate absolutely nothing, and of which we are only unable to deny the existence when we give to that term a meaning wholly opposed to the customary one.[1]

---

[1] Consciousness without a nervous system is like a man without a vertebral column—a chimera, of which in customary language we deny the " existence."

§ 10.—*The Canons of Legitimate Inference*

We cannot here discuss more fully the limits of belief and legitimate inference. We shall, however, to some extent return to the subject when considering *Causation* and *Probability* in Chapter IV. But it may not be without service to state certain canons of legitimate inference with a few explanatory remarks, leaving the reader, if he so desire, to pursue the subject further in Stanley Jevons' *Principles of Science*, or in Clifford's essay on *The Ethics of Belief*. We ought first to notice that the use of the word *belief* in our language is changing : formerly it denoted something taken as definite and certain on the basis of some external authority ; now it has grown rather to denote credit given to a statement on a more or less sufficient balancing of probabilities.[1]

The change in usage marks the gradual transition of the basis of conviction from uncriticising faith to weighed probability. The canons we have referred to are the following :—

1. Where it is impossible to apply man's reason, that is to criticise and investigate at all, there it is not only unprofitable but anti-social to believe.

Belief is thus to be looked upon as an adjunct to knowledge, as a guide to action where decision is needful, but the probability is not so overwhelming as to amount to knowledge. To believe in a sphere where we cannot reason is anti-social, for it is a matter of common experience that such belief prejudices action in spheres where we can reason.

We cannot demonstrate that a man without a backbone may not exist " outside " the physical universe, only he would not be a man and would exist " nowhere." The existence of something of which we can postulate nothing at nowhere can never be legitimately inferred from conceptions based on sense-impressions. Such a man would be like Meister Eckehart's deity, who was a non-god, a non-spirit, a non-person, a non-idea, and of whom, he says, any assertion must be more false than true.

[1] Compare the older use in Biblical passages, such as " Jacob's heart fainted for he believed them not," and " Except ye see signs and wonders ye will not believe," or in Locke's definition of belief as adherence to a proposition of which one is *persuaded* but does not know to be true, with such modern usage as " I believe that you will find a cab on the stand, and that the train starts at half-past eight."

2. We may infer what we cannot verify by direct sense-impression only when the inference is from known things to unknown things of the like nature in similar surroundings.

Thus we may not infer an "infinite" consciousness outside the physical surroundings of finite consciousness ; we may not infer a man in the moon, however like in nature to ourselves, because the physical surroundings in the moon are not such as we find man in here, etc., etc.

3. We may infer the truth of tradition when its contents are of like character and continuous with men's present experience, and when there is reasonable ground for supposing its source to lie in persons knowing the facts and reporting what they knew.

The tradition that Wellington and Blücher won the battle of Waterloo fulfils the necessary conditions, while the miracle of Karl the Great and the adder fulfils neither condition.

4. While it is reasonable in the minor actions of life, where rapidity of decision is important, to infer on slight evidence and believe on small balances of probability, it is opposed to the true interests of society to take as a permanent standard of conduct a belief based on inadequate testimony.

This canon suggests that the acceptance, as habitual guides to conduct, of beliefs based on insufficient evidence, must lead to the want of a proper sense of the individual's responsibility for the important decisions of life. I have no right to believe at seven o'clock that a cab will be on the stand at eight o'clock, if my catching the train at half-past is of vital importance to others.

§ 11.—*The External Universe*

Before we draw from our present discussion any conclusions as to the facts of science we must return once more to the immediate sense-impression and examine its nature a little more closely. We are accustomed to talk of the "external world," of the "reality" outside us. We speak of individual objects having an existence independent of our own. The store of past sense-impressions, our thoughts and memories, although most probably they have beside their psychical element a close correspondence with some physical change or impress in the brain, are yet spoken of as *inside* ourselves. On the other hand, although if a sensory nerve be divided anywhere short of the brain we lose the corresponding class of sense-impression, we yet speak of many sense-impressions, such as form and texture, as existing outside ourselves. How close then can we actually get to this supposed world outside ourselves? Just as near as but no nearer than the brain terminals of the sensory nerves. We are like the clerk in the central telephone exchange who cannot get nearer to his customers than his end of the telephone wires. We are indeed worse off than the clerk, for to carry out the analogy properly we must suppose him *never to have been outside the telephone exchange, never to have seen a customer or any one like a customer—in short, never, except through the telephone wire, to have come in contact with the outside universe.* Of that " real " universe outside himself he would be able to form no direct impression ; the real universe for him would be the aggregate of his constructs from the messages which were brought by the telephone wires in his office. About those messages and the ideas raised in his mind by them he might reason and draw his inferences ; and his conclusions would be correct—for what? For the world of telephonic messages, for the type of messages which go through the telephone. Something definite and valuable he might know with regard to the spheres of action and of thought of his telephonic subscribers, but outside those spheres he could have no experience. Pent up in his office he could never have seen or touched even a telephonic subscriber *in himself.* Very much in the position of such a telephone clerk is the conscious *ego* of each one of us seated at the brain terminals of the sensory nerves. Not a step nearer than those terminals can the *ego* get to the " outer world," and what in and for themselves are the subscribers to its nerve exchange it has no means of ascertaining. Messages in the form of sense-impressions come flowing in from that "outside world," and these we analyse, classify, store up, and reason about. But of the nature of "things-in-themselves," of what may exist at the other end of our system of telephone wires, we know nothing at all.

But the reader, perhaps, remarks, " I not only see an object, but I can *touch* it. I can trace the nerve from the tip of my finger to the brain. I am not like the telephone clerk, I can follow my network of wires to their terminals and find what is at the other end of them." Can you, reader ? Think for a moment whether your *ego* has for one moment got away from his brain - exchange. The sense-impression that you call touch was just as much as sight felt only at the brain end of a sensory nerve. What has told you also of the nerve from the tip of your finger to your brain ? Why, sense-impressions also, messages conveyed along optic or tactile sensory nerves. In truth, all you have been doing is to employ one subscriber to your telephone exchange to tell you about the wire that goes to a second, but you are just as far as ever from tracing out for yourself the telephone wires to the individual subscriber and ascertaining what his nature is in and for himself. The immediate sense-impression is just as far removed from what you term the " outside world " as the store of impresses. If our telephone clerk had recorded by aid of a phonograph certain of the messages from the outside world on past occasions, then if any telephonic message on its receipt set several phonographs repeating past messages, we have an image analogous to what goes on in the brain. Both telephone and phonograph are equally removed from what the clerk might call the "real outside world," but they enable him through their sounds to construct a universe ; he projects those sounds, which are really inside his office, outside his office, and speaks of them as the external universe. This outside world is constructed by him from the contents of the inside sounds, which differ as widely from things-in-themselves as language, the symbol, must always differ from the thing it symbolises. For our telephone clerk sounds would be the real world, and yet we can see how conditioned and limited it would be by the range of his particular telephone subscribers and by the contents of their messages.

So it is with our brain; the sounds from telephone and phonograph correspond to immediate and stored sense-impressions. These sense-impressions we project as it were outwards and term the real world outside ourselves. But the things-in-themselves which the sense-impressions symbolise, the "reality," as the metaphysicians wish to call it, at the other end of the nerve, remains unknown and is unknowable. Reality of the external world lies for science and for us in combinations of form and colour and touch—sense-impressions as widely divergent from the thing "at the other end of the nerve" as the sound of the telephone from the subscriber at the other end of the wire. We are cribbed and confined in this world of sense-impressions like the exchange clerk in his world of sounds, and not a step beyond can we get. As his world is conditioned and limited by his particular network of wires, so ours is conditioned by our nervous system, by our organs of sense. Their peculiarities determine what is the nature of the outside world which we construct. It is the similarity in the organs of sense and in the perceptive faculty of all normal human beings which makes the outside world the same, or *practically* the same, for them all.[1] To return to the old analogy, it is as if two telephone exchanges had very nearly identical groups of subscribers. In this case a wire between the two exchanges would soon convince the imprisoned clerks that they had something in common and peculiar to themselves. That conviction corresponds in our comparison to the recognition of other-consciousness.

§ 12.—*Outside and Inside Myself*

We are now in a position to see clearly what is meant by "reality" and the "external world." Any group of

---

[1] Not *exactly* the same, for the range of the organs of sense and the powers of perception vary somewhat with different individual men, and probably enormously, if we take other life into account.

immediate sense-impressions we project outside ourselves and hold to be part of the external world.   As such we call it a *phenomenon*, and in practical life term it *real*. Together with the immediate sense-impression we often include something drawn from our store of past sense-impressions, which experience has taught us to associate

FIG. I.

with the immediate sense-impression.   Thus we assume the blackboard to be *hard*, although we may only have seen its shape and colour.   What we term the real world is thus partly based on immediate sense-impressions, partly on stored sense-impresses ; it is what has been called a *construct*.   For an individual the distinction between the real world and his thought of it is the presence of some immediate sense-impression. Thus the distinction of what is "outside" and what is "inside" myself at any instant depends entirely on the amount of immediate sense-impression. This has been very cleverly represented by the well-known German scientist, Professor Ernst Mach. In the accompanying sketch our professor may be seen lying on his back, and having closed his right eye, the picture represents what is presented to his left eye :—

"In a frame formed by the ridge of my eyebrow, by my nose, and my moustache, appears a part of my body, so far as it is visible, and also the things and space about it. . . . If I observe an element, A, within my field of vision, and investigate its connection with another element, B, within the same field, I go out of the domain of physics into that of physiology or psychology, if B, to use the apposite expression that a friend of mine employed upon seeing this drawing, passes through my skin." [1]

From our standpoint, neglecting for simplicity the immediate contributions of any other senses than that of sight, the picture represents that part of the professor's sense-impressions which for the instant forms his "outside world"; the rest was "inside"—existed for him only as a product of stored sense-impresses.

There is no better exercise for the mind than the endeavour to reduce the perceptions we have of "external things" to the simple sense impressions by which we know them. The arbitrary distinction between outside and inside ourselves is then clearly seen to be one merely of everyday practical convenience. Take a needle ; we say it is thin, bright, pointed, and so forth. What are these properties but a group of sense-impressions relating to form and colour associated with conceptions drawn from past sense-impressions ? Their immediate source is the activity of certain optic nerves. These sense-impressions form for us the *reality* of the needle. Nevertheless, they and the resulting construct are projected outside ourselves, and *supposed* to reside in an external thing, "the needle."

[1] "The Analysis of the Sensations—Anti-metaphysical," *The Monist*, vol. i. p. 59.

Now by mischance we run the needle into our finger ; another nerve is excited and an unpleasant sense-impression, one which we term painful, arises. This, on the other hand, we term " in ourselves," and do not project into the needle. Yet the colour and form which constitute for us the needle are just as much sense-impressions within us as the pain produced by its prick. The distinction between ourselves and the outside world is thus only an arbitrary, if a practically convenient, division between one type of sense-impression and another. The group of sense-impressions forming what I term *myself* is only a small subdivision of the vast world of sense-impressions. My arm is paralysed, I still term it part of me ; it mortifies, I am not quite so certain whether it is to be called part of me or not ; the surgeon cuts it off, it now ceases to be a part of that group of sense-impressions which I term " myself." Obviously the distinction between " outside " and " inside," between one individuality and a second, is only a practical one. How many of the group of sense-impressions we term a tree are light and atmosphere effects ? What might be termed the limits of the group of sense-impressions which we term an individual cannot be scientifically drawn. But to this point we shall return later.

§ 13.—*Sensations as the Ultimate Source of the Materials of Knowledge*

When we find that the mind is entirely limited to the one source, sense-impression, for its contents, that it can classify and analyse, associate and construct, but always with this same material, either in its immediate or stored form, then it is not difficult to understand what, and what only, can be the facts of science, the subject-matter of knowledge. Science, we say at once, deals with conceptions drawn ultimately from sense-impressions, and its legitimate field is the whole content of the human mind. Those who assert that science deals with the world of external phenomena are only stating a half-truth. Science only appeals to the world of phenomena—to immediate sense-impressions—with the view of testing and verifying the accuracy of its conceptions and inferences, the ultimate basis of which lies, as we have seen, in such immediate sense-impressions.   Science deals with the contents of the mind, the "inside" world, and the aim of its processes of classification and inference is precisely that of instinctive or mechanical association, namely, to enable the exertion, best calculated to preserve the race and give pleasure to the individual, to follow on the sense-impression with the least expenditure of time and of intellectual energy. Science is in this respect an economy of thought—a delicate tuning in the interests of the individual of those organs which receive sense-impressions and those which expedite activity.   The mind with scientific knowledge brings with the greatest rapidity and with the least intellectual strain fitting conceptions drawn from its store of sense-impressions to bear on its immediate sense-impressions, *i.e.* on the phenomenal world.

Turn the problem round and ponder over it as we may, beyond the sense-impression, beyond the brain terminals of the sensory nerves we cannot get. Of what is beyond them, of "things-in-themselves," as the metaphysicians term them, we can know but one characteristic, and this we can only describe as a capacity for producing sense-impressions, for sending messages along the sensory nerves to the brain.   This is the sole scientific statement which can be made with regard to what lies beyond sense-impressions.   But even in this statement we must be careful to analyse our meaning.   The methods of classification and inference, which hold for sense-impressions and for the conceptions based upon them, cannot be projected outside our minds, away from the sphere in which we know them to hold, into a sphere which we have recognised as unknown and unknowable.   The laws, if we can speak of laws, of this sphere must be as unknown as its contents, and therefore to talk of its contents as *producing* sense-impressions is an unwarranted inference, for we are asserting *cause and effect*—a law of phenomena or sense-impressions

—to hold in a region beyond our experience.[1] We *know* ourselves, and we *know* around us an impenetrable wall of sense-impressions.   There is no necessity, nay, there is want of logic, in the statement that behind sense-impressions there are "things-in-themselves" *producing* sense-impressions.   About this supersensuous sphere we may philosophise and dogmatise unprofitably, but we can never know usefully.   It is indeed an unjustifiable extension of the term knowledge to apply it to something which cannot be part of the mind's contents.   What is behind or beyond sense-impressions may or may not be of the same character as sense-impressions, we cannot say.   We feel the *surface* of a body to be hard, but its core may be either hard or soft, we cannot say; we can only legitimately call it a hard-surfaced body.   So it is with sense-impressions and what may be behind them; we can only say sense-impression-stuff, or, as we shall term it, with a somewhat divergent meaning from the customary, *sensation*.   By sensation we shall accordingly understand that of which the only knowable side is sense-impression.   Our object in using the word *sensation* instead of sense-impression will be to express our ignorance, our absolute agnosticism, as to whether sense-impressions are "produced" by unknowable "things-in-themselves," or whether behind them may not be something of their own nature.[2]   The outer world is for science a world of sensations, and sensation is known to us only as sense-impression.

[1] This will appear clearer when we have discussed the scientific meaning of *cause and effect*.   See Chapter IV.

[2] Herein lies the arid field of metaphysical discussion.   Behind sense-impressions, and as their source, the materialists place *Matter;* Berkeley placed *God;* Kant, and after him Schopenhauer, placed *Will;* and Clifford placed *Mind-stuff*.   Professor E. Mach in the paper referred to on p. 65 has reduced the outer world to its known surface, sense-impression, which he terms sensation—leaving no possible unknowable *plus* which we intend to signify by our use of the word sensation.   Such a theory cannot lead to scientific error, but it does not seem a justifiable inference from sense-impression.   The variety of inferences cited above shows the quagmire which has to be avoided, especially when the inferences are drawn with a view of influencing judgment in the world of sense.

§ 14.—*Shadow and Reality*

The reader who comes to these problems for the first time may feel inclined to assert that if this world of sense-impressions is the world of scientific knowledge, then science is dealing with a world of shadows and not of real substances. And yet, if such a reader will think over what happens when he knocks his elbow against the table, I think he will agree that it is the sense-impressions of hardness, and perhaps of pain, which are for him the realities, while the table, as a "source of these sense-impressions," is the shadow. Should he impatiently retort : " I see the table—four-legged, brass-handled, with black oak top shining under the elbow-grease of a past generation—there is the reality," let him stop for a moment to inquire whether his reality is not a construct from immediate and stored sense-impressions, of exactly the same character as the previous sense-impression of hardness. He will soon convince himself that the *real* table lies for him in the permanent association of a certain group of sense-impressions, and that the shadow table is what might be left were this group abstracted.

Let us return for a moment to our old friend the blackboard, represented for us by a complex of properties (p. 40). In the first place we have size and shape, then colour and temperature, and, lastly, other properties like hardness, strength, weight, etc. Clearly the blackboard consists for us in the permanent association of these properties, in a construct from our sense-impressions. Take away the size and shape, leaving all the other properties, and the group has ceased to be the blackboard, whatever else it may be. Suppose the colour to go, and again the blackboard has ceased to be. Finally, if the hardness and weight were to vanish, we might *see* the ghost of a blackboard, but we should soon convince ourselves that it was not the "reality" we had termed blackboard. Now, as the reader may be thinking that this blackboard has had too long an existence, at least in our pages, let us employ a carpenter to pull it to pieces and construct out of it a four-legged table. To cloak the obvious deficiencies of such a table we will cause it to be coated with a thick layer of enamel. We have now a four-legged red table. It is no longer a blackboard, and any person not knowing its origin would think us quite mad if we termed it a blackboard. We should probably, however, make our selves intelligible to him by stating that the "same material" as was once in a blackboard is now in the red table. For practical purposes this is very proper and convenient, but will it help us to an accurate conception of individuality if we say the blackboard and the table are the *same* thing? New paint and probably nails have been added; the carpenter may have supplied some additional wood; nay, more, if we begin to use our table a leg may come off and a new one be put on; after a time a fresh top would be an advantage, thus even the "material" of the table may cease to be same as that of the blackboard. Or again, since our table is probably a bad one, we will break it up and burn it, and so the blackboard will be converted into various gases and some ashes. What has now become of it? Size and shape, temperature and colour, hardness and strength have all gone. It is true that the chemist asserts that, if we could completely collect the gases and ashes, one sense-impression at least, that of weight, would remain the same in these and the original blackboard. But can we define sameness to consist in the permanence of some one sub-group of sense-impressions, notwithstanding the divergence of the majority? That permanence may be a link in the succession of our sense-impressions, but it can hardly be taken as a basis for defining individuality. *If* the gases and ashes could be collected! They have, indeed, been scattered to the winds, and in course of time may be absorbed by other vegetable life, ultimately, perhaps, to reappear as other blackboards, or even in legs of mutton. What has become of the "thing-in-itself" behind the group of sense-impressions we termed the original blackboard? Surely there is less permanence in it than in our sense-impressions of the blackboard—far less than in that

purely mental conception of sameness of weight.   Is it
not clear that the reality of the blackboard consisted for
us in the permanent grouping together of certain sense-
impressions, and that that reality has disappeared for
ever, except as a group of stored sense-impressions?

§ 15.—*Individuality*

Let us look again at this matter from a slightly
different standpoint.   Let us consider a personal friend,
and then suppose his height, his figure, the familiar
features of his face changed ;   let his entire round of
physical characteristics be profoundly modified, or vanish
altogether.   Next let us imagine his gifts, his prejudices,
the little weaknesses which really endear him to us, his
views on literature, politics, and social problems, all his
conceptions of human life removed or changed entirely.
In short, all the sense-impressions which constitute our
friend gone.   Clearly the friend would have ceased for us
to be, his individuality would have disappeared.   The
" reality " of the friend consists for us, not in some shadowy
" thing-in-itself," but in the persistency of the majority of
the group of sense-impressions by which we identify him.
We are accustomed to speak, for practical purposes, of
the boy and the man as the same individual, but the body
and mind have changed so enormously that the man
would probably feel the boy a perfect stranger if he were
brought into his presence.   We experience an uncomfortable sense of strangeness in looking at portraits of ourselves taken twenty or thirty years ago.   The properties
of youth and man are, indeed, so widely different, that
though for practical purposes we call them the same
person, we suspect that they would cut each other if they
chanced to meet in the street.   Clearly an individual is
not characterised by any sameness in the thing-in-itself,
but by the sameness in or permanency of a certain grouping of sense-impressions ;   this is the basis of our identification.

§ 16.—*The Futility of " Things-in-themselves "*

If at different times we meet with two groups of sense-impressions which differ very little from each other, we term them the same object or individual, and in practical life the test of identity is sameness in sense-impressions. The individuality of an object consists for us in the sameness of the great majority of our sense-impressions at two instants of time. In the case of growth, or rapid change in a group of sense-impressions, these instants must be taken closer and closer together as the rapidity increases. An impress of this sameness is then formed in the mind of the observer, and this constitutes in the case of the " external world " the recognition of individuality, in the case of the " internal world " the feeling of the continuity of the *ego*.

The considerations of this section upon what we are to understand by an individual thing are more important than they may appear to the reader at first sight. Are we forced to assume a shadowy " thing-in-itself " behind a group of sense-impressions in order to account for the permanency of objects, their existence as individuals? We have seen by the examples cited that the thing-in-itself would have to be supposed as transient as the sense-impressions, the permanency of which it is introduced to explain.[1] We are not, however, thrown back on any metaphysical inquiry as to things-in-themselves, in order to define for practical and scientific purposes the sameness of objects. Looking out of my window I see in a *certain* corner of my garden an ash-tree, with boughs of a *certain* form and shape, the sun is playing upon it and a *certain* light and shade is visible, the wind is turning over the leaves of the western branches. All this forms a complex group of sense-impressions. I close my eyes, and on opening them I have again a complex group of sense-

[1] Unless, indeed, we follow the crude materialism of Büchner, who takes the special sense-impressions which we term material to be the basis of all other sense-impressions, or to be the thing-in-itself. The individuality of the object is then thrown back on the sameness of the *unknown* elements of matter : see Chapter VII.

impressions, but slightly differing from the last, for the sun has left some leaves and fallen on others, and the wind is still ; but there is a sameness in the great majority of the sense-impressions of the two groups, and accordingly I term them one and the same individual tree—the ash-tree in my garden. If any one tells me that the sameness is due to some "thing-in-itself" which introduces the permanency into the group of sense-impressions, I can as little accept or deny his assertion as he forsooth can demonstrate anything about this shadowy thing-in-itself. He may call it *Matter*, or *God*, or *Will*, or *Mind-stuff*, but to do so serves no useful purpose, for it lies beyond the field of conception based on sense-impressions, beyond the sphere of logical inference or human knowledge. It is idle to postulate shadowy unknowables behind that real world of sense-impression in which we live. So far as they affect us and our conduct they are sense-impressions ; what they may be beyond is fantasy, not fact ; if indeed it be wise to assume a *beyond*, to postulate that the surface of sense-impressions which shuts us in, must of necessity shut something beyond out. Such unknowables do not assist us in grasping why groups of sense-impressions remain more or less permanently linked together. Our experience is that they are so linked, and their association is at the present, and may ever remain, as mysterious as is now the process by which the impresses of past sense-impressions are involuntarily linked together in the brain. Why is the thought "garden" in my mind invariably followed by the thought "cats"? The psychical basis of the association is not what I mean. I recognise it in the repeated experience of the havoc which the feline race has wrought in *my own* garden. But what is the *physical* nexus between the two conceptions as impresses in my brain? No one can say ; and yet this problem should be easier to answer than that of the nexus between the immediate sense-impressions we term objects. When physiological psychology has answered the former problem, then it will perhaps cease to be foolish for us to discuss the latter. Meanwhile let us confess our ignorance

and work where a harvest may even at present be
garnered.

§ 17.—*The Term Knowledge is Meaningless if applied to Unthinkable Things*

We are now, I think, in a position to clearly grasp
what we mean by the facts of science ; we see that its
field is ultimately based upon sensations. The familiar
side of sensations, sense-impressions, excite the mind to
the formation of constructs and conceptions, and these
again, by association and generalisation, furnish us with
the whole range of material to which the scientific method
applies. Shall we say that there are limits to the scientific
method—that our power of knowledge is imprisoned
within the narrow bounds of sense-impression ? The
question is an absurd one until it has been demonstrated
that a definition can be found for knowledge, which shall
include what does not lie in the plane of men's thought.
Our only experience of thought is associated with the
brain of man ; no inference can possibly be legitimate
which carries thought any further than nervous systems
akin to his. But human thought has its ultimate source
in sense-impressions, beyond which it cannot reach. We
can therefore only show that our knowledge is of necessity
limited by demonstrating that there are problems within
the sphere of man's thought, the only sphere where
thought can be legitimately said to exist, which can never
be solved. Such a demonstration I, for one, have never
met with, and I believe that it can never be given. We
must one and all confess that within the sphere of
thinkable things our knowledge is still the veriest shred.
We may even go so far as to assert that unto complete
knowledge we shall never attain in finite time ; but this
admission differs widely from the assertion that knowledge is possible as to things outside thought, but yet,
however possible, must be unattainable. Such an assertion must seem hopelessly absurd unless we use knowledge
as a term for some relationship which exists between

things outside thought. But even this strained use of the term, apart from its confusion, leads us no further than the statement that an unmeaning x exists among an unthinkable y and z.

SUMMARY

1. Immediate sense-impressions form permanent impresses in the brain which psychically correspond to memory. The union of immediate sense-impressions with associated stored impressions leads to the formation of "constructs," which we project "outside ourselves," and term phenomena. The real world lies for us in such constructs and not in shadowy things-in-themselves. "Outside" and "inside" oneself are alike ultimately based on sense-impressions; but from these sense-impressions by association, mechanical and mental, we form conceptions and draw inferences. These are the facts of science, and its field is essentially the contents of the mind.

2. When an interval elapses between sense-impression and exertion filled by cerebral activity marking the revival and combination of past sense-impressions stored as impresses we are said to think or to be conscious. Other-consciousness is an inference, which, not yet having been verified by immediate sense-impression, we term an *eject*; it is conceivable, however, that it could become an object. Consciousness has no meaning beyond nervous systems akin to our own; it is illogical to assert that all matter is conscious, still more that consciousness or will can exist outside matter.

3. The term knowledge is meaningless when extended beyond the sphere in which we may legitimately infer consciousness, or when applied to things outside the plane of thought, *i.e.* to metaphysical terms dignified by the name of conceptions although they do not ultimately flow from sense-impressions.

LITERATURE

These notices being only intended to indicate easily readable matter for lay students, it would be idle to provide here a list of philosophical classics. I therefore refer with some hesitation to Kant's Kritik der reinen Vernunft (Eng. Trans. by Max Müller). At the same time I know no elementary treatise on Kant's view of "things-in-themselves." As moderate in length and easy intelligible I cite :—

BERKELEY, G.—An Essay towards a New Theory of Vision, 1709; A Treatise concerning the Principles of Human Knowledge, 1710; and Three Dialogues between Hylas and Philonous, 1713. (All to be found in vol. i. of Wright's edition of the Works of G. B., 1843.)

CLIFFORD, W. K.—Lectures and Essays ("Body and Mind" and "On the Nature of Things-in-Themselves"). Further : Seeing and Thinking. Macmillan's "Nature" Series, 2nd ed., 1880.

HUXLEY, T. H.—Hume. Macmillan, 1879.

MACH, E.—Beiträge zur Analyse der Empfindungen, 1886.   Further:
"The Analysis of the Sensations—Anti-metaphysical," The Monist,
vol. i. pp. 48-68 ; "Sensations and the Elements of Reality," ibid.
pp. 393-400.

MORGAN, C. LL.—Animal Life and Intelligence, chaps. viii. and ix.
Arnold, 1891.

PEARSON, K.—The Ethic of Freethought ("Matter and Soul").   A. and
C. Black, 1901.

CHAPTER III

THE SCIENTIFIC LAW

§ 1.—*Résumé and Foreword*

THE discussions in my first two chapters have turned upon the nature of the method and the material of modern science. The material of science corresponds, we have seen, to all the constructs and concepts of the mind. Certain parts of this material, namely, constructs associated with immediate sense-impressions, we project outwards and speak of as physical facts or phenomena ; others, which are obtained by the mental processes of isolation and co-ordination from stored sense-impressions, we are accustomed to speak of as mental facts or concepts. In the case of both these classes of facts, the scientific method is the sole path by which we can attain to knowledge. The very word knowledge, indeed, only applies to the product of the scientific method in this field. Other methods, here or elsewhere, may lead to fantasy, as that of the poet or of the metaphysician, to belief or to superstition, but never to knowledge. As to the scientific method, we saw in our first chapter that it consists in the careful and often laborious classification [1] of facts, in the comparison of their relationships and sequences, and finally in the discovery by aid of the disciplined imagination of a brief statement or *formula*, which in a few words resumes a wide range of facts. Such a formula, we have

---

[1] The reader must be careful to recollect that *classification* is not identical with collection. It denotes the systematic association of kindred facts, the collection, not of all, but of relevant and crucial facts.

seen, is termed a *scientific law.* The object served by the discovery of such laws is the economy of thought ; the suitable association of conceptions drawn from stored sense-impressions, permits the fitting exertion to follow with the minimum of thought upon the receipt of an immediate sense-impression. The knowledge of scientific law enables us to replace or supplement mechanical association, or instinct, by mental association, or thought. It is the *forethought*, by aid of which man in a far higher degree than other animals is able to make the fitting exertion on the receipt of a novel group of sense-impressions.

We are accustomed to speak of scientific law, or at any rate of one form of it termed " natural law," as something universally valid ; we hold it to be as true for all men as for its original propounder. Nay, there are not wanting those who assert that natural law has a validity quite independent of the human minds which formulate, demonstrate, or accept it. We can easily observe that there is really something *sui generis* about the validity of natural law. The philosopher who propounds a new system, or the prophet who proclaims a new religion, may be absolutely convinced of the truth of his statement ; but it is the result of experience from time immemorial that he cannot *demonstrate* that truth so that conviction is produced in the mind of every rational being. A philosophic or a religious formula—for example, the idealism of Berkeley, the scepticism of Hume, or the self-renunciation of the mediaeval mystics—however sure its teachers may be that it is capable of rational demonstration, really appeals to the individual temperament, and is accepted or rejected according to the emotional sympathies of the individual. On the other hand, a formula, like that which Newton propounded for the motion of the planetary system, will be accepted by every rational mind which has once understood its terms and clearly analysed the facts which it resumes.[1] This is sufficient to indicate

[1] *One* system of planetary gravitation is accepted throughout the civilised world, but more than a dozen distinct theological systems and almost as many philosophical schools hardly suffice even for our own country.

that there must be some wide difference between philosophic and scientific systems, between theological and
scientific formulae. I shall endeavour in this chapter to
ascertain wherein this difference lies, to discover what is
the meaning of the word law when it is used in science, and
in what sense we can say that scientific law has universal
validity.

§ 2.—*Of the Word Law and its Meanings*

The term *law* probably recalls to the reader, in the
first place, the rules of conduct proclaimed by the state
and enforced under more or less heavy penalties against
certain classes of its citizens. Austin, the most luminous
English writer on jurisprudence,[1] who has devoted a very
large portion of his well-known work to a discussion of
the meaning of the word *law*, remarks :—

" A law, in the most general and comprehensive
acceptation in which the term, in its literal meaning, is
employed, may be said to be a rule laid down for the
guidance of an intelligent being by an intelligent being
having power over him."

He further goes on to observe that where there is such
a rule there is a command, and where there is a *command*
a corresponding *duty*. From this standpoint Austin proceeds to discuss the various types of law, such as civil,
moral, and divine law. It will be at once seen that with
Austin's definition of law there is no place left for law in
the scientific sense. He himself recognises this, for he
writes :—

" Besides the various sorts of rules which are included
in the literal acceptation of the term law, and those which
are by a close and striking analogy, though improperly,
termed laws, there are numerous applications of the term
law, which rest upon a slender analogy and are merely
metaphorical or figurative. Such is the case when we
talk of *laws* observed by the lower animals ; of *laws*
regulating the growth or decay of vegetables ; of *laws*

---

[1] *Lectures on Jurisprudence*, 4th ed.   London, 1879.

determining the movements of inanimate bodies or masses. For where *intelligence* is not, or where it is too bounded to take the name of *reason*, and therefore is too bounded to conceive the purpose of a law, there is not the *will* which law can work on, on which duty can incite or restrain. Yet through the misapplications of a *name*, flagrant as the metaphor is, has the field of jurisprudence and morals been deluged with muddy speculation " (p. 90).

Now Austin was absolutely in the right to emphasise the immense distinction between the use of the term *law* in science and its use in jurisprudence. There can be no doubt that the use of the same name for two totally different conceptions has led to a great deal of confusion. But on the one hand, if the flagrant misapplication of the scientific meaning of the word law to the fields of jurisprudence and morals has deluged them with " muddy speculation," the there is equal certainty on the other hand that the misapplication of the legal and moral sense of the term has been equally disadvantageous to clear thinking in the field of science. Austin probably had in his mind, when he wrote the above passage, works like Hegel's *Philosophy of Law*, in which we find the conception of the permanent and absolute character of scientific law applied to build up a system of absolute civil and moral law which somehow realises itself in human institutions. To the mind which has once thoroughly grasped the principle of evolution in its special factor of natural selection, the civil and moral laws of any given society at a particular time must appear as ultimate results of the struggle for existence between that society and its neighbours. The civil and moral codes of a community at any time are those which are on the average best adapted to its current needs, and best calculated to preserve its stability. They are very plastic, and change in every age with the growth and variation of social conditions. What is lawful is what is not prohibited by the laws of a particular society at a particular time ; what is moral is what tends to the welfare of a particular society at a particular time. We are all well acquainted with the continual change of civil law ; in fact we maintain an important body, Parliament, the chief function of which is to modify and adapt our laws, so that they shall be best fitted at each period to assist the community in its struggle for existence. Of the changes in moral law we are, perhaps, less conscious, but they are none the less real. There are very few acts which have not been moral at some period in the growth of one or other society, and there are in fact many questions with regard to which our moral judgment is totally different from that of our grandfathers. It is the relativity, or variability with age and community, of civil and moral law, which led Austin, I think, to speak somewhat strongly of the speculation which confuses such law with law in the absolute sense of science. A law in the legal or moral sense holds only for individuals and individual communities, and is capable of repeal or modification. A law of science will be seen in the sequel to hold for all normal human beings so long as their perceptive and reasoning faculties remain without material modification. The confusion of these two ideas is productive of that " muddy speculation " which finds analogies between natural laws and those of the spiritual or moral world.

Now if we find that two quite distinct ideas unfortunately bear the same name, we ought, in order to avoid confusion, to re-name one of them, or failing this, we ought on all occasions to be quite sure in which of the two senses we are using the name. Accordingly in my first chapter, in order to keep clear of the double sense of the word law, I endeavoured to replace it, when used in the scientific sense by some such phrase as the "brief statement or formula which resumes the relationship between a group of facts." Indeed it would be well, were it possible, to take the term *formula*, as already used by theologians and mathematicians, and use it in place of scientific or natural law. But the latter term has taken such root in our language that it would be hard indeed to replace it now. Besides, if the word law is to be used in one sense only, we may ask why it is the scientist rather than the jurist who is to surrender his right to the word ? The jurists say that historically they have the older claim to the word—that civil law existed long anterior to scientific law. This, in a certain sense, is perfectly true,[1] because the earliest attempts to codify laws for the conduct of men living in communities preceded any conscious recognition of scientific law. Now this leads us directly to a very important distinction, which, if it be neglected, is the source of much confusion. Does law exist before it receives expression and recognition? According to Austin, law in the juridical sense certainly does not, for such a law involves a " command," and a " corresponding duty "— that is, expression and recognition. What are we to say, then, with regard to scientific law—does it really exist before man has given expression to it? Has the word any meaning when unassociated with the mind of man? I hold that we must definitely answer " no " to both these questions, and I believe that the reader who has carefully followed my second chapter will see at once the grounds for this statement. A scientific law is related to the perceptions and conceptions formed by the perceptive and reasoning faculties in man ; it is meaningless except in association with these ; it is the *résumé* or *brief expression* of the relationships and sequences of certain groups of these perceptions and conceptions, and exists only when formulated by man.

§ 3.—*Natural Law relative to Man*

Let us take that branch of scientific law which deals with the so-called " outside world "—natural law. We have seen that this outside world is a *construct*. It consists of objects constructed partly from immediate sense-impressions, and partly from the store of impresses. For this reason the " outside world " is essentially conditioned by the perceptive and retentive faculties in man. Even the metaphysicians, who postulate " things-in-themselves," admit that sense-impressions in nowise *resemble* them, and that *man's* sense-impressions, so far from representing the

---

[1] For final conclusions as to the historical right to the word, see p. 94.

entire product of "things-in-themselves," are probably but the smallest portion of their "capacity for producing" sense-impression. Hence to talk about natural law as existing in "things-in-themselves" and apart from man's mind is again to assert an unmeaning x among an unthinkable y and z (p. 75). If nature for man is conditioned by his perceptive and retentive faculties, then natural law is conditioned by them also. It has no relation to something above and beyond man, but solely to the special products of his perceptive faculty. We have no right to infer its existence for things without a perceptive faculty, or even for perceptive faculties not closely akin to man's. I believe that a great deal of the obscurity involved in popular ideas about " Nature " would have been avoided had this been borne in mind.

A good instance of the *relativity* of natural law is to be found in the so-called *Second Law of Thermo-dynamics*. This law resumes a wide range of human experience, that is, of sequences observed in *our* sense-impressions, and embraces a great number of conclusions not only bearing on practical life, but upon that dissipation of energy which is even supposed to foreshadow the end of all life. The appreciation of the relativity of natural law is so important that the reader will, I trust, pardon me for citing the entire passage in which Clerk-Maxwell discusses this instance : [1]—

" One of the best-established facts in thermo-dynamics is that it is impossible in a system enclosed in an envelope which permits neither change of volume nor passage of heat, and in which both the temperature and pressure are everywhere the same, to produce any inequality of temperature or of pressure without the expenditure of work. This is the second law of thermo-dynamics, and it is undoubtedly true so long as we can deal with bodies only in mass, and have no power of perceiving or handling the separate molecules of which they are made up. But if we conceive a being whose faculties are so sharpened that he can follow every molecule in its course, such a

[1] *Theory of Heat*, 3rd ed. p. 308. Longmans, 1872.

being, whose attributes are still as essentially finite as our own, would be able to do what is at present impossible to us. For we have seen that the molecules in a vessel of air at uniform temperature are moving with velocities by no means uniform, though the mean velocity of any great number of them, arbitrarily selected, is almost exactly uniform. Now let us suppose that such a vessel is divided into two portions, A and B, by a division in which there is a small hole, and that a being,[1] who can see the individual molecules, opens and closes this hole, so as to allow only the swifter molecules to pass from A to B, and only the slower ones to pass from B to A. He will thus, without expenditure of work, raise the temperature of B and lower that of A, in contradiction to the second law of thermo-dynamics."

To render this passage clear to the lay reader, we have only to add that in this kinetic theory the temperature of a gas depends upon the mean speed of its molecules. Now the Second Law of thermo-dynamics resumes with undoubted correctness a wide range of human experience, and is, to that extent, as much a law of nature as that of gravitation. But the kinetic theory of gases, whether it be hypothetical or not, enables us to conceive a demon having a perceptive faculty differing rather in degree than quality from our own, for whom the Second Law of thermo-dynamics would not necessarily be a law of nature. Such a conception enables us to grasp how relative what we term nature is to the faculty which perceives it. Scientific law does not, any more than sense-impression, lie in a universe outside and unconditioned by ourselves. Clerk-Maxwell's demon would perceive nature as something totally different from our nature, and to a less extent this is in great probability true for the animal world, and even for man in different stages of growth and civilisation. The worlds of the child and of the

---

[1] This " being " has become known to fame as " Clerk-Maxwell's demon," but it must be noted that Clerk-Maxwell supposes the being's attributes " essentially finite as our own "—a peculiarity not usually associated with demons.

savage differ widely from that of normal civilised man. One half of the perceptions which the latter links together in a law of nature may be wanting to the former. Our law of the tides could have no meaning for a blind worm on the shore, for whom the moon had no existence.[1] By the contents and the manner of perception the law of nature is essentially conditioned for each perceptive faculty. To speak, therefore, of the universal validity of a law of nature has only meaning in so far as we refer to a certain type of perceptive faculty, namely, that of a normal human being.

§ 4.—*Man as the Maker of Natural Law*

The other problem with which we are concerned is the existence or non-existence of a scientific law before it has been postulated. Here the reader will feel, perhaps, inclined to remark : " Admitted that ' Nature ' is conditioned by man's perceptive faculty, surely the sequences of man's perceptions follow the same law whether man has formulated that law in words or not ? The law of gravitation ruled the motion of the planets ages before Newton was born." Yes and no, reader ; the answer must depend on how we define our terms. The sequences involved in man's perception of the motion of the heavenly bodies were doubtless much the same to Ptolemy and Newton ; to primitive man and to ourselves the motion of the sun is a common perception, but a sequence of sense-impressions is not in itself a law. That planets move, that a chick takes its origin from the egg, may be

---

[1] This point is well brought out by Prof. Lloyd Morgan in his *Animal Life and Intelligence*. After pointing out the widely different character of the sense organs in man and insects, he continues :—

" Remember their compound eyes with mosaic vision, coarser by far than our retinal vision, and their ocelli of problematical value, and the complete absence of muscular adjustments in either one or the other. Can we conceive that, with organs so different, anything like a similar perceptual world can be elaborated in their insect mind ? I for one cannot. Admitting therefore that their perceptions may be fairly surmised to be analogous, that their world is the result of construction, I do not see how we can for one moment suppose that the perceptual world they construct can in any accurate sense be said to resemble ours " (pp. 298-9, 356-7, 361).

sequences of sense-impressions, they may be facts to be
dealt with by science, but they are not laws in themselves, at least not in any useful interpretation of the
word. The changes of the whole planetary system might
be perceived, and even those perceptions translated into
words with a fulness surpassing that of our most accurate
modern observer, and yet neither the sequence of perceptions in itself nor the description involve the existence
of any law. The sequence of perceptions has to be
compared with other sequences, classification and generalisation have to follow; conceptions and ideas, pure products
of the mind, must be formed, before a description can be
given of a range of sequences which, by its conciseness
and comprehensiveness, is worthy of the name of scientific
law.

Let it be noted that in this it is not only the process
of reaching scientific law which is mental, but that the
law itself when reached involves an association of natural
facts or phenomena with mental conceptions, lying quite
outside the particular field of those phenomena. Without
the mental conceptions the law could not be, and it only
comes into existence when these mental conceptions are
first associated with the phenomena. The law of gravita-
tation is not so much the discovery by Newton of a rule
guiding the motion of the planets as his invention of a
method of briefly describing the sequences of sense-
impressions, which we term planetary motion. He did
this in terms of a purely mental conception, namely,
mutual acceleration.[1] Newton first brought the idea of
mutual acceleration of a certain type into association with
a certain range of phenomena, and was thus enabled to
state a formula, which, by what we may term mental
shorthand, resumes a vast number of observed sequences.
The statement of this formula was not so much the
discovery as the *creation* of the law of gravitation. We
are thus to understand by a law in science, *i.e.* by a "law
of nature," a *résumé* in mental shorthand, which replaces

___

[1] The reader will find mutual acceleration fully defined and discussed in
Chapter VIII.

for us a lengthy description of the sequences among our sense-impressions. Law in the scientific sense is thus essentially a product of the human mind and has no meaning apart from man. It owes its existence to the creative power of his intellect. There is more meaning in the statement that man gives laws to Nature than in its converse that Nature gives laws to man.

§ 5.—*The Two Senses of the Words "Natural Law"*

We have now traced at least one point of analogy between juridical and scientific law which I think escaped Austin, namely, both are the product of human intelligence. But we have at the same time seen the wide distinction between the two. The civil law involves a command and a duty ; the scientific law is a description, not a pre-scription. The civil law is valid only for a *special* community at a *special* time ; the scientific law is valid for *all* normal human beings, and is unchangeable so long as their perceptive faculties remain at the same stage of development.[1] For Austin, however, and for many other philosophers too, the law of nature was not the mental formula, but the repeated sequence of perceptions. This repeated sequence of perceptions they projected out of themselves, and considered as part of an external world unconditioned by and independent of man. In this sense of the word, a sense unfortunately far too common to-day, natural law could exist before it was recognised by man. In this sense natural law has a much older ancestry than civil law, of which it appears to be the parent. For tracing historically the growth of civil law, we find its origin in unwritten custom. The customs which the struggle for existence have gradually developed in a tribe become in course of time its earliest laws. Now, the farther we go back in the development of man, through more and more complete barbarism to a simply animal

---

[1] The average perceptive faculty is probably still changing slightly, however insensibly. Nevertheless the perceptive faculty is now among men fairly stable in type, as compared with the rapid change it must have under-gone during man's evolution from a lowly form of life.

condition, the more nearly we find customs merging in instinctive habits.   But the instinctive habit of a gregarious animal is very much akin to what Austin would have termed a natural law.   The laws relating to property and marriage in the civilised states of to-day can be traced back with more or less continuity to the instinctive habits of gregarious animals.   The historical origin, therefore, of civil law is to be sought in natural law in its older sense. Indeed this fact was recognised by the early Roman jurists, who refer to a *lex naturae* as existing alongside the civil law.   This law of nature they considered that animals as well as men had a knowledge of, and they made special reference to it in relation to marriage and the birth of children.   Now it is clear that, however flagrant in Austin's opinion the metaphor may be when we speak of the *laws* observed by animals, still the use of the word law in this sense is a very old one even among jurists themselves.

§ 6.—*Confusion between the two Senses of Natural Law*

But the Roman lawyers merely took the idea of natural law from the Greek philosophers, and it is to the Stoics especially that we owe a conception of law which is of value as illustrating the kind of obscurity which still attaches to the expression natural law in many minds.   The Stoics defined nature as the universe of things, and they declared this universe to be guided by reason.   But reason, because it is a directive power, forbidding and enjoining, they called law.   Now the law of nature they considered to take in some manner its rise in nature itself—there was no source of law to nature outside nature—and they accordingly defined this law of nature as a force inherent in the universe.   They further asserted that since reason cannot be twofold, and since man has reason as well as the universe, the reason in man and the universe must be the same, and therefore the law of nature must be the law by which men's actions ought to be guided.

The string of dogma and unwarranted inference marking

this argument—which, however, has only reached us at second-hand [1]—is characteristic enough. Yet the argument is noteworthy, for we find in it the three meanings of the term law with which we have been dealing hopelessly confused. The Stoics pass from the scientific law to the *lex naturae*,—the mere sequence of phenomena,—and then to the civil or moral law without in the least observing the magnitude of their spring; and what these early philosophers accomplished in this way has been surpassed by the devotees of philosophy and natural theology in later ages. One example will, perhaps, suffice for our present investigation. Richard Hooker, a divine of the sixteenth century, who achieved a remarkable reputation for himself by stating paradoxes based on a confusion between natural and moral law, thus defines *law* in general :—

" That which doth assign unto each thing the kind, that which doth moderate the force and power, that which doth appoint the form and measure of working, the same we term a Law " (*Ecclesiastical Polity*, Bk. I. ii.).

Hooker further considers that all things, including nature, have some operations " not violent or casual." This leads him to assert that such operations have " some fore-conceived end." Hence he holds that nature is guided by law, and that this law is a product of reason. Unlike the Stoics, Hooker placed this reason in a worker, God, outside and not inherent in Nature, otherwise his doctrine and the conclusions he draws from it closely resemble theirs. He was, however, aware of the elastic character of his definition of law, for he writes :—

" They, who thus are accustomed to speak, apply the name Law unto that only rule of working which a superior authority imposeth ; whereas we, somewhat more enlarging the sense thereof, term any kind of rule or canon whereby actions are framed, a law " (Bk. I. iii.).

The views of Hooker and the Stoics thus briefly sketched deserve careful consideration by the reader, as

---

[1] Marcus Aurelius, iv. 4, and Cicero, *De legibus*, i. 6-7. *Cf.* T. C. Sandars, *The Institutes of Justinian*, p. xxii. Longmans, 1878.

they suggest the type of fallacy into which we fall by ill-defined use of the term natural law.[1] In the first place these philosophers start from the conception of natural law as the mere concatenation of phenomena, the succession or routine of sense-impressions. In the next place as materialists they project these sense-impressions into a real outside world, unconditioned by and independent of man's perceptive faculty. Then they infer reason behind the concatenation of phenomena. Now reason is known to us only in association with consciousness, and we find consciousness only with the accompaniment of a certain type of nervous organism. Thus to infer reason in what has been previously postulated as outside and independent of this type of nervous organism is unjustifiable ; it may be dogma, but it is not logic. It makes little difference whether, with the Stoic, we assert that reason is inherent in nature, or, like Hooker, place the lawgiver outside nature as at once its creator and director. Both assertions lie completely outside the field of knowledge, and, as we have said of the like statements before, they logically refer to an unmeaning x existing among an unthinkable y and z (*i.e.* "realities" unconditioned by man's perceptive faculty).

§ 7.—*The Reason behind Nature*

But how, it may be asked, has the conception that reason exists behind phenomena become so widespread ? Why have so many philosophers and theologians, nay, even scientists,[2] used the " argument from design " ? The

---

[1] The study of fallacy in concrete examples ought to play a greater part in our educational curriculum. Certain works have a permanent value in this respect. I can conceive no better exercises for a student of logic or jurisprudence than an analysis of the paralogisms in Book I. of Hooker's *Ecclesiastical Polity ;* for a student of physics than a discovery of the fallacies in Mr. Grant Allen's *Force and Energy ;* or for both than a critical study of Drummond's *Natural Law in the Spiritual World ;* while a more difficult study in pseudo-science will be found in the first part of J. G. Vogt's *Das Wesen der Elektrizität und des Magnetismus.* The power of criticism and the logical insight thus attainable are in many respects as advantageous as the appreciation of method which results from the perusal of genuine science.

[2] *E.g.* Sir G. G. Stokes, in his otherwise most suggestive and masterly *Burnett Lectures on Light.*

duty of science does not end with showing an argument to be fallacious ; it has to investigate the origin of the fallacy and show the nature of the process by which it has arisen. In the present case I do not think we have far to seek. Briefly stated, the "argument from design" consists in the production of evidence from the laws of nature, tending to exhibit those laws as the product of a rational being or of reason in one or another form. Now, although in the law of nature defined as a mere concatenation of phenomena, as a sequence of sense-impressions, there is, so far as I can perceive, no evidence of reason in any intelligible sense of the word, yet in the law of science, and in that branch of it which in this work we have termed natural law, there is every evidence of reason. So soon as man begins to form conceptions from his sense-impressions, to combine, to isolate, and to generalise, then he begins to project his *own* reason into phenomena, to replace in his mind the stored sense impressions of past concatenations of phenomena by those brief *résumés* or formulae which describe the sequences of sense-impressions in mental shorthand. He begins to confuse the scientific law, the product of his own reason, with the mere concatenation of phenomena, the natural law in the sense of Hooker and the Stoics. As he projects his sense-impressions outside himself, and forgets that they are essentially conditioned by his own perceptive faculty, so he unconsciously severs himself from the products of his own reason, projects them into phenomena, only to refind them again and wonder what reason put them there. Here, in the double sense of the word natural law, lies the origin of much obscure speculation.

The reason we find in natural phenomena is surely put there by the only reason of which we have any experience, namely, the human reason. The mind of man in the process of classifying phenomena and formulating natural law introduces the element of reason into nature, and the logic man finds in the universe is but the reflection of his own reasoning faculty. A dog, if able to recognise the instinct which guides his actions, might very naturally suppose instinct and not reason to be the basis of natural phenomena, reflecting his own source of action into all he observed around him. Indeed, it seems to me more logical to find instinct than to find reason behind the setting and rising of the sun, for instinct at least does not presuppose consciousness. Perhaps if our dog were a Stoic dog the instinct would seem to him inherent in the universe itself, while had he been reared at the parsonage he would certainly fancy his kennel the product of an instinct supercanine. But both dog and man, in thus arguing beyond the sphere of legitimate inference, are also breaking a fundamental canon of the scientific method. This canon is practically due to Newton, and forbids us to seek superfluous causes for natural phenomena.[1] We ought not to look for new causes to account for any group of phenomena until we have shown that no known cause is capable of "explaining" it. In our next chapter we shall see more clearly what is to be understood by the words "cause" and "explanation," but for the present Newton's canon suffices to show us that the Stoics were unscientific in seeking for unknown or unknowable "reasons" inherent in nature, until they had demonstrated that the only rational faculty known to them—namely, that of man— was insufficient to account for the rational element they professed to observe in nature. What is reason? Where may we infer its existence? Can we proceed from this admissible reason to the rational element in natural law? —these are the questions the Stoics ought logically to have asked themselves. Our wonder ought not to be excited by the idea that "so vast a range of phenomena are ruled (*sic !*) by so simple a law as that of gravitation," but we ought to express our astonishment that the human mind is able to express by so brief a description such wide sequences of sense-impressions. This capacity of

[1] *Causas rerum naturalium non plures admitti debere, quam quae & verae sint & earum Phaenomenis explicandis sufficiunt. Natura enim simplex est & rerum causis superfluis non luxuriat.* Principia. (Editio Princeps, 1687, p. 402.) This "simplicity of nature" is, of course, pure dogma, but the *regula philosophandi* which forbids us to revel in superfluous causes is fundamental to our view of science as an economy of thought.

itself suggests some harmony, some relation between the perceptive and reasoning faculties in man—a matter to which I shall return later.

§ 8.—*True Relation of Civil and Natural Law*

Proceeding from Austin's definition of law, we have found it necessary to distinguish between two different ideas frequently confused under the term "natural law," namely, the mere concatenation of phenomena and the mental formula which gives brief expression to their sequences. Before we devote our undivided attention to the latter as the scientific conception of natural law, it may be of interest to clear up one or two remaining points with regard to civil and scientific law. While Austin, thinking especially of natural law in the old sense, states that any relation between the two is merely metaphorical, both the Stoics and Hooker conceive that the reason, or the lawgiver to be recognised behind phenomena, ought to guide man's moral conduct. Now if these philosophers were looking upon natural law as the product of the human reason there would be little to require further comment ; but, as we have seen, this is far from the case. The Stoics tell us that reason cannot be twofold, that it must be the same reason in both man and the universe, and that therefore the civil law of man is identical with natural law.[1] The inference is of course unjustifiable, for the *same* reason may be at work in two quite distinct fields. It is important to notice, however, that in one sense civil and moral laws are natural products ; they are products of particular phases of human growth. This growth is itself capable of treatment by the scientific method, and the sequence of its stages can be expressed by scientific formulae, or—looking at civil and moral law as objective phenomena—by natural laws. Thus civil law is a natural product, and not

[1] Up to the " sameness of the reason " there is little exception to be taken to the argument, but few of us would agree with the dictum of that ancient and upright judge, Sir John Powell, that "nothing is law that is not reason."

identical with natural law—any more than the particular
configuration of the planetary system at this moment is
identical with the law of gravitation.   We are now, I
think, in a position to draw a clear distinction between
civil (or moral) law and natural law.   Civil law takes its
origin in natural law in the old sense (p. 88), while its
growth and variation can, in broad outline at least, be
described in the brief formulae of science, or in natural
laws in the scientific sense.   Civil and moral laws are the
natural product of societies, and of classes within society,
struggling in the early days for self-preservation, and in
these later days for a maximum of individual and class
comfort.

A civil law, according to Austin, is a rule laid down
for the guidance of an intelligent being by an intelligent
being having power over him.   Such a rule varies with
every age and every society.   On the other hand, a natural
law is not laid down by one intelligent being for another ;
it involves no command or corresponding duty, and it is
valid for all normal human beings.   It has taken centuries
for men to arrive at a full appreciation of this distinction,
and it would be well could the distinction be now emphasised by the specialisation of the word *law* in one or
other of its senses.   We sadly need separate terms for the
routine of sense-impressions, for the brief description or
formula of science, and for the canon of social conduct, or,
in other words, for the perceptive order, the descriptive
order, and the prescriptive order.   Historically we cannot
say that any of these orders has the higher claim to the
title *law*, for the Roman ideas of law must at least be
traced back to their Greek parentage.   Here, in the Greek
word νόμος, law, the confusion centres, and at the same
time the historical origin of the confusion becomes apparent.   This word shows us that civil law originated in
custom, and yet Plato derives it from " distribution of
mind." [1]   Anything from the harmony of nature to the
strains of a song was for the Greek *law*.   In the conception of order or sequence, therefore, we see the historical

---

[1] *The Laws*, iv. 714, and see also iii. 700, and vii. 800.

origin of law in all its senses, and thus no claim to priority on the part of either jurist or scientist can be historically proven. No individual writer can hope with success to remould such old-established usage as is associated with the word law, and all he can strive to do is to keep clearly distinct in the mind of his readers the sense in which the word on each occasion is used.[1]

§ 9.—*Physical and Metaphysical Supersensuousness*

Having now analysed our ideas of law, and reached a definition of law in its scientific sense, it may be well even at the cost of repetition, to discuss at greater length our conclusions and their application to a reasoned theory of life. From the material provided by the senses, either directly or in the form of stored sense-impresses, we draw conceptions. About these conceptions we reason, endeavouring to ascertain their relationships and to express their sequences in those brief statements or formulae which we have termed scientific laws. In this process we often analyse the material of sense-impressions into elements which are not in themselves capable of forming distinct sense-impressions ; we reach conceptions which are not capable of direct verification by the senses ; that is to say, we can never, or at least we cannot at present, assert that these elements have objective reality (see our p. 51). Thus physicists reduce the groups of sense-impressions which we term material substances to the elements *molecule* and *atom*, and discuss the motion of these elements, which have never been, and perhaps never can become, direct sense-impressions. No physicist ever saw or felt an individual atom. Atom and molecule are intellectual conceptions by aid of which physicists classify phenomena and formulate the relationships between their sequences. From a certain standpoint, therefore, these conceptions of

---

[1] For the remainder of this work I shall, for convenience, however, speak of natural law in the old sense, or, as a mere routine of perceptions, as law in the *nomic* sense. Law in the nomic sense is thus no product of the reason, but a pure *order* of perceptions, while Bramhall's coinage *anomy* may be conveniently used for a breach in the routine of perceptions.

the physicist are *supersensuous*, that is, they do not at present represent direct sense-impressions ; but the reader must be careful not to confuse this kind of supersensuousness with that of the metaphysician.   The physicist looks upon the atom in one or other of two different ways : either the atom is real, that is, capable of being a direct sense-impression, or else it is ideal, that is, a purely mental conception by aid of which we are enabled to formulate natural laws.[1]   It is either a product of the perceptive faculty, or of the reflective or reasoning faculty in man.   It may pass from the latter to the former, from the ideal stage to the real ; but till it does so, it remains merely a conceptual basis for classifying sense-impressions, it is not an actuality.   On the other hand, the metaphysician asserts an existence for the supersensuous which is unconditioned by the perceptive or reflective faculties in man.   His supersensuous is at once incapable of being a sense-impression, and yet has a real existence apart from the imagination of men.   It is needless to say that such an existence involves an unproven and undemonstrable dogma.   Nevertheless, the magnitude of the gulf between the supersensuous of the physicist and that of the metaphysician is frequently neglected, and we are told that it is as logical to discuss " things-in-themselves " as molecules and atoms !

§ 10.—*Progress in the Formulating of Natural Law*

By the formation of conceptions, which may or may not have perceptual equivalents in the sphere of sense-impression, the scientist is able to classify and compare phenomena.   From their classification he passes to formulae or scientific laws describing their sequences and relationships.   The wider the range of phenomena embraced, and the simpler the statement of the law, the more nearly we consider that he has reached a " fundamental law of nature."   The progress of science lies in the continual discovery of more and more comprehensive

---

[1] That is, it is part of a physicist's mental shorthand.

formulae, by aid of which we can classify the relationships and sequences of more and more extensive groups of phenomena. The earlier formulae are not necessarily wrong,[1] they are merely replaced by others which in briefer language describe more facts.

We cannot do better than examine this process very briefly in a special case, namely, the motion of the planetary system. An easily observed part of this motion was the daily passage of the sun, its rising in the East and setting in the West. A primitive description of the motion consisted in the statement that the *same* sun which set in the West passed, hidden by northern mountains, along the surface of the *flat* earth and rose again in the East. The description was clearly very insufficient, but it was a first attempt at a scientific formula. An obvious improvement was soon made by limiting the surface of the earth and supposing the sun to go below the solid earth. The motion of the sun taken in conjunction with the motion of the stars led early astronomers to conclude that the earth was fixed in mid-space, and sun and stars were daily carried round it. The description thus improved was still far from complete ; the sun was observed to vary its position with regard to the fixed stars. Gradually and laboriously facts were accumulated, and in time those early astronomers concluded that the sun went round yearly in the same circle, this circle itself being carried round with the starry heavens once in a day. This formula embraced a wider field of phenomena than the earlier ones, and probably was as exact a description as men's perceptions of earth and sun allowed when it was invented. Hipparchus improved it by placing the earth not exactly in the centre of the sun's circle, and thus more accurately described certain apparent irregularities in the sun's motion. A still more complete description was adopted

---

[1] They are what the mathematician would term "first approximations," true when we neglect certain small quantities. In Nature it often happens that we do not observe the existence of these small quantities until we have long had the "first approximation" as our standard of comparison. Then we need a widening, not a rejection of "natural law."

by Ptolemy (A.D. 140) nearly three hundred years after Hipparchus, who, fixing the spherical earth, considered sun and moon to move in circles yearly round the earth, and the other planets in circles, whose centres again described circles round the earth. The whole of this system revolved daily round the earth with the stars. This, the famous Ptolemaic system, remained for many centuries the current formula, and even to this day the eccentrics of Hipparchus and epicycles of Ptolemy are not without service as elements of the more modern description. It would be wrong, I think, to say that the Ptolemaic system was an erroneous *explanation*, it was simply an insufficient attempt to *describe* in brief and accurate language a too limited range of phenomena. Then at the end of the Middle Ages came Copernicus, who got rid of the cumbersome sphere carrying the fixed stars by simply considering the earth to rotate round its axis, and of the epicycles, if not of the eccentrics, by treating the sun, not the earth, as the central point of the system. Here was an immense advance in brevity and accuracy of description ; but still more facts remained to be included, more difficulties to be analysed and overcome. This work was largely done by Keppler, who conceived the earth and planets to move in certain curves termed ellipses, of which the sun occupied a non-central point termed the focus. The formula of Keppler is one of the greatest achievements of the scientific method ; it was the work of a disciplined imagination analysing a laborious and minute classification of facts.[1] A more wide-embracing statement than that of Keppler was not only possible, however, but required ; and this was provided by Newton in a single formula which embraces not only the motion of the planets, but that of their moons and of bodies at their surfaces. This formula is the well-known law of gravitation, but it is just as much a *description* of what takes place in planetary motion as Keppler's laws are a

---

[1] The elaborate observations of Tycho Brahé. Keppler not only stated the form of the planetary path but the mode of its description in his famous three laws.

description—it is simply a briefer, more accurate, and more wide-embracing statement. The one can just as fitly as the other be termed a natural law.

The law of gravitation is a brief description of *how* every particle of matter in the universe is altering its motion with reference to every other particle. It does not tell us *why* particles thus move ; it does not tell us *why* the earth describes a certain curve round the sun. It simply resumes, in a few brief words, the relationships observed between a vast range of phenomena. It economises thought by stating in conceptual shorthand that routine of our perceptions which forms for us the universe of gravitating matter.

We have in the law of gravitation an excellent example of a scientific law. We see in its evolution the continual struggles of the human mind to reach a more and more comprehensive and exact formula, and at last Newton reaches one so simple and so wide-embracing that many have thought nothing further can be achieved in this direction. " Here," says Paul du Bois-Reymond, " is the limit to our possible knowledge." If the reader once grasps the characteristics of this law of Newton's he will understand the nature of all scientific law. Men study a range of facts—in the case of nature the material contents of their perceptive faculty—they classify and analyse, they discover relationships and sequences, and then they describe in the simplest possible terms the widest possible range of phenomena. How idle is it, then, to speak of the law of gravitation, or indeed of any scientific law, as *ruling* nature. Such laws simply *describe*, they never *explain* the routine of our perceptions, the sense-impressions we project into an " outside world."

The scientific law, while thus the product of a rational analysis of facts, is always liable to be replaced by a wider generalisation. Such replacement of one formula by another is indeed the regular course of scientific progress. The only final test we have of the truth of any law, of the sufficiency of its description, the only proof that our intellect has been keen enough to reach a formula extending to the whole range of facts it professes to resume, is the actual comparison of the results of the formula with the facts themselves—that is, historical observation or physical experiment.   This test is all that marks the division between scientific hypothesis and scientific law, and the scientific law itself must, with every increase of our perceptive powers, return to the position of hypothesis and be anew put to the test of experience. Yet what philosophic system, what fantasy of the metaphysical mind in the region of the supersensuous has stood like Newton's formula of gravitation without the least change, the least variation in its statement, for more than two hundred years?   Assuredly none ; they have all shifted their ground with every advance of man's positive knowledge.   They have not stood the test of experience ; they are phantasms, not truth ; for, as Sir John Herschel has said :—

" The grand, and indeed only, character of truth is its capability of enduring the test of universal experience, and coming unchanged out of every possible form of fair discussion."

§ 11.—*The Universality of Scientific Law*

The universality, the absolute character, which we attribute to scientific law is really relative to the human mind.   It is conditioned :—

1. By the perceptive faculty.   The outside world, the world of phenomena, must be practically the same for all normal human beings.

2. By the reflective faculty.   The processes of association and logical inference, and the inner world of stored impresses and conceptions must be practically the same for all normal human beings.

Now, when we classify a number of things together and give them the same name, we can only mean to signify that they closely resemble each other in structure and action.   Hence when we speak of *human* beings we are referring to a class which in the normal civilised condition have perceptive and reflective faculties nearly akin. It is therefore not surprising that normal human beings perceive the same world of phenomena, and reflect upon it in much the same manner. The "universality" of natural law, the "absolute validity" of the scientific method, depends on the resemblance between the perceptive and reflective faculties of one human mind and those of a second. Human minds are, within limits, all receiving and sifting-machines of one type. They accept only particular classes of sense-impressions—being like automatic sweetmeat-boxes which, if well constructed, refuse to act for any coin but a penny—and having received their material they arrange and analyse it, provided they are in working order, in practically the same manner. If they do not arrange and analyse it in this manner, we say that the mind is disordered, the reason wanting, the person mad. The sense-impressions of a madman may be as much reality for him as our sense-impressions are for us, but his mind does not sift them in the normal human fashion, and for him, therefore, our laws of nature are without meaning.

§ 12.—*The Routine of Perceptions is possibly a Product of the Perceptive Faculty*

The idea of the human mind as a sorting-machine is not without suggestion with regard to another important matter, namely, the routine nature of our sense-impressions. How far does this routine of sense-impressions depend upon the perceptive faculty? How far does it lie outside that faculty in the unknown and unknowable beyond of sensation (p. 68)? The question is one to which at present no definite answer can be given, and perhaps one to which no answer can ever be found. If, with the materialists, we make matter the thing-in-itself, we throw the routine back on something behind sense-impressions, and, therefore, unknowable. Precisely the same happens if, with Berkeley, we attribute the routine to the immediate action of a deity. Materialist and idealist are here at one in casting the routine of sense-impression into the unknowable. But the business of the scientist is to know, and therefore he will not lightly assent to throwing anything into the unknowable so long as known "causes" have not been shown to be insufficient. The scientific tendency would therefore be to consider the routine of our perceptions as due in some way to the structure of our perceptive faculty before we appeal to any supersensuous aid. Far, indeed, as science at present stands from any definite solution of the problem, there are yet one or two points which it may not be unprofitable to consider.

In the first place, have we any evidence that the perceptive faculty is a *selective* machine? We have already seen that it is possible at times for us to be unconscious of sensations which on other occasions we may keenly appreciate (p. 43). We have seen that the outside world constructed by an insect in all probability differs widely from our own (p. 85). To assume, therefore, sensations which form no part of our consciousness, perhaps no part of any consciousness, is not an illogical inference, for we proceed only from the known to what is like the known (p. 60), to an eject which might have been, or may one day be, an object.[1] No better way of realising the different selective powers of diverse perceptive faculties can be found than a walk with a dog. The man looks out upon a broad landscape, and the signs of life and activity he sees in the far distance may have deep meaning for him. The dog surveys the same landscape indifferently, but his whole attention is devoted to matters in his more immediate neighbourhood, of which the man is only indirectly conscious through the activity of the dog. Many things may be going on in the distance, which, if at hand, would have considerable interest for the

---

[1] "A feeling can exist by itself without forming part of a consciousness," writes Clifford in a paper, the main conclusion of which seems to me, however, quite unproven. ("On the Nature of Things-in-Themselves," *Lectures and Essays*, vol. i. p. 84.)

dog : some way off the man perceives the rabbits in the
field skirting the copse, quite in the distance a flock of
sheep on the high-road, and behind them the shepherd with
his collie—all these remain unobserved by the dog, or if
observed, unreasoned on.   Clearly the sense-impressions
corresponding to the distant landscape are far less complex and intense in the dog than in the man.   The
perceptive faculty in the dog selects certain sense-impressions, and these form for it reality ; that of the man
selects another and probably far more complex range,
which form in turn reality for him.   Both may be again
compared to automatic sweetmeat-boxes, which only work
on the insertion of coins of definite and different value.
Objective reality does not consist of the same sense-
impressions for man and dog.

    If we pass downwards from man to the lowest forms
of life, we shall find the range of sensations perceived
becoming less and less complex till they cease altogether
as perceptions with the cessation of consciousness.   Hence,
if we accept the theory of the evolution of man from the
lowliest types of life, we see a wild field of variation in
the matter of the perceptive faculty open to him.   Man
will evolve a power of perceiving those sensations, the
perception of which will on the whole help him in the
struggle for existence.[1]

    Now, step by step with the perceptive faculty the
reflective or reasoning faculty is developed ; the power
of sifting and arranging perceptions, the power of rapidly
passing from sense-impression to fitting exertion (p. 46),
is seen to be a factor of paramount importance to man in
the battle of life.   Without our being able at present to
clearly understand the relation between the perceptive
and reflective faculties in man, or the nature of their co-
ordination, it is still reasonable to suppose a close relation
between the two ; the one largely selects those perceptions
which the other is capable of analysing and resuming in

---

[1] Light and vision, sound and hearing, extension and touch, are known
not to be identical in range.   See Lord Kelvin's *Popular Lectures and
Addresses*, vol. i. pp. 278-90.

brief formulae or laws. Within sufficiently wide limits the intensity of the perceptive faculty appears in all forms of life proportional to the reasoning faculty.[1] A world of sense-impressions in no way amenable to man's reason would be very prejudicial to man's preservation. In this plight a man, like an idiot or insane person, would be incapable of analysis, or would analyse wrongly ; the fitting exertion would not follow on the sense-impression, and any such man would have small chance of surviving among men whose perceptive and reasoning faculties were attuned. Possibly some types of idiocy and madness are the outcome of atavism, a return to variations of the human mind in which perceptive and reflective faculties are not co-ordinated—variations which on the whole have been eliminated in the struggle for existence. If this interpretation be at all a correct one—if, namely, the perceptive faculty can be so moulded in the process of evolution as to accept some and reject other sense-impressions ; if, further, the perceptive and reflective faculties have been developed in co-ordination, so that the former accepts what, in wide limits, can be analysed by the latter—then we have advanced some way towards understanding why the routine of perceptions can be expressed in brief formulae by the human reason. The relation between natural law in the nomic (p. 95, *footnote*) and in the scientific sense becomes more intelligible when we thus attribute the routine of the perceptions to the machinery of the perceptive faculty.

It will not, however, do to press this interpretation too far ; or at least we must be careful to remember that, while the perceptive faculty has developed the power of perceiving solely sense-impressions *capable* of being dealt with by the reflective faculty, it does not follow that they have already been dealt with by the latter faculty. Other-

---

[1] That woman has greater perceptive, man greater reflective power, is one of those futilities which has been used as an excuse for hindrances to woman's development of both faculties. Exceptions of course there are, but the general rule seems to be that the deeper the intellectual power in both sexes, the wider is the range of perceptions and the more delicately sensitive is the nervous system.

wise we shall be abruptly confuted by the fact that there are
many groups of sense-impressions which we receive and yet
have not classified and reduced to simple formulae.   There
are many phenomena of which we can at present only
confess our ignorance.   Compare, for example, what we
know of the tides and the weather.   Had Odysseus and
his men been stranded high and dry by a spring tide on
the Thrinacian Isle they would probably have offered a
hecatomb to Poseidon, praying him to send another spring
tide on the morrow.   A modern mariner, more wise and
less pious than Odysseus, would have consumed the kine
of Helios in peace for a fortnight, and then have taken
his departure with comparative ease.   On the other hand,
the modern mariner, like Odysseus of old, might still pray
for calm weather, thus projecting his inability to formulate
a scientific law into want of routine and possible anomy
(p. 95) in the sequence of his perceptions.   If we believe
in the capacity of the reflective faculty for ultimately reducing to a brief formula or law all types of phenomena,
if we believe in the co-ordination of perception and reflection, then the weather will not probably appear a very
strong argument against our hypothesis.   It must at least
be confessed that the discovery of a hundred or a five
hundred years' period in the weather would sadly discomfort those who delight in assuming that some one group
of perceptions at least must be beyond the analysis of the
reflective faculty.   Yet such a discovery would not now
be more remarkable than that of the Chaldean *Saros* or
eclipse period [1] must have been to those who looked upon
eclipses as an arbitrary interference with their perceptions,
and prayed and drummed vigorously for a restoration of
the light of sun or moon.   The coeval development of
the perceptive and reflective faculties associated with a
power of selecting sensations in the former is possibly an
important, but it may not be the sole, factor in the
marvellous power which the reason possesses of describing

[1] The Chaldeans had discovered that eclipses of the sun and moon recur
in a cycle of eighteen years and eleven days, and were thus able to predict
the dates of their occurrence.

wide ranges of phenomena by simple laws. There is another point which undoubtedly deserves notice. Our sense-impressions are indeed complex in their grouping, but they come to us by very few and comparatively simple channels, namely, through the organs of sense. The simplicity of the scientific law may therefore be partly conditioned by the simplicity of the modes in which sense-impressions are received.

The arguments of this section are, of course, very far from conclusive. They are only meant to suggest the possibility that the perceptive faculty may in itself determine largely or in part the routine of our perceptions. If this be true, it will seem less of a marvel that the co-ordinated reflective faculty should be able to describe the "outside universe" by comparatively simple formulae. On the whole this seems a more scientific hypothesis than those which make the routine depend on supersensuous entities, and which then—to account for the power of the human reason to analyse nature—endow those entities with reason akin to man's, thus postulating thought and consciousness apart from the associated physical machinery which alone justifies our inferring its existence. The hypothesis we have discussed, unproven as it may be, postulates reason no further than we may logically infer it, and at the same time attempts to account for the power of analysing the routine of the perceptions, which is undoubtedly possessed by the human reflective faculty.

§ 13.—*The Mind as a Sorting-Machine*

It is not hard to imagine by extension of existing machinery a great stone-sorting machine of such a character that, when a confused heap of stones was thrown in pell-mell at one end, some sizes would be rejected, while the remainder would come out at the other end of the machine sifted and sorted according to their sizes. Thus a person who solely regarded the final results of the machine might consider that only stones of certain sizes had any existence, and that such stones were always arranged according to their sizes. In some such way as this, perhaps, we may look upon that great sorting-machine—the human perceptive faculty. Sensations of all kinds and magnitudes may flow into it, some to be rejected at once, others to be sorted, all orderly, and arranged in place and time. It may be the perceptive faculty itself, which, without our being directly conscious of it, contributes the ordered sequence in time and space to our sense-impressions. The routine of perception may be due to the recipient, and not characteristic of the material. If anything like this be the case, then (granted a co-ordination of perceptive and reasoning faculties), it will be less surprising that, when the human mind comes to analyse phenomena in time and space, it should find itself capable of briefly describing the past, and of predicting the future sequences of all manner of sense-impressions. From this standpoint the nomic natural law is an unconscious product of the machinery of the perceptive faculty, while natural law in the scientific sense is the conscious product of the reflective faculty, analysing the process of perception, the working of the sorting-machine. The whole of *ordered* nature is thus seen as the product of one mind—the only mind with which we are acquainted—and the fact that the routine of perceptions can be expressed in brief formulae ceases to be so mysterious as when we postulate a twofold reason, one type characteristic of " things-in-themselves," beyond our sense-impressions, and another type associated with the machinery of nervous organisation.

§ 14.—*Science, Natural Theology, and Metaphysics*

The reader, I trust, will treat the matter of the last two sections as pure suggestion and nothing more. What we are sure of is a certain routine of perceptions and a capacity in the mind to resume them in the mental short-hand of scientific law. What we have no right to infer is that order, mind, or reason—all human characters or human conceptions falling on this side of sense-impressions

—exist on the other side of sense-impressions, in the unknown plus of sensations or in things-in-themselves. Whatever there may be on that side, we cannot logically infer it to be like anything whatever on this side. As men of science we must remain agnostic. If, however, it be possible to conceive the order, the routine of perceptions as being due to anything on this side of sense-impression, we shall have withdrawn from the beyond the last anthropomorphic element, and left it that chaos behind sense-impression, whereof to use the word knowledge would be the height of absurdity.

To positive theology, to *revelation*, science has no rejoinder. It works in a totally different plane. Only when belief enters the sphere of possible knowledge, the plane of reality, must science sternly remonstrate ; only when belief replaces knowledge as a basis of conduct is science driven to criticise, not the reality, but the morality of belief. Quite different, however, is the relation of science to natural theology and metaphysics, when they assert that reason can help us to some knowledge of the supersensuous. Here science is perfectly definite and clear ; natural theology and metaphysics are pseudo-science. The mind is absolutely confined within its nerve-exchange ; beyond the walls of sense-impression it can logically infer nothing. Order and reason, beauty and benevolence, are characteristics and conceptions which we find solely associated with the mind of man, with this side of sense-impressions. Into the chaos beyond sensation we cannot as scientists project them ; we have no ground whatever for asserting that any human conception will suffice to describe what may exist there, for it lies outside the barrier of sense-impressions from which all human conceptions are ultimately drawn. Briefly chaos is all that science can logically assert of the supersenuous —the sphere outside knowledge, outside classification by mental concepts. If the Brahmins believe that the world arose from the instinct of an infinite spider, for so it has been *revealed* to them, we may wonder what the conceptions *instinct* and *spider* may be in their minds, and remark that their belief is without meaning for us.   But if they assert that the phenomenal world gives in itself evidence of being spun from the bowels of this monster, then we pass from the plane of belief to that of reason and science, and laugh their fantasy to scorn.

§ 15.—*Conclusions*

It may seem to the reader that we have been discussing at unjustifiable length the nature of scientific law.   Yet therein we have reached a point of primary importance, a point over which the battles of systems and creeds have been long and bitter.   Here the materialists have thrown down the gauntlet to the natural theologians, and the latter in their turn have endeavoured to deck dogma with the mantle of science.   The world of phenomena for the materialists was an outside world unconditioned by man's perceptive faculty, a world of "dead" matter subjected for all time to unchangeable nomic laws (p. 95), whence flowed the routine of our perceptions.   The Stoics, with greater insight, found these laws replete with reason, but, dogmatic in turn, they postulated a reason akin to man's inherent in matter.   The natural theologians, like the materialists, found "dead" matter, but, like the Stoics, they saw strong evidence of reason in its laws ; this reason they placed in an external lawgiver.   Meta-physician and philosopher filled the measure of obscurity by hypotheses as to mind-stuff, and will and consciousness which had not become consciousness, existing behind the barrier of sense-impression.   Science—refusing to infer wildly where it cannot know, and unwilling to assume new causes where the old have not yet been shown insufficient —treats the "dead matter" of the materialist as a world of sense-impressions.   These sense-impressions appear to follow an unchanging routine capable of expression in the brief formulae of science because the perceptive and reflective faculties are machines of practically the same type in all normal human beings.   Like the Stoics, the scientist finds evidence of reason in his examination of natural phenomena, but he is content to think that this reason may be his own till he discovers evidence to the contrary. He recognises that the so-called law of nature is but a simple *résumé*, a brief description of a wide range of his own perceptions, and that the harmony between his perceptive and reasoning faculties is not incapable of being traced to its origin. Natural law appears to him an intellectual product of man, and not a routine inherent in " dead matter." The progress of science is thus reduced to a more and more complete analysis of the perceptive faculty—an analysis which unconsciously and not unnaturally, if illogically, we too often treat as an analysis of something beyond sense-impression. Thus both the material and the laws of science are inherent in ourselves rather than in an outside world. Our groups of perceptions form for us reality, and the results of our reasoning on these perceptions and the conceptions deduced from them form our only genuine knowledge. Here only we are able to reach truth—to discover similarity and to describe sequence—and we must remorselessly criticise every step we take beyond, if we would avoid the " muddy speculation " which will ever arise when we attempt to extend the field of knowledge by obscure definitions of natural law.

If it should seem to the reader that I have too narrowly circumscribed, not the field of *possible human* knowledge, but the meaning of the word knowledge itself, he must remember the danger which arises when we employ terms without concise meaning and clearly defined limits. The right of science to deal with the beyond of sense-impressions is not the subject of contest, for science confessedly claims no such right. It is within the field of knowledge as we have defined it, especially at points where our knowledge is only in the making, that the right of science has been questioned. It is easy to replace ignorance by hypothesis, and because only the attainment of real knowledge can in many cases demonstrate the falseness of hypothesis, it has come about that many worthy and otherwise excellent persons assert an hypothesis to be true, because science has not yet by positive knowledge demonstrated its falsehood. Here in the untilled part of the heritage of science, lies the playground of the undisciplined imagination. *Mine*, says Science, is the hinderland of the sensuous, and she hastens so soon as possible to make her occupation effective. She does not claim the supersensuous, for that sphere is excluded by her definition of knowledge.

Science, we are told, does not explain the origin of life ; science does not explain the development of man's higher faculties ; science does not explain the history of nations. If by explain [1] is meant " describe in a brief formula," let us admit that science has yet far from fully analysed these phenomena. What, then, must follow the admission ? Why, an honest confession of our ignorance and not mistrust in our fundamental principles— no meaningless hunt after unknown origins in the super-sensuous, until the known field of perceptions has been shown incapable of yielding the needful basis. To-day our churches still offer up prayers for the weather, and the mystery of Saturn's rings is hardly fully solved ; fifty years ago we could give no plausible account of the origin of species. The mystery of the latter was used as striking evidence of the insufficiency of science and as a valid argument for an anomy, a separate creation of each type of life. Driven from one stronghold of ignorance, those who delight in the undisciplined imagination rather than in positive knowledge, only seek refuge in another. The part played years ago by our ignorance as to the origin of species is now played by our supposed ignorance as to the origin of the higher faculties in man. As well take refuge in the weather or in the mystery of Saturn's rings, for they also belong to the world of sense-impressions and therefore are material with which the scientific method can and will ultimately cope.

Does science leave no mystery ?   On the contrary,

---

[1] No objection can be raised to the words *explain* and *explanation* if they be used in the sense of the descriptive *how*, and not the determinative *why*. The former interpretation is the sole one given to them in this work.

it proclaims mystery where others profess knowledge. There is mystery enough in the universe of sensation and in its capacity for containing those little corners of consciousness which project their own products, of order and law and reason, into an unknown and unknowable world. There is mystery enough here, only let us clearly distinguish it from ignorance within the field of possible knowledge. The one is impenetrable, the other we are daily subduing.

SUMMARY

1. Scientific law is of a totally different nature from civil law ; it does not involve an intelligent lawgiver, a command and a corresponding duty. It is a brief description in mental shorthand of as wide a range as possible of the sequences of our sense-impressions.

2. There are two distinct meanings to natural law : the mere routine of perception, and the scientific law or formula describing the field of nature. The "reason" in natural law is only obvious when we speak of law in the latter sense, and it is then really placed there by the human mind. Thus the supposed reason behind natural law does not enable us to pass from the routine of perceptions to anything of the nature of reason behind the world of sense-impression.

3. The fact that the human reflective faculty is able to express in mental formulae the routine of perceptions may be due to this routine being a product of the perceptive faculty itself. The perceptive faculty appears to be selective and to have developed in co-ordination with the reflective faculty. Of the world outside sensation science can only logically infer chaos, or the absence of the conditions of knowledge ; no human concept, such as order, reason, or consciousness, can be logically projected into it.

LITERATURE

AUSTIN, J.—Lectures on Jurisprudence. London, 1879. (Especially Lectures I. to V.)

HUME, D.—Dialogues concerning Natural Religion (pp. 375-468 of vol. ii. of the Philosophical Works, edited by Green and Grose).

STUART, J.—A Chapter of Science ; or, What is a Law of Nature? London, 1868. (A series of six lectures, of which the first five can still be read with some profit, if read cautiously, whilst the last forms for the student of logic a useful study in paralogisms.)

CHAPTER IV

CAUSE AND EFFECT—PROBABILITY

§ 1.—*Mechanism*

THE discussion of the previous chapter has led us to see that law in the scientific sense only describes in mental shorthand the sequences of our perceptions. It does not explain *why* those perceptions have a certain order, nor *why* that order repeats itself; the law discovered by science introduces no element of necessity into the sequence of our sense-impressions; it merely gives a concise statement of *how* changes are taking place. That a certain sequence has occurred and recurred in the past is a matter of experience to which we give expression in the concept *causation*; that it will continue to recur in the future is a matter of belief to which we give expression in the concept *probability*. Science in no case can demonstrate any inherent necessity in a sequence, nor prove with absolute certainty that it must be repeated. Science for the past is a description, for the future a belief; it is not, and has never been, an explanation, if by this word is meant that science shows the *necessity* of any sequence of perceptions. Science cannot demonstrate that a cataclysm will not engulf the universe to-morrow, but it can prove that past experience, so far from providing a shred of evidence in favour of any such occurrence, does, even in the light of our ignorance of any necessity in the sequence of our perceptions, give an overwhelming probability against such a cataclysm. If the reader has once fully grasped that science is an intellectual *résumé* of past experience and a mental balancing of the probability of future experience, he will be in no danger of contrasting the "mechanical explanation" of science with the "intellectual description" of mythology.

Twenty-five years ago (1885) the late Mr. Gladstone wrote a remarkable article in *The Nineteenth Century* in which he inveighed against the "dead mechanism" to which he asserted men of science reduced the universe. He contrasted the *mechanical* with the *intellectual*, and bravely set what he termed the "majestic process of creation" described in the first chapter of Genesis against the Darwinian theory of evolution. He afterwards repeated several of his arguments in a more elaborate work.[1] Now, if men even of ability can state paradoxes of this kind, we may be fairly certain that their error arises from some widespread confusion in the use of terms, and it befits us to inquire how popular and scientific usage differ as to the word *mechanical*. Unfortunately, some more or less superficial works on natural science give currency to the notion that mechanics supply a code of rules which nature of inherent necessity obeys. We are told in books published even within the last few years that mechanics is the science of force, that force is the cause which produces or tends to produce change of motion, and that force is inherent in matter. Force thus appears to the popular mind as an agent inherent in unconscious matter producing change. This agent is very naturally contrasted with the will of a living being, the consciousness of a capacity to produce motion. In matter this consciousness cannot be inferred, and thus force is contrasted as a "dead" agent with will as a "living" agent. The mind which has not probed behind the unphilosophical axioms and definitions of current physical text-books sympathises with Mr. Gladstone's revolt against the "dead mechanism" to which, in the imagination of both, science reduces the universe. Now "matter" is for us a group of sense-impressions and "matter in motion" is a sequence of sense-impressions. Hence that which causes change of

---

[1] *The Impregnable Rock of Holy Scripture.* London, 1890.

motion [1] must be that which determines a sequence of sense-impressions, or, in other words, it is the source of a routine of perceptions. But the source of such routine, as we have seen, lies either in the field of the unthinkable beyond sense-impressions, or else in the nature of the perceptive faculty itself. The "cause of change in motion" thus either lies in the unthinkable or is a substantive part of the machinery of perception ; in neither case can it with any intelligible meaning of the words be spoken of as a "dead agent." In the former case the cause of change is unknowable, in the latter it is unknown, and may long remain so, for we are very far at present from understanding how the perceptive faculty can condition a routine of perceptions. Science does not deal with the unknowable, and if force be not unknowable, but unknown, then mechanics as the science of force would as yet have made no progress. The reality is indeed different from this. One of the greatest of German physicists, Kirchhoff, thus commences his classical treatise on mechanics : [2]—

"Mechanics is the science of motion ; we define as its object the complete *description* in the *simplest* possible manner of such motions as occur in nature."

In this definition of Kirchhoff's lies, I venture to think, the only consistent view of mechanism and the true conception of scientific law. Mechanics does not differ, as so often has been asserted, from biology or any other branch of science in its essential principles. The laws of motion no more account than the laws of cell-development for the routine of perception ; both solely attempt to describe as completely and simply as possible the repeated sequences of our sense-impressions. Mechanical science no more explains or accounts for the motions of a molecule or of a planet than biological science accounts for the growth of

[1] We shall see reason in the sequel for asserting that " motion " is a conception, rather than a perception—a scientific mode of representing change of sense-impressions, rather than a sense-impression itself. In this chapter, however, the term " motion " is used in its popular sense for a well-marked class of sequences of sense-impressions.

[2] *Vorlesungen über mathematische Physik.* Band I. Mechanik, S. 1. Berlin, 1876.

a cell. The difference between the two branches of science is rather quantitative than qualitative ; that is, the descriptions of mechanics are simpler and more general than those of biology. So wide-embracing and general are the laws of motion, so completely do they describe our past experience of many forms of change, that with a considerable degree of confidence we believe they will be found to describe all forms of change. It is not a question of reducing the universe to a "dead mechanism," but of measuring the amount of probability that one description of change of a highly generalised and simple kind will ultimately be recognised as capable of replacing another description of a more specialised and complex character. It is not taking biology out of one branch of what might be termed *descriptive* science and removing it into another—that of *prescriptive* science. Here by *prescriptive* science I denote an imaginary aspect of science, which mechanics are too frequently supposed to present, namely, that of deducing some inherent necessity in the routine of perceptions, instead of merely describing that routine in simple statements. When, therefore, we say that we have reached a "mechanical explanation" of any group of phenomena, we only mean that we have described in the concise language of mechanics a certain routine of perceptions. We are neither able to explain why sense-impressions have a definite sequence, nor to assert that there is really an element of necessity in the phenomena. Regarded from this standpoint the laws of mechanics are seen to be essentially an intellectual product, and it appears absolutely unreasonable to contrast the mechanical with the intellectual when once these words are defined in an accurate manner.

§ 2.—*Force as a Cause*

If force be looked upon as the cause of change, in the sense that it necessitates a certain routine of perceptions, then we have no means of dealing with force. It may lie in the structure of the perceptive faculty, or it may be any of the phantasms with which metaphysicians fill the beyond of sense-impression. Force will not, therefore, aid us in our search for a scientific conception of *cause*. As we have seen that there are two or even three ideas conveyed by the one term law, so there are at least two ideas associated with the word cause, and their confusion has also led to as much "muddy speculation." Let us first investigate the popular idea of cause, and then see how this is related to the scientific definition. A very slight amount of observation has shown men that certain sequences of change *apparently* arise from the voluntary action, the will of a living agent. I take up a stone ; no one can predict with certainty what I shall do with it. What follows my picking up the stone is to all appearances a new sequence quite independent of any which preceded it. I can let it fall again ; I can put it into my pocket, or I may throw it into the air in any direction and with any of a great variety of speeds. The result of my action may be a long sequence of physical phenomena, to describe which mechanically would require the solution of complex problems in sound, heat, and elasticity. The sequence, however, appears to start in an act of mine, in *my* will. *I* appear to have called it into existence, and in ordinary language I am spoken of as the *cause* of the resulting phenomena. In this sense of the word cause I appear to differ qualitatively from any other stage in the sequence. Had the hand of a stronger man compelled mine to throw the stone, I should at once have sunk into a link in the chain of phenomena ; he, not I, would have been *the* cause of the resulting motion.

It is certainly true that even in popular usage intermediate stages in the sequence will occasionally be spoken of as causes. If the stone from my hand break a window, the cause of the broken window might very likely be spoken of as the moving stone. But although this usage, as we shall see afterwards, is an approach to the scientific usage of the word cause, it yet involves in the popular estimation an idea of enforcement which is not in the latter. That the stone moving with a certain speed *must* produce the destruction of the window is, I think, the idea involved in thus speaking of the moving stone as the cause of the breakage. But were our perceptive organs sufficiently powerful, science conceives that we should see before the impact particles of window and particles of stone moving in a certain manner, and after the impact the same particles moving in a very different manner. We might carefully *describe* these motions, but we should be unable to say why one stage would follow another, just as we can describe *how* a stone falls to the earth, but not say *why* it does. Thus, scientifically the idea of *necessity* in the stages of the sequence—stone in motion, broken window—or the idea of enforcement would disappear ; we should have a routine of experience, but an unexplained routine. When we speak, however, of the stages of a sequence in ordinary life as causes, I do not think it is because we are approaching the scientific standpoint, but I fear it arises from our associating, through long usage, the idea of *force* with the stone. The stone is the cause of certain new motions, just as I am looked upon as the cause of certain motions in the stone—that is, both stone and I are supposed to *enforce* subsequent stages in the sequence. Now the reader who has once dismissed the notion of force as a cause, which I think he will probably be prepared to do, will perhaps admit that there is no element of enforcement, but merely a routine of experience in the motions of particles of stone and glass. Still he may say that the will of a living agent does seem to him a cause of motion in the necessarian sense. Nor would he be in this unreasonable, for I must confess that to attribute sequences of motion to will seems at first sight a more scientific hypothesis than to attribute them to an unknown and possibly unknowable source *force*.

§ 3.—*Will as a Cause*

It is not unnatural that human beings should be impressed at a very early stage of their mental growth with the real, or at any rate apparent, power which lies in their will of originating "motion." In this manner we find that most primitive peoples attribute all motions to some will behind the moving body; for their first conception of the cause of motion lies in their own will. Thus they consider the sun as carried round by a sun-god, the moon by a moon-god, while rivers flow, trees grow, and winds blow owing to the will of the various spirits which dwell within them. It is only in the long course of ages that mankind more or less clearly recognises will as associated with consciousness and a definite physiological structure; then the spiritualistic explanation of motion is gradually displaced by the scientific description; we eliminate in one case after another the direct action of will in the motion of natural bodies.[1] The idea, however, of enforcement, of some necessity in the order of a sequence, remains deeply rooted in men's minds, as a fossil from the spiritualistic explanation which sees in will the cause of motion. This idea is unfortunately preserved in association with the scientific description of motion, and in the materialist's notion of force as that which *necessitates* certain changes or sequences of motion, we have the ghost of the old spiritualism. The force of the materialist is the will of the old spiritualist separated from consciousness. Both carry us into the region beyond our sense-impressions, both are therefore *metaphysical;* but perhaps the inference of the old spiritualist was, if illegitimate, less absurdly so than that of the modern materialist, for the spiritualist did not infer will to exist beyond the sphere of consciousness with which he had always found will associated.

Force as cause of motion[2] is exactly on the same footing as a tree-god as cause of growth—both are but names which hide our ignorance of the *why* in the routine of our

---

[1] The spiritualistic explanation still of course exists where the scientific analysis is incomplete. We continue to appeal to a spirit "at whose command the winds blow and lift up the waves of the sea and who stilleth the waves thereof," or who "sends a plague of rain and waters."

[2] Force as a name used for a particular *measure* of motion will be found in our chapter on the "Laws of Motion" to involve no obscurity, and to be in itself a convenient term.

perceptions. The necessity in a law of nature has not the logical *must* of a geometrical theorem, nor the categorical *must* of a human law-giver; it is merely our experience of a routine, whose stages have neither logical nor volitional order.

§ 4.—*Secondary Causes involve no Enforcement*

Let us endeavour to see a little more closely how the idea of any inherent necessity in the particular order taken by our perceptions disappears from the scientific conception of a sequence of motions—at least from all but the first stage, if the sequence arise from an apparent act of will. Still speaking in the popular sense, we will term the act of will, if it exists, a first cause, and the successive stages of the sequence secondary causes. Our present proposition is that the scientific description of motion involves no idea of enforcement in the successive stages of motion. We shall see in the sequel that the whole tendency of modern physics has been to describe natural phenomena by reducing them to conceptual motions. From these motions we construct the more complex motions by aid of which we describe actual sequences of sense-impressions. But in no single case have we discovered *why* it is that these motions are taking place; science describes how they take place, but the *why* remains a mystery. To term it force might not be so productive of obscurity as it is, were there any suggestion in the elementary text-books that the cause of motion, or of change in motion, may be the structure of the perceptive faculty, or will, or the deity, or any unknowable x amid an unthinkable y and z. The glib transition from force as a cause to force as a measure of motion too often screens the ignorance which it is as much the duty of science to proclaim from the house-tops as it is its duty to assert knowledge on other points. Primitive man placed a sun-god behind the sun (as some of us still place a storm-god behind the storm), because he did not see how and why it moved. The physicist now proceeds to describe *how* the sun moves, by describing how a particle of earth and a particle of sun move in each other's presence. The description of that motion is given by Newton's law of gravitation, but the *why* of that motion is just as mysterious to us as the motion of the sun to the barbarian.[1] No one knows why two ultimate particles influence each other's motion. Even if gravitation be analysed and described by the motion of some simpler particle or ether-element, the whole will still be a description, and not an explanation, of motion. Science would still have to content itself with recording the *how*. In what we have termed secondary causes, therefore, science finds no element of enforcement, solely the routine of experience. But the idea of will as a first cause has been over and over again associated with secondary causes. Aristotle, noting the difficulty of explaining why motions take place, introduced not only God as a first cause, but, like primitive man, made God an immediate source of the enforcement in every secondary cause. God, Aristotle held, is continually imparting motion to all the bodies in the universe, and so producing phenomena. Aristotle's doctrine was accepted by the mediaeval schoolmen, and for many centuries remained fundamental in philosophical and theological writings. Schopenhauer, the German metaphysician, perceiving that the only known apparent first cause of motion was will, placed will behind all the phenomena of the universe, much like the barbarian who postulates the will of a storm-god behind the storm.[2]

[1] The reader will find it profitable to analyse what is meant by such statements as that the law of gravitation *causes* bodies to fall to the earth. This law really describes how bodies do fall according to our past experience. It tells us that a body at the surface of the earth falls about sixteen feet towards the earth in the first second, and at the distance of the moon about $\frac{1}{3700}$ part of this distance in the same time. The law of gravitation describes the rate at which a body falls, or, better, the rate at which its motion is changed at diverse distances, and the force of gravitation is really a certain measure of this change of motion, and no useful purpose can be served by defining it as the cause of change in motion. Other physical laws ought to be interpreted in the same anti-metaphysical manner.

[2] Sir John Herschel went so far as to identify gravitation and will ! (*Outlines of Astronomy*, arts. 439-40). Other samples of the same animistic tendency will be found in the writings of the late Dr. J. Martineau and the late Dr. W. B. Carpenter.

But however little logical basis these metaphysical specu-
lations possess—all failing to satisfy our canons of legitimate inference (p. 59)—they still suffice to mark the
distinction between the popular or metaphysical conception of cause as enforcement, and the scientific conception
of cause as the routine of experience. Every association
of inherent necessity with secondary causes is a passage
from physics to metaphysics, from knowledge to fantasy.
Historically, I think, the whole association can be traced
back through the old spiritualism to the sequences of motion
which the will as a first cause can apparently enforce.
Here, then, it befits us to ask two questions: Does the
will in any way really account for motion? Is there any
ground for supposing the will to be an arbitrary first cause?

§ 5.—*Is Will a First Cause?*

Now, in attempting to answer these questions
scientifically we must bear in mind that what we term
will is only known to us in association with consciousness,
and that we can only infer consciousness where we find
a certain type of nervous system. Does will as an
apparently spontaneous producer of motion throw any
light on the mystery of motion? Does it in any way
explain the particular sequences motions take? To be
consistent we shall have to suppose, with Aristotle, that
every phase of motion is the direct product of a conscious
being. Let us return to the example of the stone.
Apparently, by the arbitrary action of my will, I set the
stone in motion. I appear in doing this as a first cause.
But a complex sequence of motions now arises. Each
stage of this sequence I can conceive myself mechanically
describing, but I am quite unable to assert the necessity,
the *why* of these stages. For example, the stone falls to
the ground, and I can say approximately how many feet
it will fall in the first and in the following seconds. That
is the result of past experience used to predict the
future, the result of the classification of phenomena
resumed in the law of gravitation; but this law does not

explain the *why* of the motion. If I grant that my will set the stone in motion, I cannot suppose it to continue in motion for the same reason, for any amount of willing after the stone has left my hand will not, in the majority of cases, be in the least able to influence its motion. Hence even in motion started by a conscious being, we have at once a mystery. My will might explain the origin, it cannot explain the continuance of the motion. If will is to help us at all, we must postulate it as producing motion at every stage. But clearly this will is not my will ; it must be some other will. Here we are only restating the solutions of primitive man with his spiritualism behind nature, of Schopenhauer with his undefined will behind all phenomena, of Aristotle when he says God moves all things. But this solution involves an extension of the notion of will beyond the sphere where we may legitimately infer its existence— *i.e.* beyond the physiological structure with which, in our experience, we have always found it associated. Like the hypothesis of force it postulates an unthinkable x outside sense-impressions. It carries us no-whither. Will cannot, therefore, be looked upon as necessitating a sequence of motion, any more than what we have termed a secondary cause, for in the great majority of cases if will be supposed to start a motion, it cannot enforce its continuance in a particular sequence, and so far as the will is concerned the motion might cease at its birth.

§ 6.—*Will as a Secondary Cause*

Will thus appears, like the secondary cause, as a stage in the routine of perceptions. Our experience shows us that in the past an act of will occurred at a certain stage in a routine of perceptions, but we cannot assert that there was anything in the act itself which *enforced* the stages which followed. Does will, however, differ on closer analysis from other secondary causes in being the *first* stage of an observed routine ? This leads us to our second question (p. 122), and the answer to it is really involved in the views on consciousness which have been developed in our second chapter.

We have seen that the difference between a voluntary and involuntary exertion lies in the latter being conditioned only by the immediate sense-impression, while the former is conditioned by stored sense-impresses and the conceptions drawn from them. Where consciousness exists, there there may be an interval between sense-impression and exertion, this interval being filled with the "resonance," as it were, of associated but stored sense-impresses and their correlated conceptions. When the exertion is at once determined by the immediate sense-impression (which we associate with a construct projected *outside* ourselves), we do not speak of will, but of reflex action, habit, instinct, etc. In this case both sense-impression and exertion appear as stages in a routine of perceptions, and we do not speak of the exertion as a first cause, but as a direct effect of the sense-impression ; both are secondary causes in a routine of perceptions, and capable of mechanical description. On the other hand, when the exertion is conditioned by the stored sense-impresses, it appears to be conditioned by something *within* ourselves ; by the manner in which memory and past thought have linked together stored sense-impresses and the conceptions drawn from them. No other person can predict with absolute certainty what the exertion will be, for the contents of our mind are not objects to him. None the less the inherited features of our brain, its present physical condition owing to past nurture, exercise, and general health, our past training and experience are all factors determining what sense-impresses will be stored, how they will be associated, and to what conceptions they will give rise. By this we are to understand that, if we could bring into the sphere of perception the processes that intervene in the brain between immediate sense-impression and conscious exertion, we should find them just as much routine changes as what precedes the sense-impression or follows the exertion. In other words, will, when we analyse it, does not appear as the first cause in a routine of perceptions, but merely as a secondary cause or intermediate link in the chain. The "freedom of the will" lies in the fact that exertion is conditioned by our own individuality, that the routine of mental processes which intervenes between sense-impression and exertion is perceived physically neither by us nor by any one else, and psychically by us alone. Thus will as the first cause of a sequence of motions explains nothing at all; it is only a limit at which very often our power of describing a sequence abruptly terminates.

So much is this recognised by modern science, that special branches of it are entirely devoted to describing the sequences of secondary causes, the routine which precedes special determinations of the will. Science tries to describe how will is influenced by desires and passions, and how these again flow from education, experience, inheritance, physique, disease, all of which are further associated with climate, class, race, or other great factors of evolution. Thus, with the advance of our positive knowledge we come more and more to regard individual acts of will as secondary causes in a long sequence, as stages in a routine which can be described—stages, however, at which the routine changes its at present knowable side from the psychical to the physical. An act of will thus appears as a secondary cause, and no longer as an arbitrary first cause. Evil acts flow indeed from an anti-social will, and as hostile to itself society endeavours to repress them; but the anti-social will itself is seen as a heritage from a bad stock, or as arising from the conditions of past life and training. Society begins more and more to regard incorrigible criminals as insane, and slight offenders as uneducated children.

From the standpoint of science no two brains are alike, the complexity of the parts and of their commissures differs from individual to individual; it is due to heritage, to training, to experience. The difference constitutes the mental individuality of a man, when we view it from the psychical side. From the physical side we can in part only describe its action and link its centres and commissures with psychical action. Destroy a commissure and a man may understand language, but have lost the link to connect the stored impresses of word-meanings with the organ that controls word-sounds ; he suffers from *aphasia.* Destroy other commissures and other groups of stored impresses may disappear, conscience and the moral sense may become extinct. The psychic is closely allied with the physical, the individuality with what admits of mechanical description. Free-will and consciousness are associated with the interval between sense-impression and exertion, the physical of the outside world becomes the physical of the inner world (p. 65) ; it is the play of the individuality, of a brain the product of a certain heritage, a certain training, a certain experience. Had we knowledge enough we can hardly doubt that all this brain action might be described " mechanically." This would not in the least explain the psychic side of the brain-motions, but it would show free-will making no breach in mechanical routine, volition no arbitrary bringing into play of " vital forces " but the introduction into the " outer world " of the action of an " inner " mechanism, the individuality. I act as I do, because I am I, and that wonderful psychic " I," built up of heritage, training, and experience, is associated with a physical " I " built up at the same time, a wonderful " mechanism," which represents it on the physical side. Is there such a thing as free-will ? Certainly, if free-will means acting in accordance with the character, the individuality of the *ego.* Does free-will connote a breach in mechanical causation, in the law of motion or the principle of energy ? We have no reason to suppose it does, for the interval between sense-impression and exertion—the thought- and consideration-interval—is filled by the play of the physical brain, the marvellous complex upon which no element of race, of ancestry, of education or of experience has failed to leave a more or less indelible impress. It is the physical mechanism corresponding to the psychic individuality, which makes necessity and free-will one and the same thing. But the " necessity " of mechanism is no categorical *must*, it is the descriptive *how* of the formula, the mere summary of what has been observed, the inexplicable routine.

§ 7.—*First Causes have no Existence for Science*

We have now reached some very important conclusions with regard to will as a cause. In the first place, the only will known to us (or the only *like* will that we can logically infer to exist) is seen not to be associated with an arbitrary power to originate, alter, or stop a motion. It appears merely as a secondary cause, as a stage in a routine, but one where the knowable side of the routine changes from the psychical to the physical. Further, there lies in this will no power of enforcing a sequence of motions. The will as first cause is merely a limit arising from some impossibility in our powers of further following the physical side of a routine, or of discovering its further psychical side ; it is merely another way of saying : At this point our ignorance begins. The moment the only will we know or infer ceases to appear. as the arbitrary originator or enforcer of a sequence, so soon as it sinks to a stage—if a remarkable stage—in a routine, then it becomes idle to suppose will as the backbone of natural phenomena. Will, as the creator and maintainer of nature, is either a familiar term used anew for some unknown and unthinkable existence, or if used in the only sense now intelligible to us, that of a secondary cause or stage in a routine, it gives us no assistance in comprehending routine. We are just as wise if we drop this will behind phenomena, and content ourselves with observing that there is a routine in perceptions. This, in fact, is what science does, not unnecessarily multiplying causes, when no simplification of perceptions arises from postulating their existence.

We have seen that the conception of will as an arbitrary source of motion arose historically, and not unnaturally, from a portion of the routine of which will is a stage being both physically and psychically screened from the observer, because it was buried in the individuality of another person. We have further noticed that as will and motion are more carefully analysed, the conception that will originates motion ceases to have any consistency. But with will as first cause falls to the ground any possible experience of first causes on our part. We can no longer infer even the possibility of the existence of first causes, for there is nothing like them in our experience, and we cannot by the second canon of logical inference (p. 60) pass from the known to something totally unlike it in the unknown. Science knows nothing of first causes. They cannot, as Stanley Jevons has supposed,[1] be inferred from any branch of scientific investigation, and where we see them asserted we may be quite sure they mark a permanent or temporary limit to knowledge. We are either inferring something in the beyond of sense-impression, where knowledge and inference are meaningless words, or we are implying ignorance within the sphere of knowledge,[2] in which case it is more honest to say : " Here, for the present, our ignorance begins," than, " Here is a first cause."

§ 8.—*Cause and Effect as the Routine of Experience*

We are now in a position, I think, to appreciate the scientific value of the word cause. For science, cause, as originating or enforcing a particular sequence of perceptions, is meaningless—we have no experience of anything which originates or enforces something else. Cause, however, used to mark a stage in a routine, is a clear and

[1] In the remarkably unscientific chapter entitled "Reflections on the Results and Limits of Scientific Method," with which his, in so many respects, excellent *Principles of Science* concludes.

[2] The latter alternative—the temporary limit in ignorance—has been the chief source of "first causes." So long as the routine of history cannot be traced back more than a few centuries, we find no difficulty in asserting that the world began 6000 years ago. So long as we do not grasp the evolution of life from its most primitive types, we postulate a first cause creating each type (Paley). So long as we do not observe the various grades of animal intelligence and consciousness, we suppose a soul implanted in every human being at birth. So long as we do not see that the mutual motion of two atoms is as mysterious as the life changes in a cell, we postulate a total difference between the two kinds of motion and a separate creation of life.

valuable conception, which throws the idea of cause entirely into the field of sense-impressions, into the sphere where we can reason and can reach knowledge. Cause, in this sense, is a stage in a routine of experience, and not one in a routine of inherent necessity. The distinction is, perhaps, a difficult one, but it is all the more needful that the reader should fully grasp it. If I write down a hundred numbers at chance—say by opening carelessly the pages of a book—there results a sequence of numbers beginning, say—

141, 253, 73, 477, 187, 585, 57, 353, . . . etc.,

in which I cannot predict from any two or three or more numbers those which will follow. The number 477 does not enable me to say that 187 will follow it, the numbers which precede 187 in no way enforce or determine those which follow it. On the other hand, if I take the series—

1, 2, 3, 4, 5, 6, 7, 8, . . .

each individual number leads (by addition of 1) to the immediately following number, or in a certain sense determines it. The first series can, however, be written down so often that we learn it by rote, *i.e.* that it becomes a routine of experience. The analogy must not, of course, be pressed far, but it may still be of service. There is nothing in any scientific cause which compels us of inherent necessity to predict the effect. The effect is associated with the cause simply as a result of past direct or indirect experience. Or again, perhaps the matter may be grasped more clearly from a geometrical analogy. If I form the conception of a circle, it follows of inherent necessity that the angle at the circumference on any diameter is a right-angle. The one conception flows not as a result of experience but as a logical necessity from the other. No sequence of sense-impressions involves in itself a logical necessity. The sequence might be chaotic like our first series of numbers ; it has become for us a routine by repeated experience. The noteworthy fact in a routine of perceptions lies not so much in the particular order of the stages in the sequence as in the result of experience that this order can very clearly repeat itself.

The reader may perhaps wonder how, if the sequences of sense-impressions are really of the chaotic nature represented by our first series of numbers, it is possible to describe such sequences apart from their repetition by those brief formulae we term scientific laws. As the perceptive faculty presents us, indeed, with the sequence, it is undeniably more like the second than the first series of numbers, for natural phenomena can without doubt be largely described by certain brief laws. We must rather put the actual case in the following form. We observe a person whose motives are quite unknown to us writing down the series—

$$1, 2, 4, 8, 16, 32,$$

and at present he has reached the number 32. A law describing the series is obvious—each number is twice the preceding one. With a great degree of probability we infer that he will now write down 64, especially if we have seen him write the series up to and beyond 32 before. But there is nothing of logical necessity about his writing 64 after the preceding numbers. Those numbers, when we know the law, suggest his doing so, but do not enforce it.

We are now in a position to define *cause* as used in science. Whenever a sequence of perception D, E, F, G is invariably preceded by the perception C, or the perceptions C, D, E, F, G always occur in this order, that is, form a routine of experience, C is said to be a *cause* of D, E, F, G, which are then described as its effects. No phenomenon or stage in a sequence has only one cause, all antecedent stages are successive causes, and, as science has no reason to infer a first cause, the succession of causes can be carried back to the limit of existing knowledge, and beyond that *ad infinitum* in the field of conceivable knowledge. When we scientifically state causes we are really describing the successive stages of a routine of experience.

Causation, says John Stuart Mill, is uniform [1] antecedence, and this definition is perfectly in accord with the scientific concept.

§ 9.—*Width of the Term Cause*

The word cause, even in its scientific sense, is somewhat elastic. It has been used to mark uniform conjunction in space as well as uniform antecedence in time ; while if we take an actually existing group of perceptions, say the particular ash-tree in my garden, the causes of its growth might be widened out into a description of the various past stages of the universe. One of the causes of its growth is the existence of my garden, which is conditioned by the existence of the metropolis ; another cause is the nature of the soil, gravel approaching the edge of the clay, which again is conditioned by the geological structure and past history of the earth. The causes of any *individual* thing thus widen out into the unmanageable history of the universe. The ash-tree is like Tennyson's " flower in the crannied wall " : to know all its causes would be to know the universe. To trace causes in this sense is like tracing back all the lines of ancestry which converge in one individual ; we soon reach a point where we can go no further owing to the bulk of the material. Obviously science in tracing causes attempts no task of this character, but at the same time it is useful to remember how essentially the causes of any finite portions of the universe lead us irresistibly to the history of the universe as a whole. This thought suggests how closely knit together are in reality the most diverse branches of our positive knowledge. It shows us how difficult it is for the great building of science to advance rapidly and surely unless its various parts keep pace with each other (p. 13). Practically science has to content itself with tracing one line of ancestry, one range of causes at a time, and this not for a special and individual object like the ash-tree in my garden, but for ash-trees or even trees in

[1] " Uniformity " and " sameness " are, in the perceptual world, however, only relative terms (*see* Chapter V. § 6).

general. It is because science for its descriptive purposes deals with general notions or conceptions, that the words cause and effect have been withdrawn from the sphere of sense-impressions, from phenomena to which they strictly belong, and applied to the world of conceptions and ideas, where, indeed, there is logical necessity but no true cause and effect. To this point I shall return under § 11.

§ 10.—*The Universe of Sense-Impressions as a Universe of Motions*

The reader can hardly fail to have been impressed in his past reading and experience with the great burden of explanation which is thrown on that unfortunate metaphysical conception *force*. He will undoubtedly have heard of the "mechanical forces" ruling the universe, of the "vital forces" directing the development of life, and of the "social forces" governing the growth of human societies.[1] He may perhaps have concluded, with the present writer, that the word is not infrequently a fetish which symbolises more or less mental obscurity. But the reason for the repeated occurrence of the word is really not far to seek. Wherever motion, change, or growth were postulated, there in the old metaphysics force as the cause of change in motion was to be found. The frequent use of the word force was due to the almost invariable association of *motion* with our perceptions, or, in more accurate language, to the analysis of nearly all our sense-impressions by aid of conceptual motions. For example, a coal fire may be said to be a cause of warmth. Here we mean that the group of sense-impressions we term coal,

---

[1] A good illustration of the obscurity attaching to the use of the words force and cause may be taken from the recently (1900) published *History of Human Marriage*, by E. Westermarck. The author writes : "Nothing exists without a cause, but this cause is not sought in an agglomeration of external or internal forces." He thus implies that a cause ought to be sought in this unintelligible "agglomeration of external and internal forces." Now, what the author attempts to do is to *describe* the various stages through which marriage has passed, and then to express the sequence of these stages by brief formulae, such as those of natural selection. To use the word *force* hopelessly obscures his method

followed by the group we term combustion, has invariably in our experience been accompanied by the sense-impression warmth.   We may, if we are chemists, be able to describe the chemical processes, the atomic changes or motions to which the phenomenon of combustion has been reduced ; we may, if we are physicists, describe the motion of the ethereal medium, to which the phenomenon of radiation of heat has been reduced ; we may, if we are physiologists, be able to describe the nerve-motions by aid of which the molecular motion of the finger-tips is interpreted as the sense-impression warmth at the brain. In all these cases we are dealing with the sequences of various types of motion, into which we anaylse or reduce a variety of sense-impressions.   Just as in the special case of gravitation, we can also describe these sequences and can frequently give a measure to the motions which we conceive to take place, but we are still wholly unable to state *why* these motions occur.   We may talk, if we please, about the forces of combustion, the forces of radiation, or even the forces inherent in nerve-substance ; we might indeed say that the warmth, of which combustion is the cause, is due to " an agglomeration of external or internal forces," but in using such phrases we do not introduce an iota of new knowledge, but too often a whole alphabet of obscurity.   We hide the fact that all knowledge is concise description, all cause is routine.

Now it deserves special note that the sequences with which we are dealing are all reducible to descriptions of motion, or of change.   We need not start arbitrarily with the combustion of the coal ; its chemical constitution as an element in the sequence of causes can, for example, be carried back through a long past history in the evolution of coal, and we cannot logically infer (p. 128) any beginning or first cause in this sequence.   Sequences of motion or of change in natural phenomena go backwards and forwards through an infinite range of causes, and to begin or end them anywhere with a first or last cause is simply to say that at such a point the sphere of knowledge ends with an unthinkable *x*.   The universe thus appears to the scientist as a universe of varying motions, motions the *why* of which is unknown, but the sequences of which are, according to our experience, invariably repeating themselves.   The cause of motion in the scientific sense lying in the sphere of sense-impressions [1] cannot be the *why* of motions, we must seek it in some *uniform antecedent* of the motion—such, for example, as the past history of the motion, the relative position of the moving bodies, and so forth.   How such antecedents are true scientific causes of motion we shall see in our Chapter VIII. devoted to the " Laws of Motion."

§ 11.—*Necessity belongs to the World of Conceptions,*
not to that of Perceptions

At this point the reader may feel inclined to say : " But surely there is as much necessity that a planet describing its elliptic orbit should at a certain time be in a certain position, as that the angles on the diameter of a circle should be right-angles ? "   With this I entirely agree. The *theory* of planetary motion is in itself as logically necessary as the theory of the circle ; but in both cases the logic and necessity arise from the definitions and axioms with which we mentally start, and do not exist in the sequence of sense-impressions which we hope that they will, at any rate approximately, describe.   The necessity lies in the world of conceptions, and is only unconsciously and illogically transferred to the world of perceptions.

This difference may be well illustrated by an example due to Mr. James Stuart, formerly Professor of Mechanism in Cambridge.   Suppose I were to put a stone on a piece of flat ground and walk round it in that particular curve termed an ellipse, which a planet describes about the sun. We will further suppose the stone to be at that particular point termed the focus which in the case of an elliptic orbit is actually occupied by the sun ; and lastly, I will

---

[1] That the frequently cited " muscular sensation of force " is really only a sense-impression interpreted as one of motion will be shown at a later stage of our work.

walk round so that a line drawn from the stone to me sweeps out equal areas in equal times, a fundamental characteristic of the laws of planetary motion. Now my motion might be very fairly *described* by the law of gravitation, but it is quite clear that no force from the stone to me, no law of gravitation, could logically be said to cause my motion in the ellipse. We might in *imagination* conceive a point changing its motion according to the law of gravitation and tracing out my ellipse ; it might keep pace with me, and would, of logical necessity, cover equal areas in equal times. This logical necessity would flow from our definition, our conception, namely, that of a gravitating point. This point might be used to describe my elliptic motion, and to predict my positions in the future, but no observer would be logical in inferring that the necessary sequence of positions involved in the concept of a gravitating point could be transferred, or projected into a necessity in the sequence of his perceptions of my motion. I might go round the ellipse a hundred times in the same manner and then stop or go off in an entirely different path. The sole legitimate inference of the observer would then be that the law of gravitation was not a sufficiently wide-embracing formula to describe more than a portion of my motion.[1] This difference between necessity in conception and routine in perception ought to be carefully borne in mind. The corpuscular, the elastic-solid, and the electro-magnetic theories of light all involve a series of conclusions of logical necessity,

[1] The example cited is given by Mr. Stuart on p. 168 of his *Chapter of Science.* It is there used to support the argument of primitive man ; my will causes me to go round the ellipse, therefore will causes the planets to go round in ellipses, and hence Mr. Stuart passes to Aristotle's God as continual mover of all things. That will is only found associated with certain types of material nervous systems is not used by Mr. Stuart, however, to logically infer the material nature of his first cause. He passes by the juggle of a common name from the known to the unthinkable outside the sphere of knowledge and science. The real truth which his *Chapter of Science* contains as to the characteristics of natural law is hopelessly vitiated by his theological standpoint. "I know," he says, "no result of science which could go to discredit any single thing in all the Bible" (p. 184). Mr. Stuart's "science" is thus incomparably more retrograde than the modern Cambridge theology which discredits Noah's Ark.

and we may use these conclusions as a means of testing our perceptions.   So far as they are confirmed, the theory remains valid as a description ; if, on the other hand, our sense-impressions differ from these conclusions, the conclusions have just as much mental necessity, but the theory while valid for the mind is not valid as a description of the routine of perceptions.   It is only the very great probability deduced from past experience of routine that enables us to speak of the "invariable order of the universe," or enables scientists to assert that facts which have hitherto proved obstinate will be ultimately embraced by the already well-established laws of nature.   Not in the field of causation, but in that of conception do we deal with certainties.

§ 12.—*Routine in Perception is a necessary condition of Knowledge*

While in the nature of perceptions themselves there appears nothing tending to enforce an order D, E, F, G rather than F, G, D, E, there is still a real need, if thought is to be possible, that the perceptive faculty should always repeat the sequence in *nearly* the *same* order.   In other words, repetition or routine is an essential condition of thought ; the actual order of the sequence is immaterial, but whatever it may be, it must nearly repeat itself if knowledge is to be possible.   We express this briefly in the law : *That the same* (Chapter V. § 6) *set of causes is always accompanied by the same effect.*   That the future will be like our experience of the past is the sole condition under which we can predict what is about to happen and so guide our conduct.   But thought has been evolved in the struggle for existence as a guide to conduct, and therefore could not have been evolved had this condition been absent.   If after the sense-impressions D, E, F, G, the sense-impression H does not uniformly follow, but unexpected A, J, or even Z, occurs just as often, then knowledge becomes impossible for us, and we must cease to think.   The power of thinking—or of associating groups and sequences of sense-impressions, immediate or stored—vanishes if these groups and sequences have no premanent elements by which they can be classified and compared.

In the struggle for existence man has won his dictatorship over other forms of life by his power of foreseeing the effects which flow from antecedent causes—not only by his memory of past experience, but by his power of codifying natural law, that is, by his power of generalising experience in scientific statements. It was not necessary for his success that he should know *why* phenomena take place, but only that he should know *how* they take place, that he should be able to observe in them a routine, a repeated sequence as a basis for his knowledge. We have only to consider in some simple case—say that of the combustion of coal—what would follow for man if the resulting sense-impression were not uniform—if it were, for example, either intense warmth or intense cold—to appreciate that invariable order in the sequence of sense-impressions is an absolute condition for man's knowledge, and therefore for the foresight by aid of which he has won his dictatorship. In the chaos behind sensations, in the " beyond " of sense-impressions, we cannot infer necessity, order or routine, for these are concepts formed by the mind of man on this side of sense-impressions. Yet if the supremacy of man is due to his reasoning faculty, so the condition for the existence of man as a reasoning being is routine in his perceptions, invariable or nearly invariable order in the sequences of his sense-impressions. We can neither assert nor deny that this routine is due to something beyond sense-impression, for in that " beyond " the word routine is meaningless, and we can neither assert nor deny where we are dealing with a field to which the word knowledge cannot be applied. All we can assert is that the reasoning faculty in man connotes a perceptive faculty presenting sense-impressions in some almost invariable order. That this routine is due to the nature of the perceptive faculty itself—to factors, of which we are unconscious in its constitution, akin to the conscious association and memory of the reasoning faculty—is a plausible if unproven hypothesis.   It is one, however, as we have seen, suggested by the contemporaneous growth of perception and reason, and strengthened by the impossibility of any form of perceptive faculty, such as we find in the insane, surviving in the struggle for existence (p. 104).

While a nearly invariable order in the sequence of sense-impressions is thus seen to be an essential characteristic of the perceptive faculty of a rational being, the power to understand the why and wherefore of any sequence is not so.   It would undoubtedly be of great intellectual interest to know *why* bodies fall to the earth, but *how* they invariably fall is the practical knowledge, which now enables us to build machines and which enabled our fore-fathers to throw stones, and thus helped them as it helps us in the struggle for existence.   Broadly speaking, here as elsewhere, the perceptive faculty has developed along lines which strengthen man's powers of self-preservation, and not along those which would merely minister to his intellectual curiosity.

Anything, be it noted, that tends to weaken our con-fidence in the uniform order of phenomena, in what we have termed the routine of perceptions, tends also to stultify our reasoning faculty by destroying the sole basis of knowledge.   It decreases our power of foresight and lessens our strength for the battle of life.   For this reason theosophists and spiritualists with their modern miracles contradicting the long-experienced routine of perceptions are very unlikely to form a society sufficiently stable to survive in the struggle for existence.   Every ecstatic and mystical state weakens the whole intellectual character of those who experience it, for it impairs their belief in the normal routine of preceptions.   The abnormal perceptive faculty, whether that of the madman or that of the mystic, must ever be a danger to human society, for it under-mines the efficiency of the reason as a guide to conduct. Conviction, therefore, of the uniform order of phenomena is essential to social welfare.

But the reader may object that although this con-viction be essential to social welfare, it does not follow that it is well based. Belief in a fetish may be essential to the welfare of a primitive tribe, and he who does not believe in it may be exterminated ; yet this does not demonstrate the rational character of the belief. It is right, therefore, that we should investigate whether our conviction is well based, and to this point we shall devote the remaining sections of this chapter.

In concluding the present section we may resume the results reached as follows :—

In the order of perceptions (cause and effect) no inherent necessity can be demonstrated.

In the uniformity with which sequences of perceptions are repeated (the routine of perceptions) there is also no inherent necessity, but it is a necessary condition for the existence of thinking beings that there should be a routine in perceptions. The necessity thus lies in the nature of the thinking being and not in the perceptions themselves ; thus it is conceivably a product of the perceptive faculty.

§ 13.—*Probable and Provable*

Stanley Jevons in his discussion of the theory of probability, which forms one of the most valuable and interesting portions of his *Principles of Science*, remarks that the etymology of the word *probable* does not help us to understand what probability is and where it exists :—

" For, curiously enough, *probable* is ultimately the same word as *provable*—a good instance of one word becoming differentiated to two opposite meanings " (p. 197).[1]

Now we have seen that certainty belongs only to the sphere of conceptions ; that inherent necessity has a meaning in the mental field of logic, but that we cannot postulate it in the universe of perceptions ; that the " necessity of natural law " is really an unjustifiable phrase. The word *proof*, therefore, used in the sense of a

---

[1] The source of both words must be sought, I think, in the mediaeval Latin *proba*, a sample, test, or trial. Thus *probare* is used in the sense of extracting a fact by torture, and *probabilis* is that which by aid of the *proba* has been attested and approved.

demonstrable certainty, applies only to the sphere of conceptions. What are we, then, to understand when the word *proof* is applied to natural phenomena? Shall we say that it is incorrect to use the word *prove* at all in such relationship? Yet our leading men of science do use it. Here is a passage from Lord Kelvin's lecture on "The Six Gateways of Knowledge." [1] He is discussing the possibility of our having a "magnetic sense," and he writes :—

" I cannot think that that quality of matter in space —magnetisation—which produces such a prodigious effect upon a piece of metal, can be absolutely without any— it is certainly not without any—effect whatever on the matter of a living body ; and that it can be absolutely without any *perceptible* effect whatever on the matter of a living body placed there, seems to me not *proved* even yet, although nothing has been found."

The word *prove* is here distinctly used of something being demonstrable in the field of perception. There is clearly an inference involved, and this inference is easily seen to be that of the routine of perceptions, namely, that if something has once been perceived, it will under precisely the same circumstances be again perceived. Our conviction of this routine is not a certainty, but, as we have seen, a probability. Hence, when we are speaking of the sphere of perceptions we must remember that provable is ultimately the same word as probable. The association of the two words does not therefore seem without profit ; and the etymology may after all serve to remind us of the character of our knowledge in the field of perception.

The problem before us is the following one : A certain order of perceptions has been experienced in the past, what is the probability that the perceptions will repeat themselves in the same order in the future? The probability is conditioned by two factors, namely : (1) In most cases the order has previously been very often repeated, and (2) past experience shows us that sequences

[1] *Popular Lectures and Addresses*, vol. i. p. 261. London, 1889.

of perceptions are things which have hitherto repeated themselves without fail. Thus there is past experience of repetition in the class, as well as in the individual, strengthening the probability of a future recurrence of the same sequence. The probability that the sun will rise to-morrow is not only conditioned by men's past experience of the sun's motion, but by their past experience of the uniform order in natural phenomena. There is no need to repeat a cautiously conducted experiment a great number of times to *prove*—that is, to establish an overwhelming probability in favour of—a certain sequence of perceptions. The overwhelming probability drawn from past experience in favour of *all* sequences repeating themselves at once embraces the new sequence. Suppose the solidification of hydrogen to have been *once* accomplished by an experimenter of known probity and caution, and with a method in which criticism fails to detect any flaw. What is the probability that on repetition of the same process the solidification of hydrogen will follow? Now Laplace has asserted that the probability that an event which has ocurred p times and has not hitherto failed will occur again, is represented by the fraction $\frac{p+1}{p+2}$. Hence in the case of hydrogen the probability of repetition would only be $\frac{2}{3}$, or, as we popularly say, the odds would be two to one in its favour. On the other hand, if the sun has risen without fail a million times, the odds in favour of its rising to-morrow would be 1,000,001 to 1. It is clear that on this hypothesis there would be practical certainty with regard to the rising of the sun being repeated, but only some likelihood with regard to the solidification of hydrogen being repeated. The numbers, in fact, do not in the least represent the degrees of belief of the scientist regarding the repetition of the two phenomena. We ought rather to put the problem in this manner: p different sequences of perception have been found to follow the same routine, however often repeated, and none have been found to fail, what is the probability that the $(p + 1)$th sequence of perceptions will have a routine? Laplace's theorem shows us that the odds are $(p + 1)$ to one in favour of the new sequence having a routine.   In other words, since p represents here the infinite variety of phenomena in which men's past experience has shown that the same causes are on repetition followed by the same effect, there are overwhelming odds that any newly-observed phenomenon may be classified under this law of causation.[1]   So great and, considering the odds, reasonably great is our belief in this law of causation applying to new phenomena, that when a sequence of perception does not appear to repeat itself, we assert with the utmost confidence that the same causes have not been present in the original and in the repeated sequence.

§ 14.—*Probability as to Breaches in the Routine of Perceptions*

Laplace has even enabled us to take account of possible " miracles," anomies, or breaches of routine in the sequence of perceptions.   He tells us that if an event has happened p times and failed q times, then the probability that it will happen the next time, is $\frac{p+1}{p+q+2}$, or the odds in favour of its happening are $p + 1$ to $q + 1$. Now if we are as generous as we possibly can be to the reporters of the miraculous, we can hardly assert that a well-authenticated breach of the routine of perceptions has happened *once* in past experience for every 1000 million cases of routine.   In other words, we must take p equal to 1000 million times q, or the odds against a miracle happening in the next sequence of perceptions would be about 1000 millions to one.   It is clear from this that any belief that the miraculous will occur in our immediate experience cannot possibly form a factor in the conduct of practical life.   Indeed the odds against a miracle occurring are so great, the percentage of permanently diseased or temporarily disordered perceptive

---

[1] A somewhat greater probability in favour of a new sequence which has repeated itself r times repeating itself on the $(r + 1)$th trial will be given below.

faculties so large as compared with the percentage of asserted breaches of routine, and the advantage to mankind of evolving an absolutely certain basis of knowledge so great,[1] that we are justified in saying that miracles have been *proved* incredible—the word *proved* being used in the sense in which alone it has meaning when applied to the field of perceptions (p. 140).

§ 15.—*The Basis of Laplace's Theory lies in an Experience as to Ignorance*

I have said enough, I think, to indicate that if Laplace's theorems be correct and can be fairly applied to measure the probability of the repetition of events, our belief in the routine of perceptions is based upon that high degree of probability, which renders probable and provable practically the same word. Let us consider the basis of Laplace's theory a little more closely. Suppose we take a shilling and toss it, then the chances that head or tail will be uppermost are exactly equal ; unity denoting certainty, we say that the probability of a head equals $\frac{1}{2}$. If we toss it again, the chances of a head will not be altered and will again be $\frac{1}{2}$, and so on for each throw, the chance always remaining $\frac{1}{2}$. Since in two throws we might with equal probability have any of the four cases: head, head: tail, tail: head, tail: tail, head, it follows that the recurrence of head has only a probability of $\frac{1}{4}$ or $\frac{1}{2} \times \frac{1}{2}$. Similarly the probability that three heads will be tossed in succession may be easily seen by counting the possible cases to be $\frac{1}{8}$ or $\frac{1}{2} \times \frac{1}{2} \times \frac{1}{2}$; that is, the odds are seven to one against a triple recurrence. Extending this to twenty or thirty recurrences of heads, we soon find that there is an overwhelming probability against a succession of recurrences without a break.

Instead of the shilling, let us take a bag and put into

[1] This refers to the hypothesis (p. 137) that man in the course of evolution has attained a perceptive faculty which in the normal condition can only present sequences of perceptions in the form of routine. Such routine being, as we have seen, the sole basis of knowledge, is of enormous advantage to man.

it an equal number of black and white balls. The probability of a random drawing resulting in a white ball will now be $\frac{1}{2}$, and this will at each drawing, provided the balls be returned to the bag, be the probability in favour of a white ball. Now let us look upon the world of perceptions as a bag containing white and black balls, a white ball representing a routine-order and a black ball an anomy or breach of routine. Then, since we see no reason why perceptions should have a routine or should not have a routine, may we not assert that each are equally likely, or that there will be the same number of black and white balls in our bag? If this be so, then obviously the odds are seven to one against a routine-order occurring even three times without a single anomy, and are overwhelming against no breach of routine occurring at all. Yet the only supposition that we appear to have made is this: that, knowing nothing of nature, routine and anomy are to be considered as equally likely to occur. Now we were not really justified in making even this assumption, for it involves a knowledge that we do not possess regarding nature. We use our *experience* of the constitution and action of coins in general to assert that heads and tails are equally probable, but we have no right to assert before experience that, as we know nothing of nature, routine and breach of routine are equally probable. In our ignorance we ought to consider before experience that nature may consist of all routines, all anomies, or a mixture of the two in any proportion whatever, and that all such are equally probable. Which of these constitutions after experience is the most probable must clearly depend on what that experience has been like.

To return to the case of the coin, we must suppose all experience of the action of coins withdrawn from us ; it must be unknown to us, whether coins are so constituted as to have a head on both faces, a tail on both faces, or a head on one and a tail on the other. The probability of any one of these three equally probable constitutions would before experience be $\frac{1}{3}$. Now suppose we had the experience of two tosses both resulting in heads. On the first constitution of the body this would be a certain result, or its probability be represented by 1 ; on the second constitution the result would be impossible, or the probability would be zero, while on the third constitution —that of the customary coin—the probability of the result would be $\frac{1}{4}$. *Experience*, then, shows us that one constitution of the coin is impossible, and that another constitution will certainly give the observed result, while the odds against the remaining possible constitution giving it are 3 : 1. Obviously a double head is a more probable constitution for the coin than head and tail. But in what ratio is this constitution more probable than the other? This is determined by a principle due to Laplace, which we may state as follows :—

"If a result might flow from any one of a certain number of different constitutions, all equally probable before experience, then the several probabilities of each constitution after experience being the real constitution, are proportional to the probabilities that the result would flow from each of these constitutions."

Thus in our case the head-head constitution gives a probability of 1 that the observed result will arise, while head-tail only gives a probability of $\frac{1}{4}$. Hence, on Laplace's principle, the odds are four to one that our coin has a head on both sides. We must be careful to note that this result depends entirely on the assumption that coins may have *any* constitution whatever ; it ceases to have application when we have once had the experience that coins usually have a head and a tail. But it may be said, ought we not to have had the actual *experience* that coins may be of any constitution before we can predict that the individual coin which has twice turned up heads is probably a double-headed coin? Can we assume without such experience that, where we are ignorant, all constitutions are *a priori* equally probable? May we for the very reason that we know nothing "distribute our ignorance equally"? The logic of this proceeding has been called in question by more than one writer, notably

by the late George Boole.[1] We may indeed reasonably question whether it is possible to draw knowledge
out of complete ignorance. But before we can agree
with Boole that Laplace's method is nugatory, we must
ask whether, after all, his principle is not based on knowledge, namely, on that derived from the experience that
in cases where we are ignorant, there in the long run all
constitutions will be found to be equally probable.

A good example of this has been given by Professor
Edgeworth. Suppose we divide 143,678 by 7 and stop
at the fourth figure of the quotient, we have 2052 as the
result. Now we may be supposed ignorant of what the
next figure will turn out to be, and in our ignorance *all*
the digits from 0 to 9 are equally probable. Why?
Because if we divided a very great quantity of numbers
of 6 figures by 7, stopping at the fourth digit in the
quotient, we should find that the numbers of times each of
the digits from 0 to 9 would occur in the fifth place
were practically equal. In other words, statistics would
justify the "equal distribution of our ignorance," or
experience show us that in our ignorance all constitutions
were equally probable. This example may, perhaps,
suffice to show that there is an element of human experience at the basis of Laplace's assumption. The
reader who wishes to pursue this subject further may be
referred in the first place to Professor Edgeworth's
article.[2] " I submit," he writes, " the assumption that any
probability-constant about which we know nothing in particular is as likely to have one value as another, is
grounded upon the rough but solid experience that such
constants do as a matter of fact as often have one value
as another."

The reader may, however, ask why may not " nature "
change after one set of experiences and before another ?
The only answer to this question lies in the views ex-

---

[1] *An Investigation of the Laws of Thought* (London, 1854), chap. xx.
Problems Relating to the Connexion of Causes and Effects, especially pp. 363-
375.
[2] " The Philosophy of Chance," *Mind*, vol. ix. pp. 223-35, 1884.

pressed partly in earlier chapters of this work, partly in the following chapter on *Space and Time*. Nature, we have seen, is a construct of the human mind (pp. 41, 101-6, 107) ; time and space are not inherent in an outside world, but are modes of discriminating groups of sense-impressions (pp. 181, 209). Thus " nature " is essentially conditioned by our perceptive faculty, and " change " cannot be thought of as apart from ourselves. That " nature " is identical " before and after experience " will be admitted, as soon as it is recognised as probable that time and change relate to perception, and not to the " beyond " of sense-impressions. The sameness of the perceptive faculty is very likely the key to the sameness of the modes of perception. The conditions for each trial (as in throwing a die or in drawing from a bag) remaining the same, lie according to this view in the identity of the perceptive faculty.

§ 16.—*Nature of Laplace's Investigation*

We are now in a position to return to our bag of white and black balls, but we can no longer suppose an equal number of both kinds, or that routine and breach of routine are equally probable. We must assume our " nature bag " to have every possible constitution or every possible ratio of black to white balls to be equally likely ; to do this we suppose an infinitely great number of balls in all. We may then calculate the probability that with each of these constitutions the observed result, say p white balls and q black balls (or, p cases of routine, and q anomies) would arise in $p + q$ drawings.[1] This will determine, by Laplace's principle, the probability that each hypothetical constitution is the real constitution of the bag. Let these probabilities be represented by the letters P_1, P_2, P_3 . . . etc. We may then determine the probabilities on each of these constitutions that a white ball will be drawn in the $(p + q + 1)$th drawing. If these

---

[1] The reader may suppose the ball returned to the bag after each drawing.

probabilities be represented by the letters C_1, C_2, C_3 . . . etc., then by a well-known law for compounding probabilities[1] we shall find that the total probability in favour of a white ball occurring on the $(p + q + 1)$th drawing, or of a routine following on p routines and q anomies, is—

$$P_1 C_1 + P_2 C_2 + P_3 C_3 + . . .$$

Now all this is pure calculation; it involves no *new* principle, nothing the reader may not take on faith, if he is not an adept in mathematical analysis. We shall therefore suppose the calculation made[2] as Laplace made it, and the result will be found to be that given on our p. 142, namely, the probability that a white ball will be drawn is $\frac{p+1}{p+q+2}$. Or, since q is either zero or vanishingly small as compared with p, we have the overwhelming probability of the routine of perceptions being maintained on the *next* trial.

§ 17.—*The Permanency of Routine for the Future*

One particular case is worth noting. Suppose we have experienced m sequences of perceptions which have repeated themselves n times without any anomy. Suppose, further, a new sequence to have repeated itself r times also without anomy. Then in all we have had $m(n - 1) + r - 1$ repetitions, or cases of routine, and no failures; hence the probability that the new sequence will repeat itself on the $(r + 1)$th occasion is obtained by putting $p = m(n - 1) + r - 1$ and $q = o$ in the result of § 16, or the odds in favour of a routine occurring on the next occasion with the new sequence are $m(n - 1) + r$ to 1. Therefore if m and n be very great, there will be overwhelming odds in favour of the new sequence following

---

[1] The reader will find this law discussed in any elementary work on algebra. See, for example, Todhunter's *Algebra*, §§ 732 and 746.

[2] See Todhunter's *History of the Theory of Probability*, Arts. 374, 847-8 ; Boole's *Laws of Thought*, chap. xx. § 23 ; or T. Galloway, *A Treatise on Probability*, § v., " On the Probability of Future Events deduced from Experience."

routine, although r, or the number of times it has been tested, be very small.[1]

Our discussion of the probability basis for routine in the sequences of perceptions has perforce been brief, and only touched the fringe of a vast and difficult subject. Yet it may perhaps suffice to indicate that the odds in favour of that routine being preserved in the immediate future, or, indeed, for any finite interval, both with regard to old and to new groups of perceptions, are overwhelming.[2] We may be absolutely unable to demonstrate any inherent necessity for routine from our perceptions themselves, but our complete ignorance of such necessity, combined with our past experience, enables us by aid of the theory of probability to gauge roughly how unlikely it is that the possibility of knowledge and the power of thinking will be destroyed in our generation by those breaches of routine which, in popular language, we term miracles.

So much science can tell us at present ; more we can only hope to *know*, if we admit that routine flows from the nature of our perceptive faculty and not from the sphere beyond sense-impression. If science must at the present stage perforce be content with a *belief* in the immediate permanency of the universe (based on a probability

---

[1] We must be cautious in applying this formula to take a sufficiently comprehensive sequence of perceptions. We must see that the causes are really "like," before we predict on the basis of past experience of routine in perceptions a repetition of sequence in any particular case. That I have twice seen a certain river overflowing its banks, and never seen that river without a flood, will not enable me to predict that the flood will always occur when I see the river. I must add to these perceptions, those of the season of the year, of the amount of sun which has acted on the snow-fields and glaciers at its source, of the condition of its banks, etc., etc., before I have a sufficiently wide range of causes to enable me to predict from two repetitions the occurrence of a third. I must indeed show that in my supposed identical sequences there are really the same components. The reader who wishes to study this point more thoroughly must be referred to Mill's "Canons of Induction" (*System of Logic*, book iii.), an elementary discussion of which will be found in the "Lessons on Induction," pp. 210-64 of Stanley Jevons' *Elementary Lessons in Logic*.

[2] The odds in favour of a sequence repeating itself s times when the past shows p repetitions and no failure are $p + 1$ to s. The number of repeated sequences in the universe, or p, is practically infinite, so that the odds are overwhelming so long as s is finite. We cannot, however, argue from this result for an *infinite* future of repetition.

which in practical life we should term certainty), we must at the same time remember that because a proposition has not yet been proved, we have no right to infer that its converse must be true. It is not a case of balancing contradictory evidence, for not a single valid argument is to be found in the whole range of human experience for inferring a first or last cause. There may be a beginning and an end to life on our planet ; we may term these, if we please, a " first and a last catastrophe." But among the myriad planetary systems we see on a clear night there surely must be myriad planets which have reached our own stage of development, and teem, or have teemed, with life. The first and last catastrophe must have occurred a myriad times, and were we able to watch through long thousands of years the changing brilliancy of stars, the first and last catastrophe would appear to us not as a first and last cause, but as much a routine of perceptions as the birth and death of individual men.

SUMMARY

1. Cause is scientifically used to denote an antecedent stage in a routine of perceptions. In this sense force as a cause is meaningless. First cause is only a limit, permanent or temporary, to knowledge. No instance, certainly not will, occurs in our experience of an arbitrary first cause in the popular sense of the word.

2. There is no inherent necessity in the routine of perceptions, but the permanent existence of rational beings necessitates a routine of perceptions ; with the cessation of routine ceases the possibility of a thinking being. The only necessity we are acquainted with exists in the sphere of conceptions ; possibly routine in perceptions is due to the constitution of the perceptive faculty.

3. Proof in the field of perceptions is the demonstration of overwhelming probability. Logically we ought to use the word *know* only of conceptions, and reserve the word *believe* for perceptions. " I know that the angle at the circumference on any diameter of a circle is right," but " I believe that the sun will rise to-morrow." The proof that for no finite future a breach of routine will occur depends upon the solid experience that where we are ignorant, there statistically all constitutions of the unknown are found to be equally probable.

LITERATURE

BOOLE, G.—An Investigation of the Laws of Thought, chaps. xvi.-xx. London, 1854.

DE MORGAN, A.—The Theory of Probabilities. London, 1838.

EDGEWORTH, F. Y.—"The Philosophy of Chance," *Mind*, vol. ix., 1884, pp. 223-35.

GALLOWAY, T.—A Treatise on Probability. Edinburgh, 1839.

JEVONS, W. STANLEY.—The Principles of Science, chaps. x.-xii.

MILL, JOHN STUART.—System of Logic, book iii., Induction. 1st ed., 1843 ; 8th ed., 1872.

VENN, J.—The Logic of Chance. 3rd Edition. London, 1888.

The reader who wishes to study Laplace's labours at first-hand will find a guide to his memoirs and some account of the various editions of his *Théorie analytique des probabilités* in Todhunter's History of the Theory of Probability, chap. xx. He may also consult Arts. 841-857 of the same History.

CHAPTER V

CONTINGENCY AND CORRELATION——THE INSUFFICIENCY OF CAUSATION

§ 1.——*The Routine of Perceptions is Relative rather than Absolute*

IN the previous chapter we saw the foundation of the idea of causation in the routine of perceptions. There was no inherent necessity in the nature of this routine itself, but failing it the existence of rational beings, capable of conduct became practically impossible. To think may connote existence, but to act, to conduct one's life and affairs, connote of necessity a *routine* of perceptions. It is this practical necessity, which we have crystallised out as a necessity existing in "things in themselves," and made fundamental in our conception of cause and effect. So all-important is this routine for the conduct of rational beings, that we fail to comprehend a world to which the conception of cause and effect would not apply. We have made it the dominating factor in phenomena, and most of us are firmly convinced not only of its absolute truth, but of its correspondence with some reality lying behind phenomena and at the basis of all existence itself. Yet as we have seen, even in the most purely physical phenomena, the routine is a matter of experience, and our belief in it a conviction based on probability ; we can but describe experience, we never reach an " explanation," connoting necessity. Strange as it may seem also when we come to analyse this cause and effect category in actual practise, we find that it slips vaguely away from us into the intangible field of the conceptual rather than realising itself in our actual experience of phenomena. It is a conceptual limit based upon our experience, rather than a factor of phenomena as we know them.

For rational beings conducting life in time and space some routine of perceptions is essential ; without it foresight, and therefore rational conduct become impossible. But routine is a word the "atmosphere" of which is of more value than its definition. It marks a certain sameness, but not necessarily an absolute sameness. Is absolute sameness necessary to the conduct of a rational being? Is absolute sameness ever reached in the repetition of phenomena? If these questions are answered, as we believe they must be, in the negative, then we see that our routine of perceptions has become a relative idea, it marks a certain degree of sameness in repetition, the limit to which—absolute sameness—is a purely conceptual notion, which is not in human experience, but which has been extracted from that experience in the same manner as other conceptual limits, such as geometrical surfaces or the ratio of infinitesimals. Our rational being requires for his active existence a certain degree of sameness in his perceptions, he does not require for conduct *absolute* sameness. If he goes through closely the same processes to-day, he expects much the same results as yesterday ; if the preparation of what was nourishment yesterday, when repeated to-day, produces relatively the same nourishment and not a poison ; if the conduct that tended to welfare in the past, when repeated, tends to much the like degree of welfare in the present, then the degree of sameness is practically sufficient for the rational being. It is this relatively rough degree of routine in our perceptions which has led mankind ultimately to the conceptual limit of causation. But those who have not thought very carefully over this matter will exclaim : "But with exactly like causes we shall get exactly the same effects." Possibly yes, and possibly no. As far as our experience goes, nothing in the universe ever has or ever will exactly repeat itself. You cannot get exactly the like causes, because everything which has previously occurred or is simultaneously occurring in the universe is to a greater or less extent a cause of everything else. That fact is one of the reasons why the definition of cause and effect is really so vague. The sameness of the "routine" which the man in the street is familiar with may be far looser than the routine of experiment which the physicist or chemist idealises as absolute sameness; but the sameness is in both cases one of degree. The man in the street is possibly unaware that no two samples to which physicist or chemist gives the same name are ever absolutely identical; the numerical constants obtained for them always differ provided the measurements or determinations are made with extreme accuracy. No doubt the physicist will tell us that if he could get his material the same, his apparatus the same, his environment the same, and himself the same, the absolute sameness of the law of causation would be demonstrated. Possibly, but what does this admission amount to but to the statement that the law of causation does not lie in phenomena as we experience them, but is purely a mental limit drawn like any other limit as an ideal from actual experience; it is a useful conception, but in no sense a reality lying as a bedrock below phenomena. The conclusions of the physicist and the chemist are based on *average* experiences, no two of which exactly agree; at best they are routines of perception which have a certain variability. This variability they may attribute to errors of observations, to impurities in their specimens, to the physical factors of the environment, but it none the less exists and, when it is removed by a process of averaging, we pass at once from the perceptual to the conceptual, and construct a model universe, not the real universe.

§ 2.—*The Ultimate Elements of the Inorganic as of the Organic Universe may be Individual and not Same*

So familiar has this conceptual model become, that when we mention an element the hearer is likely to call to mind vacant space peopled by an immense number of identical molecules, each of the same geometrical pattern and possessing identical physical properties! Yet even if we suppose such a system, or anything resembling it, to be at the basis of reality, we should only have evidence of a certain average or statistical sameness, and not of absolute identity. Imagine a certain number of pebbles taken from the beach and sorted out into groups, the first group weighing less than 1 oz., the second between 1 and 2 oz., the third between 2 and 3 oz., and so on. Then let us take the groups from 1 to 2 oz., from 5 to 6 oz., from 13 to 14 oz., from 20 to 21 oz., etc. ; it is clear that even the hand could accurately separate out these groups, even if they were again mingled together. The members of each group would have a certain degree of sameness, and they might be sorted out mechanically. Nay, the sea might possibly act upon them for years, and yet it might be possible to practically differentiate our selected classes. To the Greek the differences of the stars were embraced in the idea of relative brilliancy, he classed them by their "magnitude." It is extremely improbable that, had a demon interchanged during the daytime two stars of the "same" magnitude, any Greek would have had the means of discovering the change. It would have passed unnoticed even if the "sameness" of magnitude had to our modern appreciation been fairly rough. The stars to the Greek were much like our sorted pebbles from the shore. But to the modern astronomer it is hardly too much to assert that every star that he has studied has its own physical and chemical individuality. He classifies them in innumerable ways scarcely conceivable to the Greek. He notices their differences from their fellows, and he knows their progressive changes. He could in the bulk of cases discover a stellar interchange, and he knows that individuality and progressive change are the characteristics of bodies which but for relative magnitude were identical to the Greek.

What, then, is the moral of these analogies? Why that in the one case where we have actual experience of an infinity of bodies we find individuality and change, although to a rougher classification we may treat them as statistically same. The absence of individuality and the persistency through all time in the same condition of our molecules is purely conceptual, not necessarily a feature of actuality. Experience gives a certain sameness and a certain variation, both are really statistical results, and we do not know whether, even if environment and observer were or could be identical, two specimens could be obtained, which to the observer of the ultimate elements would be absolutely same. It is no discredit to the great structure of modern physical chemistry to assert that the absolute sameness of the molecule is only a statistical sameness, and that an ultimate individuality, a variation within the class, may be hypothecated as a means of describing new developments which may hereafter be observed when the powers of discrimination are finer. Individuality within class differentiation has been hitherto confined to vital forms; absence of individuality and persistency asserted of inorganic matter. What if the sameness and the persistence be merely a relative distinction? What if the attempt of some biologists to replace vital variation by "unit" characters be really a retrogressive change, and the persistency and absence of individuality to which they appeal as comparable with chemical changes be ultimately a false analogy, because the sameness of chemical theory is a *statistical* experience which may ultimately admit differentiation within the class?

§ 3.—*The Category of Association, as replacing Causation*

If we realise individuality at the basis of all existence, and sameness as a relative term depending on the fineness of classification, then we see that cause and effect as measured by the routine of perceptions only connote a degree of likeness, not an absolute repetition. The law of causation is a conceptual figment extracted from phenomena, it is not of their very essence. The actual problem before mankind is a far wider one than that of "causation," and may be summed up as follows : If the "causes" have such and such a degree of likeness, how like will the "effects" be? Here in the broadest sense anything is a cause which antedates or accompanies a phenomenon, and we ask if we vary that cause to what degree we vary or change the phenomenon. If we say that variation of the cause produces no effect on the phenomenon we have absolute independence ; if we found variation of this cause absolutely and alone varied the phenomenon we should say that there was absolute dependence. Such absolute dependence of a phenomenon on a single measurable cause is certainly the exception, if it ever exists when the refinement of observation is intense enough. It would correspond to a true case of the conceptual limit—of whose actual existence we have our grave doubts. But between these two limits of absolute independence and absolute dependence all grades of association may occur. When we vary the cause, the phenomenon changes, but not always to the same extent ; it changes, but has variation in its change. The less the variation in that change the more nearly the cause defines the phenomena, the more closely we assert the association or the correlation to be. It is this conception of correlation between two occurrences embracing all relationship from absolute independence to complete dependence, which is the wider category by which we have to replace the old idea of causation. Everything in the universe occurs but once, there is no absolute sameness of repetition. Individual phenomena can only be classified, and our problem turns on how far a group or class of like, but not absolutely same, things which we term "causes" will be accompanied or followed by another group or class of like, but not absolutely same things which we term "effects."

Let us call these two groups A and B, and examine how much wider and yet more definite this new conception of correlation is than the old conception of causation. Into the group A we put any number of things A_1, A_2, A_3 . . . defined as having a certain degree of likeness. They are not absolutely same, because they really depend for sameness on an infinity of characters, only a very small number of which are or can in actual practise be examined and identified. The degree of likeness may be small, for example if A connote a man, or it may be large, for example if A be a chemist's sample of hydrogen ; in both cases, however, there is not absolute sameness either in the thing itself, or in its environment, a factor which is not, as some suppose, absolutely differentiated from or independent of the thing. We now observe our second group B, and it again has like things, B_1, B_2, B_3 . . ., things which may be phenomena, or qualities, or attributes of the things in the A group. If to a certain degree of observation or measurement, we do not or cannot distinguish A_1 from A_2 or A_3, etc., and we do not or cannot distinguish B_1 from B_2 or B_3, etc., we talk about A producing or causing B, and we have the causation idea of the physicist. But in the great bulk of cases, even if we make every attempt to reach sameness in A, we find observable or measurable differences in B. For a given A we obtain an "array" of values of B, say for a particular A_p,—which we fail to distinguish from any other of this sub-class of A's,—we find a series of perceptibly different B's, namely B_1 occurs n_{p1} times, B_2 occurs n_{p2} times, and so forth. This array of B's thus possesses *variation*. The more nearly all the B's fall into one group the less is the variation, but the extent of the variation is a matter of degree, and the finer our observing and measuring tools the more marked we discover is usually the deviation from, not the agreement with, the principle of absolute causation.[1] If, instead of taking A_p, we start with a distinguishable A_q, we find that

---

[1] Measured only with an ounce scale our pebbles (p. 155) are "same," measured with a chemical balance they are differentiated in the sub-groups.

B_1 occurs n_{p1}, B_2 occurs n_{p2} times, and so on. We thus are able to obtain a general distribution of B's for each class of A that we can form, and were we to go through the whole population, N, of A's in this manner we should obtain a table of the following kind :—

TYPE OF A OBSERVED

TYPE OF B OBSERVED

	A_1.	A_2.	A_3.	...	...	A_p.	...	...	...	Total.
B_1	n_{11}	n_{21}	n_{31}	...	...	n_{p1}	...	...	...	n_{a1}
B_2	n_{12}	n_{22}	n_{32}	...	...	n_{p2}	...	...	...	n_{a2}
B_3	n_{13}	n_{23}	n_{33}	...	...	n_{p3}	...	...	...	n_{a3}
...	...	...	...	...	...	...	...	...	...	...
...	...	...	...	...	...	...	...	...	..	...
B_s	n_{1s}	n_{2s}	n_{3s}	...	...	n_{ps}	...	...	...	n_{as}
...	...	...	...	...	...	...	...	...	...	...
...	...	...	...	...	...	...	...	...	...	...
Total	n_{1b}	n_{2b}	n_{3b}	...	...	n_{pb}	...	...	...	N

Such a table is termed a *contingency* table, and the ultimate scientific statement or description of the relation between two things can always be thrown back upon such a contingency table. If we take our population "N," wherein the relation of A and B has been observed or measured, then we note that the thing, phenomenon, or quality A occurs n_{pb} times in the form A_p; if we classify the way in which this A_p is associated with B in its different forms we note, reading down the vertical column, that A_p occurs with B_1 n_{p1} times, with B_2 n_{p2} times, with B_s n_{ps} times. In other words n_{ps} marks the number of times that A_p is associated with B_s, or the number recorded in any "cell" is the number of times the association of the A at the top of the column occurs with the B at the left of the row in which the cell lies. Once the reader realises the nature of such a table, he will have grasped the essence of the conception of association between cause and effect, and the nature of its ideal limit in causation.[1]

[1] A "solid" of such cells in multiple space is the fundamental classification, which forms the point of departure for modern theories of logic.

§ 4.—*Symbolic Measure of the Intensity of Association or Contingency*

Now, what do we mean when we say B is independent of A ? Clearly that whatever A we select we shall not alter the proportions of the observed B's. In other words the proportional distribution of B's under any A_p must be the same as the whole distribution of B's in the population or universe under discussion, *i.e.* the distribution given in the total column on the right. Expressed in symbols :

$$\frac{n_{ps}}{n_{pb}} \text{ must equal } \frac{n_{as}}{N},$$

$$\text{or } n_{ps} = \frac{n_{pb} \times n_{as}}{N}.$$

If n_{ps} be not equal to this, B is not independent of A but *contingent* on it.[1] The deviation from this result namely :

$$n_{ps} - \frac{n_{pb} \times n_{as}}{N}$$

is termed the contingency of the cell p,s ; it is the deviation in the observed number of associated A_p and B_s from the number which would occur in the case of absolute independence. Such a contingency table as we have schemed above is the numerical syllogism of observational science, which replaces for all its purposes the barren syllogism of the old Aristotelian logic. We do not say, " Some of B is A," but we state numerically how much of each class of B is associated with each category of A. In actual practise, of course, it is impossible to form a table of the whole population or the whole universe of A and B things. We take here as elsewhere a " sample " to illustrate that universe, and we have to take great precautions not only that this is a true sample, but that our inferences from the sample may

---

[1] Since ˙N may clearly be written n_{ab} the algebra of non-contingent variables may be developed from $(ab) \times (ps) = (pb) \times (as)$ as a symbolic definition of multiplication.

be applied to the universe under discussion. The theory of samples—their probable errors and legitimate use—is the chief topic of modern scientific statistics ; it cannot be considered here, but the idea of contingency is one which is fundamental and easy to grasp. It is at the basis of the wider conception of association, which is surely replacing the old limited idea of cause and effect.

Let us try and follow up this contingency idea further. Let ν_{ps} stand for what would be the content of the p,s cell if A and B were independent, then $n_{ps} - \nu_{ps}$ measures the deviation from independence with regard to this cell. But clearly such deviation must be taken relative to the total of occurrences in this cell, or $(n_{ps} - \nu_{ps})/\nu_{ps}$ is a fit measure of the contingency in the cell. Now such deviation may be in excess or defect, *i.e.* may be plus or minus, and as either are equally significant we take the square to measure them or $\{(n_{ps} - \nu_{ps})/\nu_{ps}\}^2$. Lastly, this measure ought to be taken relative to the total population, *i.e.* we multiply it by the factor ν_{ps}/N, which measures the relation of the individual cell to the whole total observed. The quantity thus obtained, or

$$\frac{(n_{ps} - \nu_{ps})^2}{\nu_{ps} \times N} ,$$

if summed for each cell, is termed the *mean square contingency* of the whole table. Since the sum of a number of squares, multiplied by positive numerical factors can, only vanish, if each square vanishes, or $n_{ps} = \nu_{ps}$ for every cell, we assert that the vanishing of the mean squared contingency is the essential condition for the independence of two characters.

Now let us turn to the other extreme and suppose that the class of B could be absolutely defined by the class of A. Then our table takes the following typical form, with one category of B only for each category of A :

[TABLE

TYPE OF A

	$A_1.$	$A_2.$	$A_3.$	...	...	$A_p.$	...	...	...	Total.
B_1	n_{11}	o	o	...	...	o	...	...	...	n_{11}
B_2	o	n_{22}	o	...	...	o	...	...	...	n_{22}
B_3	o	o	n_{33}	...	...	o	...	...	...	n_{33}
...	...	...	...	...	...	...	...	...	...	...
...	...	...	...	...	...	...	...	...	...	...
B_p	o	o	o	...	...	n_{pp}	...	...	...	n_{pp}
...	...	...	...	...	...	o	...	...	...	...
...	...	...	...	...	...	o	...	...	...	...
...	...	...	...	...	...	o	...	...	...	...
Total	n_{11}	n_{22}	n_{33}	...	...	n_{pp}	...	...	...	N

(TYPE OF B — left axis label)

Here B_1 has been absolutely associated with A_1, B_2 with A_2, etc. This is legitimate as there is no special order of any kind about the A's and the B's ; they are mere classificatory groups. Now let us find the mean square contingency for such a distribution as this, which consists of a diagonal line of cells with finite frequencies n_{11}, n_{22}, n_{33} ... n_{pp} ... and all other cells with zero frequencies. Take the first row as illustration ; the value of ν_{11} is $n_{11} \times n_{11}/N$, and we have

$$\frac{(n_{11} - \nu_{11})^2}{\nu_{11}N} = \left(1 - \frac{n_{11}}{N}\right)^2 = 1 - \frac{2n_{11}}{N} + \frac{n_{11}^2}{N}.$$

The zero cells of the first row give

$$\frac{\left(o - \frac{n_{11}n_{22}}{N}\right)^2}{\frac{n_{11}n_{22}N}{N}} + \frac{\left(o - \frac{n_{11}n_{33}}{N}\right)^2}{\frac{n_{11}n_{33}N}{N}} + \cdots$$

$$= \frac{n_{11}}{N}\left(\frac{n_{22}}{N} + \frac{n_{33}}{N} + \cdots\right) = \frac{n_{11}}{N}\left(1 - \frac{n_{11}}{N}\right).$$

Adding this to the value for the first cell we have for the mean square contingency of the first row $1 - \frac{n_{11}}{N}$, or summing for all rows, if there be m values of A, mean square contingency for whole table $= m - \frac{n_{11} + n_{22} + n_{33} + \cdots}{N}$ $= m - 1$, which depends solely on the number of classes we can distinguish among the A's. Hence we assert that when an individual A fixes also an individual B the mean square contingency depends only on the number of individuals which can be differentiated and is a unit less than this number.

In mathematical language when A absolutely fixes B, B is said to be a function of A. If for every alteration in A an alteration is found in B, and no two B's corresponding to different A's are alike, then clearly m becomes infinite in value. Or, when one quantity is a function of a second, the mean square contingency tends to an infinite value. We have thus found a certain quantity the mean squared contingency, which for absolute independence takes the value zero ; for absolute dependence, or when a functional relation exists, takes the value infinity. These are the extreme limits of relationship, which, owing to the dominance of physical notions, we are too apt to consider as the only possible categories, *i.e.* independence and absolute causation. Actually they are the extreme limits of the contingency table under which we can subsume our whole experience of the association of pairs of phenomena. These extreme limits we very shrewdly suspect are only conceptual limits to actual experience. At least many things pass in the universe for absolutely independent, which a finer power of analysis or observation would demonstrate to be associated, and another large class are asserted to be causally linked together because we cannot yet perceive the variation in the array of B's associated with a given A, but can perceive the differentiation of that array from the array corresponding to a second A. In the one case the mean square contingency is so small we cannot determine its value, in the other case so large that for practical purposes it passes for infinite.

In actual treatment of experience, however, we do not use mean square contingency as our measure of the interdependence of two things. If S represent the mean square contingency we use as our measure of independence a coefficient of contingency[1] dependent upon S and determined by $C = \sqrt{\dfrac{S}{1+S}}.$ The reason for this value is

[1] The mean square contingency and the coefficient of contingency are subject

that under certain limitations, it coincides with another measure of relationship, termed the coefficient of correlation,[1] which is of much service when the two things under discussion are continuously varying quantities. We see at once that this coefficient of contingency is absolutely dependent on the mean square contingency, it is zero, if the phenomena under consideration are absolutely independent, and it takes the value unity if for every alteration in the one, there is an individual change peculiar to it in the other; that is to say, if one phenomenon is a function of the other. Between these values, zero and unity, the coefficient can take every value, and this value measures the deviation from independence, that is, measures the approach to the conceptual limit of causation, the functional relationship, which is the narrow field in which hitherto the physicist has worked. The splendid results reached in this field have led both scientist and philosopher to overlook the fact that no experience demonstrates causation; all experience shows association, varying in every degree of closeness. The very statement of the law of causation involves antecedents—sameness of causes—which are purely conceptual and never actual. Permanence and absence of individuality in the bricks of the physical universe are only demonstrated in the same way that the bricks of a building are for many statistical purposes without individuality. The exact repetition of any antecedents is never possible, and all we can do is to classify things into like within a certain degree of observation, and record whether what we note as following from them are like within another degree of observation. Whenever we do this in physics, in zoology, in botany, in sociology, in medicine, or in any other branch of science, we really form a contingency table, and the causation of the physicist solely results from the fact—not that the contingency

to corrections, depending on the number of classificatory groups in A and B, the size of the "sample," and other matters, which have been determined and are of great importance in practical use, but are not considered here, where we only need to insist on the general logical conceptions at the basis of their use.

[1] This co-efficient is dealt with later in the *Grammar*.

coefficient of everything physical is unity—but that he has so far worked to most profit in the field, where his contingency is so near unity that he could conceptualise his relationships as mathematical functions.   That *like* effects flow from *like* causes (where the word *like* is used in contrast to the *same* of the conceptual law of causation), or that for many phenomena the contingency is high, is the source of the routine we have noted in perceptions, but the subsuming of all the phenomena of the universe under the category of contingency rather than that of causation is one epoch-making to the individual mind.

§ 5.—*The Universe as governed by Causation and as governed by Contingency*

Nearly all tradition which has hampered human thought has been the product, not directly of experience, but of mental deduction from too small a range of experience.   We have only to look at pre-Copernican systems of the universe, at such narrow conceptions as "matter" and "force," or "atom" and "ether," to see how the mental concept dominates experience, and even comes to be accepted by many as a fact of experience. It is among such conceptual bondages that the law of causation in its bald and absolute statement will ultimately come to be placed.

The universe is made up of innumerable entities, each probably individual, each probably non-permanent ; all man can achieve is to classify by measurement or observation of characteristics these entities into classes of *like* individuals. Within these classes variation can be noted, and the fundamental problem of science is to discover how the variation in one class is correlated with or contingent on the variation in a second class.   Consciously, or more often unconsciously, the man of science is for ever making contingency tables.   If for each definite individual in class A, he found an associated definite individual in class B, he would say that B was a function of A, but as a matter of fact for each selected A he invariably finds, if his powers of observation and measurement are fine enough, an array—it may be very concentrated, or it may not— of individual B's. From this array he reaches by purely conceptual processes a limit in which B is mentally represented as a function of A. A is looked upon as absolutely defining B ; we have proceeded from the facts of experience to the conceptual limit of function- ality, or to the so-called law of causation. The newer, and I think truer, view of the universe is that all existences are associated in a higher or lower degree. Existences are individual ; it is a human, a rational process which for economy of thought classifies them. Any variation within the existences in one class is found to be associated with a corresponding variation among the existences in a second class. Science has to measure the degree of stringency, or of looseness in these con- comitant variations. Absolute independence is the conceptual limit at one end to the looseness of the link, absolute dependence is the conceptual limit at the other end to the stringency of the link. The old view of cause and effect tried to subsume the universe under these two conceptual limits to experience—and it could only fail ; things are not in our experience either independent or causative. All classes of phenomena are linked together, and the problem in each case is how close is the degree of association. Likeness of causes produces likeness of effects ; we can measure the degree of likeness, whether we are dealing with a chemical reaction or with the resemblance in any aptitude between parent and child. There is no question of absolute sameness in either case ; there is a wide degree of difference in the likeness, but both problems are only variants of one and the same logical problem—the contingency problem at the basis of modern science.

The intellectual attitude which sees between all existences diverse degrees of association, not dependence and independence alone, conceptualises the universe under a new category. It frees itself at once from old and trammelling distinctions between vital and physical phenomena, which lie not in these phenomena themselves, but in the conceptual limits which man has intellectually extracted from them, and then—as his habit is—forgetful of his own creative facility, has converted into a dominant reality behind his perceptions and external to himself. All the universe provides man with is likeness in variations ; he has thrust function into it, because he desired to economise his limited intellectual energy.

§ 6.—*Classification of A and B by Measurement.* *Mathematical Function*

Thus far we have been very careful to take the broadest view of the variation in our two classes of existences. The changes we have noted in A may be purely qualitative and classificatory, and the associated changes in B may be of a like nature. There may be nothing quantitative or continuous about either set of variations. If any definite classificatory change in A is associated with another definite classificatory change in B, then we say that B is a function of A. But this conceptual limit to partial experience has been narrowed down by the mathematician and physicist to a much more special conception. The idea of variation has in the main been associated with continuous variation. A quantity B has been looked upon as a function of another quantity A, when gradual and continual change in A is accompanied by gradual and continual change in B. It is not all variations in two existences A and B which can be submitted to quantitative measurement or observation, and our contingency table demands no such characteristic in the variation of either B or A. Yet the general notion of contingency and its relation to causality can be so well illustrated by continuous variation and mathematical function that it is well to linger over this special case.

We will suppose the quantity A capable of measurement, and this measurement can be represented in excess or defect of a certain average or mean value. This deviation of A can be measured plus or minus along a horizontal line. For each individual A let us measure the associated individual B, and let the quantity of the corresponding B be measured along a vertical line represented in the middle of the figure (Fig. 2*a*) by the scale 1, 2, 3,

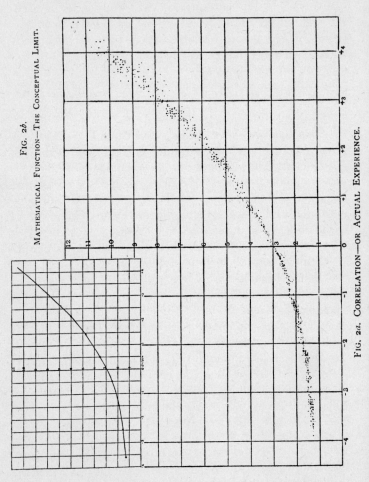

. . . 12. It is possible in this way to plot, or place, on our diagram, a point for each pair of associated A's and B's. Six hundred observations treated in this way give a diagram of dots or points like that illustrated. If any physicist made 600 to 1000 observations connecting two

variates A and B, and plotted them on a sufficiently large piece of paper, this is precisely what he would see. He would admit, as the reader does, that at any rate in his case A is not determined by B ; there is association but not causation. He would probably tell us that the scatter was due to differences in the individual observations and measurements, but this is only to admit the contention that in the actual universe nothing is same, nothing can ever be actually repeated ; in short that we can only classify like and measure the degree of association in the like which follow. Now what would the physicist do, if he ever took the time and trouble to reach a diagram of this kind ? Well, he would photograph it fifty yards off, or look at it through an inverted telescope, with the result seen in Fig. 2*b*. He has replaced experience by a conceptual limit, the contingency table with its arrays of B's for given A's has been reduced by photography, *i.e.* the mathematics of least squares, or by an inverted telescope, *i.e.* the averaging of the arrays to a smooth curve ; actual experience has been replaced by mathematical function. A knowledge of two or three numerical constants will now define for him,—what, actual experience ?—no, the conceptual limit to actual experience represented in Fig. 2*b*. That curve is the " causality " which man extracts from his experience and thrusts back into nature as if it had actual existence there. What then does it represent ? An economy of thought, an average or approximate routine of perceptions. No future routine will be the *same* as this, it will be *like* it, but not identical with it ; and the degree of deviation from this conceptual routine will be measured by the variation in the array of B's which corresponds to a given A. If that variation be very small then experience approximates to the conceptual limit ; if it be very large then the conceptual limit is of little if any value as a basis for predicting future experience. The degree of variation in B for a given A is thus a measure of the extent to which the association of these quantities is passing from independence to causal relationship. But in actual experience, given a large enough piece of paper and a sufficiency of observations, it is the dots and not the continuous curve which we reach.

Take any two measurable classes of things in the universe of perceptions, physical, organic, social or economic, and it is such a dot or scatter diagram, which we reach with extended observations. In some cases the dots are scattered all over the paper, there is no association of A and B ; in other cases there is a broad belt, there is only moderate relationship ; then the dots narrow down to a " comet's tail," and we have close association. Yet the whole series of diagrams is continuous ; nowhere can you draw a distinction and say here correlation ceases and causation begins. Causation is solely the conceptual limit to correlation when the band gets so attenuated, that it looks like a curve. Under the one category, correlation, all our experience whatever of the links between phenomena can be classified ; under the other category no actual experience whatever can be ranked ; it is a purely descriptive conceptual limit reached by statistical processes from observed phenomena : invaluable as an economy of thought, roughly corresponding to likeness of routines, but in itself providing no measure of the deviations or want of sameness that will actually be experienced in routines—to determine that requires us to know the actual variation in the arrays, the correlation, or degree of contingency. As a method of predicting the experience *likely* in the future from the experience of the past, the summary of the past expressed by function or under the category of causation has done immense service. But it is incomplete in itself, for it gives no measure of the variation in experience, and it has trammelled the human mind, because it has led to a conceptual limit dominating actual experience. We have tried to subsume all things under a perfectly inelastic category of cause and effect. It has led to our disregarding the fundamental truth that nothing in the universe repeats itself ; we cannot classify by sameness, but only by likeness. Resemblance connotes variation, and variation marks limited not absolute contingency. How often, when a new phenomenon has been observed, do we hear the question asked : What is the cause of it ? A question which it may be absolutely impossible to answer, whereas the question : To what degree are other phenomena associated with it ? may admit of easy solution, and result in invaluable knowledge.[1]

§ 7—On the Multiplicity of " Causes "

We now reach a point at which the physicist who has not thought closely on the logic of his science is apt to make a suggestion, which he believes will re-establish his conceptual causation as a reality of experience. You have, he will in effect say, fixed A and found B variable. Fix C, D, E, etc., also and you will find B becomes less variable. The argument is a very plausible one, but it is specious. Let us suppose that we have two variables A and C, and that we try to get a geometrical representation of the variation of a third variable B. In this case we must measure the quantities A and C along two lines at right angles in, say, a horizontal plane and plot the value of B perpendicular to this plane. We thus reach for the individual B a point in space, and for all B's a system of dots in three-dimensioned space. Suppose A and C were absolutely to fix the individual value of B, then these dots would lie on a surface in space, we should have a functional relation between B and A and C. But as in the case of dots in the plane, actual experience shows that when we take two variables or two " causes " A and C, we get no such surface, but a cloud or cluster of dots in space. Looked at from a distance, or by aid of an inverted telescope, this may look like an indefinitely thin surface, but actually we have merely a repetition of the problem of the curve in plan space ; we have no longer to ask how closely are the B points condensed into a curve or uniplanar functional relationship ; but how closely are

---

[1] We experience the narrowness of the causation category—and admit it—when the man in the street asks : " What is the cause of the weather ? " or " What is the cause of alcoholism or of insanity ? " The search for one cause, or a combination of causes, which will absolutely define one or the other is hopeless, but the determination of correlations between these and other phenomena is easy and is of first-class practical importance.

they condensed into a curved sheet in space. There is no greater necessity, because we have taken two variates, for the variation of B to cease than there was when we took only one ; we have spread the points of our belt in the plane over a zone in space ; we have not compelled them to lie absolutely on a surface or to fulfil a functional relationship to A and C. When we proceed to other assumed " causes," D, E, F, etc., the same idea governs the situation. If each one of these be not causally but correlatedly associated with B, we have to extend our notions of space and imagine a space with more than three dimensions, wherein there will be a belt or zone of dots still giving freedom to B, and only in the conceptual limit replaceable by a function or surface absolutely defining B. In other words, if B be contingent on A, C, D, E, etc., but not causally connected with any of them, it does not follow that B must be causally determined by all these things taken together. The origin of the idea that multiplying causes will reduce variation ultimately to zero is similar to that of most such ideas ; it is due to the thrusting of a mental conception out into phenomena, and not realising that it is actually a limit, not a reality of experience. If A in part determines B, when we disregard other factors, and C in part determines B, when we disregard all else, and similarly D and E, it is argued that all these part-determinations can be added together and the sum will finally fully determine B. The error made lies in the supposition that A, C, D, E, etc., are themselves *independent*. In the universe as we know it, all these factors are themselves to a greater or less extent associated or correlated, and in actual experience, but little effect is produced in lessening the variability of B, by introducing additional factors after we have taken the first few most highly associated phenomena. The reduction in variability that follows the consideration of these has in fact been taken as the basis of another conceptual limit—namely, that if we could take all " causes," we should always reach a unique functional relation. The theory of multiple correlation shows that freedom to vary is quite compatible with an indefinite number of determining variables, and actual experience of correlation shows it is only a few highly correlated variables that matter. "All causes" might mean the whole past history of the universe, and what would happen if the universe started afresh from the same initial conditions, nobody knows, nor will anybody profitably stay to conjecture. It might at some point go off at a tangent to its previous course, along a "singular solution" to those conceptual equations by which the scientist describes its proceedings. All actual experience tells us is that with such repetitions as we can bring about, like produces like, not absolute sameness; with many phenomena in our purview as with few there is variation, it may be very wide or it may be very narrow; and we learn that multiplicity is not essential to the approach towards high contingency, it may be as high with one as with the sum of twenty associated phenomena.

§ 8.—*The Universe as a Complex of Contingent, not Causally Linked Phenomena*

That the universe is a sum of phenomena, some of which are more, others less closely contingent on each other is the conception wider than that of causality, which we may at the present time draw from our widening experience. The aim of science ceases to be the discovery of "cause" and "effect"; in order to predict future experience it seeks out the phenomena which are most highly correlated—the cases in which the variation of B for a given A, or for a given complex of A, C, D, E, etc., is the least discoverable. From this standpoint it finds no distinction in kind but only in degree between the data, method of treatment, or the resulting "laws" of chemical, physical, biological, or sociological investigations. They all provide, or should provide, (i.) a conceptual routine, which is a functional expression of average experience, and (ii.) a measure of the possible or probable deviations from this routine, which is a guide to the amount of variation in experience. Because this is small in some physical experiences, it has been often neglected as a matter of little practical value—a routine may vary even considerably without its upsetting conduct. But this neglect is no justification for the assumption that our conceptional routine, a product of the statistical treatment of experience, represents a real functional relationship at the back of phenomena. This projection of the mental concept into the beyond of perceptions is not justified by any actual experience. There is always in non-organic as in organic phenomena a residual variation. Repetitions are like within limits, but not same, for the antecedents are only like but never same. From this standpoint the universe appears as a universe of variation rather than as a universe controlled by the law of causation in its narrowest sense. No phenomena are causal; all phenomena are contingent, and the problem before us is to measure the degree of this contingency, which we have seen lies between the zero of independence and the unity of causation. That is briefly the wider outlook we must now take of the universe as we experience it.

§ 9.—*The Measure of Correlation and its Relation to Contingency*

We can follow up the idea of the belt represented in our diagram (p. 168) in order to obtain another measure of the association of two phenomena A and B. There is complete association, a functional or causal relationship, if there be no variation in any array whatever, *i.e.* if the belt at each point thins down into a line, or there be only one value of B for each value of A. As before, let us assume that the total number of B's which occur with A_p is n_{pb}, and let the mean value of B on this array be $\bar{\beta}_p$; then if any other value of B in this array be β_p, let us consider the expression $(\bar{\beta}_p - \beta_p)^2$. It clearly cannot vanish unless $\beta_p = \bar{\beta}_p$ or the particular value of B coincides with the mean of the array. Hence it follows that if we add together all such expressions for the array, or, as it is technically expressed *sum* $(\beta_p - \bar{\beta}_p)^2$ for the array, this sum being a sum of squares can only vanish if all the points of the array close up together. This sum is written $S(\beta_p - \bar{\beta}_p)^2$ and, if divided by the number n_{pb} of cases in the array, is the mean square deviation of dots in the array, which is written $\sigma_p{}^2$, and σ_p, its square root, is termed the *standard deviation* of the array. Clearly this standard deviation is a good measure of the variation within the array, and the smaller this standard deviation is the narrower will be the "belt" at the point under consideration. Now suppose we form a quantity u, which is the mean sum of the squares of each dot from the mean dot of the array in which it lies, *i.e.*

$$u = \frac{1}{N}\left\{ S(\beta_1 - \bar{\beta}_1)^2 + S(\beta_2 - \bar{\beta}_2)^2 + \ldots + S(\beta_p - \bar{\beta}_p)^2 + \ldots \right\}$$

$$= S\left(\frac{n_{1b}}{N} \times \frac{(\beta_1 - \bar{\beta}_1)^2}{n_{1b}}\right) + S\left(\frac{n_{2b}}{N} \times \frac{(\beta_2 - \bar{\beta}_2)^2}{n_{2b}}\right) + \ldots$$

$$\qquad\qquad + S\left(\frac{n_{pb}}{N}\frac{(\beta_p - \bar{\beta}_p)^2}{n_{pb}} + \ldots\right)$$

$$= \frac{1}{N}\left(n_{1b}\sigma_1{}^2 + n_{2b}\sigma_2{}^2 + \ldots + n_{pb}\sigma_p{}^2 + \ldots \right)$$

= mean of the standard deviations squared of all the arrays, each array being "weighted" with the number of cases in the array.

Now the first line shows us that u can only be zero, when the "belt" shrivels up into a curve, *i.e.* when the association becomes functional or causal. The last line shows us that when the two phenomena are unrelated, then since every array is merely a repetition of the universe of B's,

$$\sigma_1{}^2 = \sigma_2{}^2 = \ldots = \sigma_p{}^2 = \ldots$$

and is equal to Σ^2 where Σ^2 is the standard deviation squared, $= \frac{1}{N} S(\beta - \bar{\beta})^2$, and $\bar{\beta}$ is the mean, of the whole universe of B's. Accordingly, u/Σ^2 takes every value from zero to unity as we pass from complete association to absolute independence.

Now let us look at u from another aspect

$$\begin{aligned} S(\beta_p - \bar{\beta}_p)^2 &= S(\beta_p{}^2) - 2\,S(\beta_p\bar{\beta}_p) + S(\bar{\beta}_p{}^2) \\ &= S(\beta_p{}^2) - 2n_{pb}\bar{\beta}_p{}^2 + n_{pb}\bar{\beta}_p{}^2 \\ &= S(\beta_p{}^2) - n_{pb}\bar{\beta}_p{}^2 \\ &= S(\beta_p - \bar{\beta})^2 + 2\bar{\beta}S(\beta_p) - n_{pb}(\bar{\beta}^2 + \bar{\beta}^2{}_p) \\ &= S(\beta_p - \bar{\beta})^2 - n_{pb}(\bar{\beta} - \bar{\beta}_p)^2. \end{aligned}$$

Hence

$$u = \frac{1}{N}\{S(\beta_1 - \bar{\beta})^2 + S(\beta_2 - \bar{\beta})^2 + \ldots + S(\beta_p - \bar{\beta})^2 + \ldots \}$$

$$- \frac{1}{N}\{n_{1b}(\beta - \bar{\beta}_1)^2 + n_{2b}(\beta - \bar{\beta}_2)^2 + \ldots + n_{pb}(\beta - \bar{\beta}_p)^2 + \ldots \}$$

$$= \Sigma^2 - S\left\{\frac{n_{pb}(\bar{\beta} - \bar{\beta}_p)^2}{N}\right\}.$$

But

$$\frac{S\{n_{pb}(\bar{\beta} - \bar{\beta}_p)^2\}}{N}$$

equals the standard deviation squared of the means of the arrays, each array being weighted with the number in the array. If we put η for the ratio of the standard deviation of the means of the arrays to the standard deviation of the universe of B's we have

$$\eta = \frac{1}{\Sigma}\left\{\frac{S n_{pb}(\bar{\beta} - \bar{\beta}_p)^2}{N}\right\}^{\frac{1}{2}} = \sqrt{1 - \frac{u}{\Sigma^2}}.$$

η is termed the *correlation ratio*. Clearly, if $\eta = 1$, then $u = 0$, or our belt becomes a curve, or the association is causal; if, on the other hand, $\eta = 0$, then $u = \Sigma$, or each array is reproduction in miniature of the whole population of B's, *i.e.* there is absolute independence of A and B. For values of η between 0 and 1 there is limited association of A and B, *i.e.* the variation of the belt for any array is on the average less than that of the whole population. Thus we see that the correlation ratio η precisely like the contingency coefficient C measures by values between 0 and 1 the degree of dependence of any two *measurable* phenomena.

The general resemblance in the two ideas, that of contingency and that of correlation, will be obvious to the reader. In each case we compare the variation in any array of B's with that of the whole universe of B's. If these variations have the same distribution, then there is nothing individual about the array of B's found with a particular A, and therefore B is not contingent on or correlated with A. On the other hand, if the variation in the array vanishes by all the B's of the array falling into a single cell or, the belt shrivelling up into a curve, we have absolutely dependent quantities, absolute contingency, or perfect correlation.   Thus at the two extremes our two coefficients represent by their common values zero and unity the same general ideas.   Between these extremes they do not always take identical values for the same material unless the distribution of the frequency be of a special character, which character, however, is of very wide occurrence.   It would be impossible here to discuss this point at length ; but we may state that if the number of cells in the contingency table be fairly numerous, the correlation-ratio and the coefficient of contingency will be found in practice to take numerically very close values for the same material.   Their values enable us to determine by qualitative or quantitative classifications the link between any two phenomena in the universe.   They form the basis of the newer outlook on nature, which measures the association between phenomena, and reduces causation and mathematical function to a special and extreme case of contingency.

SUMMARY

1. Routine in perceptions is a relative term ; the idea of causation is extracted by conceptual processes from phenomena, it is neither a logical necessity, nor an actual experience.   We can merely classify things as like ; we cannot reproduce sameness, but we can only measure how relatively like follows relatively like.   The wider view of the universe sees all phenomena as correlated, but not causally related.

2. Whether phenomena are qualitative or quantitative a classification leads to a contingency table, and from such a table we can measure the degree of dependence between any two phenomena.   Causation is the limit to such a table, when it contains an indefinitely large number of " cells," but in each array only one such cell is occupied.   Mathematical function arises when the belt of dots which are the actual result of all experience shrivels up into a curve.   It is a purely conceptual limit which is just as much a conceptual limit to actual experience when we use a multiplicity of " causes."

3. The intellectual gain of this contingency category lies in the fact that it sees variation as the fundamental factor in phenomena.   Determinatism is the result of supposing " sameness " instead of a mere classificatory " likeness " in phenomena.   Variation and correlation include causation and determinatism as special cases, if indeed they have any actual existence in regard to phenomena. No experience we have at present justifies us, however, in assuming them to be anything but conceptual limits created by human need for economy of thought, and as little inherent in phenomena themselves as geometrical surfaces or centres of force.

LITERATURE

No popular account of contingency and correlation exists at present, nor is there any complete text-book treatment of the subject. The reader with some mathematical knowledge may consult the original memoirs on the subject :

1. K. PEARSON.—Royal Society Proceedings, vol. lxxi. pp. 303-304.
2. K. PEARSON.—Mathematical Contributions to the Theory of Evolution, xiv. On the General Theory of Skew Correlation. Dulau and Co.
3. K. PEARSON.—Mathematical Contributions to the Theory of Evolution, xiii. On the Theory of Contingency and its Relation to Association and Normal Correlation. Dulau and Co.
4. W. PALIN ELDERTON.—Frequency Curves and Correlation. C. and E. Layton. Part ii.

CHAPTER VI

SPACE AND TIME

§ I.—*Space as a Mode of Perception*

IN our second chapter (p. 63) we saw that the distinction between "inside" and "outside" ourselves was not a very real or well-defined one. Certain of the vast complex of our sense-impressions we term inside, others again we term outside. To a savage the beginning of outside, the limit to *self*, is undoubtedly his skin ; although on occasion he may extend the idea of self farther, and be peculiarly careful of what becomes of such outward-lying portions of self as nail-parings and hair-clippings. The skin seems to him to bound self off from an outside world of non-self. The group of sense-impressions which he calls skin marks off a world which he can see and feel from one which in the normal condition is inaccessible to sight or touch. His first experiences of pain arise, or at least are perpetuated, from something within this invisible and intangible world, and the nerve-vibrations, which he classifies as pain, he postulates as inside self ; his indigestion does not seem immediately associated with the visible and tangible world outside his skin. Thus the sense-impression pain, even when associated later with a group of other sense-impressions classified as those of sight and touch, is still differentiated from them as something especially internal. I receive for a moment, and then they vanish, the feelings of hardness and pain ; both may come to the seat of my consciousness as nerve-vibrations, or even by the same nerve-vibration ; both are associated with stored impresses of past hardnesses and pains, yet I project the sense-impression hardness into something outside self, but the pain I consider as something peculiar to my inside.   I speak of *my* pain and *your* pain ; yet not of *my* hardness and *your* hardness, but of hardness as something peculiar to the table-leg.   I thus give an objective reality to one group of sense-impressions, which I refuse to another.

Now this distinction seems to me to have arisen from the historical fact that the stored sense-impresses with which we associate hardness have been drawn from the tangible and visible world " outside skin," while those with which we associate pain have been largely drawn from the intangible and invisible world " inside skin."   Even as our knowledge develops and " inside skin " becomes less intangible and invisible, even as we learn to associate pain with the stored impresses of various local organs " inside skin," we still feel it a somewhat doubtful use of language to talk of pain as " existing in space."   Gradually, however, the skin has ceased to be a well-marked boundary between outside and inside.   Self, like the soul of the metaphysicians, has disappeared from body and been concentrated in consciousness.   Self, seated (metaphorically, not physically), in the telephonic brain exchange, receives an infinite variety of messages, which we can only assume to reach self in precisely the same manner.   Yet self classes some groups of these messages together, and speaks of them as objects existing in space, while to other groups it has denied in the past, or still denies, this spacial existence.   How far is this distinction logical, how far historical ? [1]

Now we shall find that the instant we associate a number of sense-impressions in a group, and separate them in perception from other groups, we consider them " to exist in space."   Space is thus, in the first place, a

---

[1] By *historical* I mean that which arises in the natural history of man from imperfect knowledge and illogical inference.   Thus the belief in ghosts, witches, and storm-spirits is a perfectly intelligible stage in the natural history of man, but not a logical inference from any natural phenomena in the light of more perfect knowledge.

mental expression for the fact that the perceptive faculty
has separated coexisting sense-impressions into groups of
associated impressions.   This separation of immediate
sense-impressions into groups, this *discriminating* power
of the perceptive faculty, is, at any rate in the early stages
of man's development, most clearly recognised and closely
associated with the senses of sight and touch.   Hence it
comes about that the invisible and intangible "inside
skin" is at first not considered as in space.   Later, for
example, as we localise pain, or associate it with other
sense-impressions classified as visible and tangible, we
treat "inside skin" as belonging to space.   Yet we still
frequently consider the presence of visible and tangible
members a condition for a *spacial* group of sense-impressions.   Space, says Thomas Reid, is known directly by
the senses of sight and touch.   But probably a like, if
less powerful, means of discriminating groups of sense-
impressions lies in the senses of sound and smell.[1]   We
localise sounds and smells without necessarily associating
them with visible and tangible resounding and smelling
bodies.   It will, I think, be admitted on reflection that
whenever we concentrate our attention on a limited group
of associated sense-impressions, then we consider them as
spacial, or "existing in space."   We join together, owing
to past experience, certain sense-impressions as a *permanent* group, and we then mentally separate this group
from other groups.   The actual boundary of the group,
however, when we attempt to define it, is found in reality
to be vague (p. 72).   The group, although in the main a
permanent association, has a continual flow in and out of
junior partners; while some of the partners belong, on
closer examination, as much to one association as another.
The separation is thus rather practical than real; it
arises, in the first place, from the fact that in our perception certain sense-impressions are more or less

[1] One of my babies when three days old was able to distinguish between the
snapping of the fingers of the right and left hands, and to follow with the
ear the direction of the sound.   She would turn to a voice long before she
paid any attention to bodies moving quite close to her eyes.   Difference of
position was thus associated with sound.

permanently grouped together, and, in the second place, from the mental habit of concentrating our attention on one of these groups by placing about it in conception an arbitrary boundary separating it from other groups. Such arbitrary boundaries are conceptions drawn doubtless from sense-impressions of sight and touch, but they correspond, as we shall soon see, to nothing real in the world of sense-impression or in phenomena.

The coexistence of more or less permanent and distinct groups of sense-impressions is a fundamental mode of our perception ; it is one of the ways in which we perceive things apart. There is nothing in sense-impressions themselves which involves the notion of space, but whether space be " due " to something behind sense-impression or to the nature of the perceptive faculty itself we are unable at present to decide. Leibniz has defined space as the order of possible coexisting phenomena. This order may " arise " from something behind phenomena, or from the machinery of perception, but in either case the order itself is simply a mode or manner in which we perceive things. The reader must distinguish carefully between the groups of sense-impressions themselves and the order in which we perceive them to coexist. Perhaps the distinction will be best brought out by considering the letters of the alphabet :—

A, B, C, D, E, F, G, . . .

The letters may be said to have a real existence like the groups of sense-impressions we term objects. The order of the letters is merely the mode in which we perceive them to coexist as an alphabet. The " existence " we attribute to the order is thus of a totally different character from the " existence " we attribute to the letters. The alphabet has in itself no existence except for the letters it contains, but the letters, on the other hand, could have a real existence if they had never been arranged in any order or alphabet. The alphabet has merely existence as a manner of looking at all the letters together. These results may all be interpreted of coexisting groups of sense-impressions and their order *space*. A single sense-impression might, indeed, exist for us without any coexisting groups being postulated, but space would have no meaning if there were not such coexisting groups. Space is an order or mode of perceiving objects, but it has no existence if objects are withdrawn, no more than the alphabet could have an existence if there were no letters.

If the reader has once grasped this point—and it is undoubtedly a difficult and hard one (for our senses of sight and touch lead us imperceptibly to confuse the reality of sense-impressions with our mode of perceiving them),—then he will cease to look upon space as an enormous void in which objects have been placed by an agency in nowise conditioned by his own perceptive faculty ; he will begin to consider space as an order of things, but not itself a thing. To say, therefore, that a thing " exists in space " is to assert that the perceptive faculty has distinguished it as a group of sense-impressions from other groups of sense-impressions, which actually or possibly coexist. We cannot dogmatically deny that the order of coexisting phenomena " arises " from something behind sense-impressions,[1] but we may feel pretty confident that space, our mode of perceiving these phenomena, is very different from anything in the unknowable world behind sense-impressions. Once recognise space as a mode of the perceptive faculty, and it appears as something peculiar to the *individual* perceptive faculty. Without any perceptive faculty it is conceivable that sensations might exist (see p. 102), but there could not be that mode of perception we term space. The remarkable fact is this : that the order of coexisting phenomena is apparently the same at any rate for the vast majority of human perceptive faculties. Why should this mode of perception be the same for all normal human faculties—or, perhaps it would be better to say,

---

[1] Just as little ought we to assert that it does. The word *arise* suggests *causation* ; but the word causation is meaningless as a relation between the unknowable beyond of sense-impression and sense-impression itself (see pp. 68 and 127).

very approximately the same ? We express the problem and the mystery wrongly when we ask " why space seems the same to you and me " ; we ought more precisely to ask " why your space and my space are alike." Because our perceptive faculties are of the normal type, may be the immediate answer ; but how similar organising centres have come to exist in the chaos of sensations remains still to be described.

Some light perhaps may be thrown on this difficult problem by considerations which will be more fully developed in our chapter on *Life*. Man has not reached his present high stage of development solely by individualistic tendencies, but also by socialistic or gregarious tendencies. The struggle of man against man might suffice to bring about a co-ordination of the individual man's perceptive and reasoning faculties (p. 104), but in the struggle of group against group, and of group with its environment, it is clear that a great advantage would follow to any group from a close agreement of the perceptive faculties of its members, and great disadvantage to any group without this agreement. The survival of the former would be the natural result.

§ 2.—*The Infinite Bigness of Space*

" How big is space ? " is a meaningless question as it stands. " How big is space *for me* ? " admits, however, of an answer. It is just so large as will suffice to separate all things which coexist for me. Let the reader try to imagine phenomenal space apart from groups of sense-impressions and he will quickly discover how big space is for him. Space, he will at once recognise, has no meaning when we cease to perceive things *apart*—to distinguish between groups of sense-impressions. We ought constantly to bear in mind that space is peculiar to ourselves, and that we ought not reasonably to be stirred to greater admiration by any one descanting on the " magnitude of space," than we are wont to be when reflecting on the complex nature of our own perceptive faculty. The farthest star and the page of this book are both for us merely groups of sense-impressions, and the space which separates them is not in them, but is our mode of perceiving them.

There is a cheap and, unfortunately, common form of emotional science which revels in contrasting the "infinities of space" with the "finite capacities of man." As instructive samples of this we may take the following passages from a well-known man of science writing on astronomy for the people :—

"Can it be true that these countless orbs are really majestic suns, sunk to an appalling depth in the abyss of unfathomable space?"

"Yet, after all, how little is all we can see even with our greatest telescopes, when compared with the whole extent of infinite space! No matter how vast may be the depth which our instruments have sounded, there is yet a beyond of infinite extent. Imagine a mighty globe described in space, a globe of such stupendous dimensions that it shall include the sun and his system, all the stars and nebulæ, and even all the objects which our finite capacities can imagine. Yet, after all, what must be the relation of even this great globe to the whole extent of infinite space? The globe will bear to that a ratio infinitely less than that which the water in a single drop of dew bears to the water in the whole Atlantic Ocean." [1]

To speak of the mode in which we perceive coexisting phenomena as an abyss of appalling depth is perhaps rather meaningless phraseology ; but the statement that infinite space contains more than our finite capacity can imagine is hopelessly misleading. In the first place, the space of our perceptions, the space in which we discriminate phenomena, is not infinite : it is exactly commensurate with the contents of that finite capacity we term our perceptive faculty. In the second place, if by "all the objects which our finite capacities can imagine" the author means conceptions and not perceptions, he is confusing two different things—space, as the order of real

[1] Sir Robert Ball's *Story of the Heavens*, pp. 2 and 538.

coexisting phenomena, what we may term real space, and the space of our thought, the conceptual space of geometry, what we may term ideal space. This latter, as we shall see in the sequel, may be conceived as either finite or infinite, although a limited portion of ideal infinite space describes most easily the real space of our perceptions. Thus the only infinite space we know of, so far from being a real immensity overwhelming our finite capacities, is a product of our own reasoning faculty. On the other hand, cosmical space, the mode of our perception, is finite and limited by the range, not of what we imagine, but of what we actually perceive to coexist. The mystery of space, whether it be the finite space of perception or the infinite space of conception, lies in, and not outside, each human consciousness. We must seek it either in our power of distinguishing (or of perceiving apart) so many and varied groups of sense-impressions, or in our power of drawing conceptions, which enables us to pass from the finite real to the infinite ideal. Only for us, as perceiving human beings, has space any meaning; we cannot infer it where we do not find psychical machinery similar to our own.

§ 3.—*The Infinite Divisibility of Space*

The space of our perceptions, as we have seen, is finite and varies from individual to individual with the range and complexity of his perceptions. As it is just large enough for our perception of phenomena, so it is just small enough, by which we are to understand that it is not "infinitely divisible." The limit to its divisibility is the limit to our power of perceiving things apart. Our organs of sense are such that only sense-impressions of a certain intensity or amplitude fall within their cognisance. We may resolve phenomena into smaller and smaller groups of sense-impressions, but we ultimately reach a limit at which the sense-impression ceases. We may divide a piece of paper up into more and more minute fragments, but ultimately they cease to be sensible even by the aid of our most powerful microscopes.   We have then reached a limit to our mode of perceiving apart,—in ordinary parlance, to the divisibility of space.   We may possibly conceive smaller divisions, but in doing this we have passed from the sphere of the real to the ideal— from the space of perception to the space of geometry. It seems to me that this transition from perception to conception, often made quite unconsciously, is the basis of all the difficulties involved in the paradox as to the infinite divisibility of space.   The point has been referred to by Hume in his *Essay Concerning Human Understanding*,[1] where he writes as follows :—

" The chief objection against all abstract reasonings is derived from the ideas of space and time—ideas which, in common life and to a careless view, are very clear and intelligible, but when they pass through the scrutiny of the profound sciences (and they are the chief object of those sciences) afford principles which seem full of absurdity and contradiction.   No priestly *dogmas*, invented on purpose to tame and subdue the rebellious reason of mankind, ever shocked common sense more than the doctrine of the infinite divisibility of extension, with its consequences, as they are pompously displayed by all geometricians and metaphysicians with a kind of triumph and exultation.   A real quantity, infinitely less than any finite quantity, containing quantities infinitely less than itself, and so on *in infinitum* ; this is an edifice so bold and prodigious that it is too weighty for any pretended demonstration to support, because it shocks the clearest and most natural principles of human reason.   But what renders the matter most extraordinary is that these seemingly absurd opinions are supported by a chain of reasoning, the clearest and most natural ; nor is it possible for us to allow the premises without admitting the consequences."

Now the reader should carefully note the unconscious transition in this passage from the *ideas* of space and time to the infinite divisibility of *real* quantities.   The transition

[1] Section xii. part ii.   Green and Grose : *Hume's Works*, vol. iv. p. 128.

is even more marked in a footnote which accompanies the passage, and which runs thus :—

" Whatever disputes there may be about mathematical points, we must allow that there are physical points— that is, parts of extension, which cannot be divided or lessened either by the eye or imagination. These images, then, which are present to the fancy or senses, are absolutely indivisible, and consequently must be allowed by mathematicians to be infinitely less than any real part of extension ; and yet nothing appears more certain to reason than that an infinite number of them composes an infinite extension. How much more an infinite number of those infinitely small parts of extension, which are still supposed infinitely divisible."

Here the transition from perception to conception and back again is made several times over. A point mathematically defined is a conception and has no real existence in the field of perception. It is true we base this conception on our perceptive experience of things which are not points, but the mathematical point is not a *limit* to any process which could be carried on in the field of perception ; it is the limit to a process which we imagine carried on in the field of thought, in the sphere of conceptions. If Hume means by a physical point the smallest possible groups of sense-impressions which we can perceive apart, then this cannot be divided or lessened by the eye. But this physical point transferred from the field of perception to that of conception can in the imagination be divided over and over again. This remark will be more clearly appreciated when we come to deal with the geometrical conception of space. It suffices for the present to note that Hume passes from the eye to the imagination, from the mathematical to the physical, from the fancy to the senses, as if the geometrical theory of extension, that shorthand method of classifying and describing coexisting phenomena, was itself the world of phenomena. Several types of geometry can be elaborated by our rational faculty, and the results, which flow from them, will depend upon the statement of their fundamental axioms. From these types we select that one which will enable us to describe the widest range of phenomena in the briefest possible formula, or which will enable us with the greatest accuracy to classify the differences between groups of sense-impressions. We have no more right to quarrel with the geometrician's conception of the infinite divisibility of space than with his conception of the circle, or with the physicist's conception of the atom. One and all are pure ideals beyond the range of perceptual experience. What we must ask is: How far are these conceptions of service in enabling us to briefly describe and classify our perceptions; how far do they aid us in mentally storing up past experience as a guide for future action? A point and an ellipse may be absolutely absurd in the world of perceptions, but they are none the less valid and useful conceptions if they help us to describe and predict the motion of the earth about the sun. The paradoxes which Hume finds in the conclusions of geometry only exist as long as we assert that every conception has a precise counterpart in perception, and forget that science is only a shorthand description of nature and not nature itself.

§ 4.—*The Space of Memory and Thought*

Before we pass from the subject of real or perceptual space, we ought to note that this mode of perceiving phenomena appears not only in association with immediate sense-impressions, but also with the stored impresses of past experience. To be accurate, we ought perhaps to say that the mode of remembrance is akin to the mode of perception—unless, indeed, we are using the word *perception* to refer to the consciousness alike of an "external" sense-impression and of an "internal" sense-impress. In all probability these processes of what Locke would term external and internal perception are much the same, only the sources from which they draw their material are different. In this case it is sufficient to say that space as a mode of perception applies as much to

memory as to phenomena. By this method of regarding the matter we certainly gain new insight into the
manner in which space may result from the nature of the
psychical machinery. No one can look upon the space
whereby the impresses of past experience are grouped
and distinguished as a reality apart from internal perceptions ; it is too obviously a mode of the retentive
faculty. But the distinction between the world of phenomena and the world of memories lies not in the order
and relation of their contents, but in the intensity of the
stimulus and the quality of the association in the two
cases. The candles, the inkstand, the books and papers
on my table have the same order and relation, whether I
see and touch them or simply shut my eyes and recall
them as a memory, but there is a great difference in the
vividness [1] of the external and internal perceptions, and a
considerable change in the range of stored impresses with
which the contents of perception are associated in the
two cases.

Once recognise space as the mode in which we perceive
coexisting things apart, and we have either to multiply
spaces or to consider that logically all separation denotes
space. Thus our thoughts and conceptions will be found
almost invariably to involve spacial relationship, while the
psychical processes themselves are, like pain, being more
and more localised or associated with individual centres
of brain-activity. It may fairly be said that until the
spacial relationship is recognised in any field, until we are
able to perceive things apart, we have no basis for
distinction, comparison, classification, and the resulting
scientific knowledge. It is especially from the localisation
of psychical processes that we may hope for great results,
for a true science of psychology in the future. This
localisation is not a " materialisation " of thought, it is
merely an association of " internal " and " external "

---

[1] Hume's definition of belief, slightly modified, well marks the difference :
A group of immediate sense-impressions is a "more vivid, lively, forcible,
firm, steady " perception of an object than a group of stored impresses alone
is ever able to provide (*Essay Concerning Human Understanding*, Section v.
part ii.).

perceptions, both equally factors of consciousness. The association is not an association of two totally diverse and opposed things—matter and mind—but of the two phases of perception. Groups of sense-impressions in space, being conditioned by the perceptive faculty, are as much a part of the sentient being as psychical processes themselves.

Logically, then, it seems that whenever we clearly separate and distinguish coexisting things, we perceive them under the mode space ; and perception under this mode is what we ought to mean by "existence in space." Yet historically the notion of space has arisen from the separation and distinction of groups of sense-impressions, when some one or more members in each group were due to sight or touch ; for these senses are those by which groups have, in the natural history of man, been first perceived apart. Just as these groups of sense-impressions were projected outward from our consciousness, and treated as things unconditioned by our perceptive faculty, as objects independent of the sentient being, so our mode of perception was treated as inherent in them, and given an objective existence, fossils of which are still to be found in the " primeval void " of mythology and the "appalling abyss" of popular astronomy. Only gradually have we learnt to recognise that empty space is meaningless, that space is a mode of perception—the order in which our perceptive faculty presents coexistence to us. We are not compelled to postulate a space outside self for phenomena, and spaces inside self for memory, thought, and the psychical processes, but rather we must hold that the mode in which we perceive in these different fields is essentially the same, and that this mode is what we term space.

§ 5.—*Conceptions and Perceptions*

If such be the space of perception, we have next to ask : How do we scientifically describe it ? What is conceptual space—the space with which we deal in the science of geometry ? We have seen that our perceptive faculty presents sense-impressions to us as separated into groups, and further, that though this separation is most serviceable for practical purposes, it is not very exactly and clearly defined " at the limits " (p. 66). How do we represent in thought, in conception, this separation into groups which results from our mode of perception? The answer is : We *conceive* groups of sense-impressions to be bounded by *surfaces*, to be limited by straight or curved *lines*. Thus our consideration of conceptual space leads us at once to a discussion of surfaces and lines—to a study, in fact, of *Geometry*.

Several important problems at once present themselves for investigation. In the first place, have these surfaces and lines a real existence in the world of perception? Are they phenomena? Or are they ideal modes whereby we analyse the manner in which we perceive phenomena? In the second place, if they should be only ideals of conception, what is the historical process by which they have been reached? What is their ultimate root in perception?

Now there is at this stage an important remark to be made, namely, that *what is imperceptible is not therefore inconceivable*. This remark is all the more necessary, for it seems directly opposed to the healthy scepticism of Hume.[1] Yet unless it be true the whole fabric of exact science falls to the ground, neither the concepts of geometry, nor those of mechanics, would be of service ; for example, the circle and the motion of a point would be absurdities if, being imperceptible, they were really inconceivable. The basis of our conceptions doubtless lies in perceptions, but in imagination we can carry on perceptual processes to a limit which is itself not a perception ; we can further associate groups of stored sense-impresses, and form ideas which correspond to nothing in our perceptual experience.

Here a word of caution is, however, very necessary. Because we conceive a thing, we must not argue that it

[1] See especially the *Treatise on Human Nature*, part ii. *Of the Ideas of Space and Time.* Green and Grose : *Hume's Works*, vol. i. pp. 334-371.

is either possible or probable as a perception.   Indeed, the process or association by which we have reached our conception may in itself suffice to exhibit its perceptual impossibility or improbability.   The appeal to experience can alone determine whether a conception is possible as a perception.   For example, experience shows me that there is a sensible limit to the visible and tangible; hence a point, valid as a conception, can never have a real existence as a perception.   I reach this conception of a point by carrying to a limit in my imagination a process which cannot be so carried in perception.   Exactly of the same character are my conceptions of infinite distance or infinite number; they are the conceptual limits to processes, which may be *started* in perception, but cannot be carried to a limit except in the imagination.   Somewhat different from perceptual impossibility is perceptual improbability. I can conceive Her Majesty Queen Mary walking alone down Regent Street, but, tested by my experience of the past actions of royalty, this association of conceptions is hardly a perceptual probability.   These instances may be sufficient to indicate that what is improbable or impossible in perception may be valid in conception.   But we must ever be careful to bear in mind that the *reality* of the conception, its existence outside thought, can only be demonstrated by an appeal to perceptual experience. The geometrician even asserts the phenomenal impossibility of his points, lines, and surfaces ; the physicist by no means postulates the existence of atoms, molecules, and electrons as possible perceptions.   Science is content for the present to look upon these concepts as existing only in the sphere of thought, as purely the product of man's mind.   It does not, like metaphysics or theology, demand any existence in or beyond sense-impression for its conceptions until experience has shown that the conceptual limit or association can become a perceptual reality.[1]   The validity of

---

[1] Leverrier and Adams *conceived* a planet having a definite orbit as a method of accounting for the irregularities perceived in the motions of Uranus. Their conception might have been valid as a manner of describing these irregularities, if Neptune itself had never been perceived—in other words, if their conception had not become a perceptual reality.

scientific conceptions does not in the first place depend on their reality as perceptions, but on the means they provide of classifying and describing perceptions. If a rectangle and a circle have no real existence, they are still invaluable as enabling me to classify my perceptions of form, to describe, however imperfectly, the difference in shape between the face of a page of this book and of my watch. They are symbols in that shorthand by means of which science describes the universe of phenomena. The atom, if a pure conception, still enables us, by codifying our past experience, to economise thought ; it preserves within reasonable limits the material upon which we base our prediction of possible future experience. If any one tells us that the storm-god is to some minds as conceivable as the atom, we must, in the first place, reply that the conceivable is not the real ; and further, that the value to man of any ideal of conception depends upon the extent to which it subsumes the future in its *résumé* of the past. The conception storm-god may, after all, be of some value as a striking monument to our meteorological ignorance, and as a useful reminder that we must " be prepared for all weathers."

What we have at this stage to notice is that the mind is not limited to perceptual association, and that it can carry on in conception a process which may be begun but cannot be indefinitely continued in the sphere of perception. The scientific value of such conceptions, whether reached by association or as a limit, must in every case be judged by the extent to which they enable us to classify, describe, and predict phenomena.

§ 6.—*Sameness and Continuity*

Now there are two ideas reached as conceptual limits to perceptual processes which have important bearings on the geometrical representation of space. These may be expressed by the words *sameness* and *continuity*. So far as our perceptual experience goes, probably no two groups of sense-impressions are exactly the same. The sameness in each depends upon the degree of our examination and observation. To a casual observer all the sheep in a flock appear the same, but the shepherd individualises each. Two coins from one die, or two engravings from one block, will always be found to possess some distinguishing marks. We may safely assert that absolute sameness has never occurred in our experience. No "permanent" group of sense-impressions or "object" even is exactly the same at two different times. Various elements in the group have changed slightly with the time, the light, or the observer. Take a polished piece of metal and note two parts of its surface; they appear exactly alike, but the microscope reveals their want of sameness. Thus sameness is never a real limit to our experience of phenomena; the more closely we examine, the less is the sameness. Yet, as a conception, the sameness of two groups of sense-impressions is a very valid idea, and the basis of much of our scientific classification. In the sphere of perceptions sameness denotes the identity for certain practical purposes of two slightly different groups of sense-impressions. In the sphere of conceptions, however, sameness denotes absolute identity of all the members of either group; it is a limit to a process of comparison which cannot be reached in the perceptual world.

The idea of continuity, in the sense in which we are now considering the word, involves that of sameness. If I take a vessel of water, I find a certain permanent group of sense-impressions which leads me to term the contents of the vessel water; if I take a small quantity of the water out of the vessel I find the "same" group, and this still remains true if I take a smaller and smaller quantity, even to a drop. I may continue to divide the drop, but apparently as long as the portion taken remains sensible at all, there is the same group of sense-impressions, and I term the fraction of the drop water. Now the question arises, if this division could be carried on indefinitely, should we at last reach a limit at which the group of sense-impressions would change not only quantitatively, that is in intensity, but also qualitatively? If we could magnify the sense-impressions due to the infinitesimal fraction of a drop of water up to a sensible intensity, would they so differ from those characteristic of the contents of the original vessel that we should not give them the name water? Now we cannot test the effects of an indefinitely continued division in the phenomenal world, for we soon reach a stage at which we fail to get, by the means at our disposal, any sense-impressions at all from the divided substances. Our magnifiers of sense-impression have but a limited range.[1] But although in the sphere of perceptions there is no possibility of carrying division to its ultimate limit, we can yet in conception repeat the process indefinitely. If after an infinite number of divisions we conceive that the same group of sense-impressions would be found, then we are said to conceive the substance as *continuous*. We have then to ask how far the conception of continuity applies to the real bodies of our perceptual experience. From the finite process of division which is possible in perception, we might easily conclude that continuity was a property of real substances ; and there is small doubt that a slight amount of observation is favourable to the notion that many real substances are continuous, although the infinite division necessary to the conception of continuity fails to find any perceptual equivalent. Further observation and wider insight, however, contradict this notion. The physicist and the chemist bring many arguments to show us that the finite process of division which suggests continuity would, if carried to an infinite limit, show bodies to be discontinuous. On a first and untrained inspection we find a continuity and a sameness in perceptions which disappear on closer and more critical examination. The ideas conveyed in these words are found to be no real limits to the actual, but ideal limits to processes which can only be carried out in the field of conception. Bear-

---

[1] *E.g.* the microscope, the microphone, the spectroscope, etc. From the spectroscope we obtain, perhaps, positive indications of a qualitative change in many substances as the quantity is diminished.

ing this in mind we may now return to the geometrical conceptions of space.

§ 7.—*Conceptual Space.   Geometrical Boundaries*

It has been remarked (p. 192) that we conceive groups or sense-impressions to be limited by surfaces and lines. We speak of the surface of the table ; the fly-leaf of this book appears to be separated from the air above it by a plane surface and that plane to be bounded at its upper edge by a portion of a straight line.   In the first place, we have to ask whether our geometrical notions of line and plane correspond to the limits of anything we actually find in perception or whether they are purely ideal limits to processes begun in perception, but which it is impossible to carry to a limit in perception.   The answer to these questions lies in the conceptions of *sameness* and *continuity*. The geometrical ideas of line and plane involve absolute sameness in all their elements and absolute continuity. Every element of a straight line can in conception be made to fit every other element, and this however it be turned about its terminal points.   Every element of a plane can be made to fit every other element, and this without regard to side.   Further, every element of a straight line or a plane, however often divided up, is in conception, when magnified up, still an element of straight line or plane.

The geometrical ideas correspond to absolute sameness and continuity, but do we experience anything like these in our perceptions ?   The fly-leaf of this book appears at first sight a plane surface bounded by a straight line, but a very slight inspection with a magnifying lens shows that the surface has hollows and elevations in it, which quite defy all geometrical definition and scientific treatment. The straight line which seems to bound its edge becomes, under a powerful glass, so torn and jagged that its ups and downs are more like a saw-edge than a straight line. The sameness and continuity are seen to be wanting on more careful investigation.   We take a glass cube skilfully cut and polished, and its faces appear at first as true planes. But we find that a small body placed upon one of its faces does not slide off when the cube is slightly tilted. The face of the cube must, after all, be *rough*, there are hollows and projections in it which catch those of the superposed body ; our plane again appears delusive. Or we may take one of Whitworth's wonderful metal planes obtained by rubbing the faces of three pieces of metal upon each other. Here again a powerful microscope reveals to us that we are still dealing with a surface having ridges and hollows.

The fact remains, that however great the care we take in the preparation of a plane surface, either a microscope or other means can be found of sufficient power to show that it is not a plane surface. It is precisely the same with a straight line ; however accurate it appears at first to be, exact methods of investigation invariably show it to be widely removed from the conceptual straight line of geometry. It is a race between our power of representing a straight line or plane and our power of creating instruments which demonstrate that the sameness and continuity of the geometrical conceptions are wanting. Absolutely perfect instruments could probably only be constructed if we were already in possession of a true geometrical line or plane, but the instruments we can make appear invariably to win the race. *Our experience gives us no reason to suppose that with any amount of care we could obtain a perceptual straight line or plane, the elements of which would on indefinite magnification satisfy the condition of ultimate sameness involved in the geometrical definitions.* We are thus forced to conclude that the geometrical definitions are the results of processes which may be started, but the limits of which can never be reached in perception ; they are pure conceptions having no correspondence with any possible perceptual experience. What we have said of straight lines and planes holds equally of all geometrically defined curves and surfaces. The fundamental conceptions of geometry are only ideal symbols which enable us to form an approximate, but in no sense absolute analysis

of our sense-impressions. They are the scientific shorthand by which we describe, classify, and formulate the
characteristics of that mode of perception which we term
perceptual space. Their validity, like that of all other
conceptions, lies in the power they give us of codifying
past and predicting future experience.

We speak of a spherical or cubical body, and say that
it is of such and such a capacity. But no perceptual
body is ever truly spherical or cubical, and the size we
attribute to it is at best an approximate one. Further
analysis of our sense-impressions leads us in each case
to find variations from the geometrical definition and
measurement. Yet the conceptions of sphere and cube
are frequently sufficient to enable us to classify and
identify various bodies and predict the different types of
sense - impression to which these bodies correspond.[1]
Perhaps no better instance than geometry can be taken to
show how science *describes* the world of phenomena by aid
of conceptions corresponding to no reality in phenomena
themselves. That our geometrical conceptions enable us
on the whole to so effectually describe perceptual space is
only a striking instance of the practically equal development of our perceptive and reasoning faculties (p. 103).

§ 8.— *Surfaces as Boundaries*

Although perceptual boundaries do not, on ultimate
analysis, in any way correspond to any special geometrical definition such as that of plane or sphere, we
have still to inquire whether they answer to our conception of surface at all. By surface in this sense we are to
consider, not something of which it would be possible to
analyse the properties by any of the known processes of
geometry, but any *continuous* boundary between two
groups of sense-impressions or bodies.[2] Is there a con-

[1] Our whole system of measuring size will be found to be based on
geometrical conceptions having no actuality in perception.

[2] " *That which has position, length and breadth but not thickness*, is called
surface."

" The word *surface* in ordinary language conveys the idea of extension in
two directions ; for instance, we speak of the surface of the earth, the surface

tinuous boundary between the open page of this book and the air above it? Would it be possible to say at any distinct step of the passage from air to paper, here air ends and paper begins? At this point we reach one of the most important problems of science. Are we to consider the groups of sense-impressions which we term bodies *continuous* or not? If bodies are not continuous, then it is clear that boundaries are only mental symbols of separation, and on deeper analysis correspond to no exact reality in the sphere of sense-impression.

Would every element of the surface of a body still appear to us a continuous boundary, however small the element and however much we magnified it up? If I could take the hundredth part of a square inch of this page and magnify it to a billion times its present size, would there still appear a continuous boundary between air and paper?

Consider the boundary of still water. It furnishes us with the impression of a continuous surface. On the other hand, examine a heap of sand closely, and it appears to have no continuous boundary at all. Are there any reasons which would lead us to suppose that, if we could sufficiently magnify a small element of this page of paper, it would produce in us sense-impressions not of continuity but of discontinuity? Would it look, supposing it were still visible, like the surface of water, or rather like a heap of sand, a pile of small shot, or, better still, like a starry patch of the heavens on a clear night? No group of stars is in perception separated from another by a line or surface. We can *imagine* such boundaries drawn across the heavens, but we do not *perceive* them.

---

of the sea, the surface of a sheet of paper. Although in some cases the idea of the thickness or the depth of the thing spoken of may be present in the speaker's mind, yet as a rule no stress is laid on depth or thickness. When we speak of a *geometrical surface*, we put aside the idea of depth and thickness altogether " (H. M. Taylor, *Pitt Press Euclid*, i.-ii. p. 3). It seems to me that in ordinary language there is something more than length and breadth involved—there is an idea of *continuous boundary*. It is difficult to say how far this idea is really involved in the word extension. A veil may have extension in two directions, but it fails to fulfil our idea of surface because it is not a continuous boundary.

We have, then, to ask whether the boundary between paper and air, if immensely magnified, would look sideways, not indeed like a geometrical line, but roughly like the first or second of these figures :—

FIG. 3a.

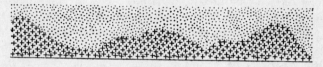

FIG. 3b.

Now no direct answer can really be given to this question, because bodies cease to impress us sensibly long before we reach the point at which the appearance of continuity might be expected to disappear. We cannot predict what our sense-impressions would be if we could magnify a drop of water up to the size of the earth. But we may put the question in a slightly different way. We may ask : Would it enable us to classify and describe phenomena better if we *conceived* bodies to be continuous as in Fig. 3a, or discontinuous as in Fig. 3b? The physicist promptly replies : I can only conceive bodies to be discontinuous. Discontinuity is essential to the methods by which I describe and formulate my sense-impressions of the phenomenal world.

§ 9.—*Conceptual Discontinuity of Bodies. The Atom*

Foremost among the physicist's reasons for postulating the discontinuity of bodies is the elasticity which we notice in all of them. Air can be placed under a piston in a cylinder and compressed ; a bar of wood can be bent —in other words, a portion of it squeezed and another portion stretched. Even the amounts by which we can squeeze iron or granite are capable of measurement. Now it is very hard, I think impossible, to *conceive* how we can alter the size of bodies if we suppose them continuous. We feel ourselves compelled to assert that, if the parts of a body move closer together, they must have something free of body into which they can move. If a body were continuous and yet compressible, there appears to be no reason why it should not be indefinitely compressible, or indefinitely extensible, both results repugnant to our experience. Further, our sense-impressions of temperature in both gaseous and solid bodies, and of colour in solid bodies, the phenomena of pressure in gases, and those of the absorption and emission of light, are easily analysed and described, if we conceive the ultimate parts of bodies to have a capacity for relative motion ; but there is no possibility of conceiving such a motion if all the parts of a body are continuous. A crowd of human beings seen from a great height may look like a turbulent fluid in motion at every point. But we know from experience that this motion is only possible because there is some void in the crowd. It may become so densely packed that motion is no longer practicable. Thus it is with that relative motion of the parts of bodies upon which so much of modern physics depends ; absolutely close packing, that is continuity, seems to render it impossible. It is only by reducing in conception the complex groups of sense-impressions, which we term bodies, into simple elements directly depending on the motion of discontinuous systems,—of what we may term granular or starlike systems,—that we have been able to resume phenomena in the wide-reaching laws of physics and chemistry. The relative motion of the ultimate parts of bodies, involving the idea of discontinuity, is one of the fundamental conceptions of modern science (p. 133). These ultimate parts of bodies we are accustomed to speak of as *atoms* ; groups of atoms which apparently repeat themselves over and over again in the same body— something like planetary systems in the starry universe— we term *molecules*. The generally accepted atomic or

molecular theory of bodies postulates essentially their
discontinuity.   Take, for example, a spherical drop of
water—to follow Lord Kelvin—suppose it to be as big
as a football, then if we could magnify the whole drop up
to the size of the earth, the structure, he tells us, would be
more coarse-grained than a heap of small shot, but probably less coarse-grained than a heap of footballs.[1]

Now I propose later to return to the atomic hypothesis.
At present I will only ask the reader to look upon atom
and molecule as *conceptions* which very greatly reduce the
complexity of our description of phenomena.   But what
it is necessary to notice at this stage is : that the conception atom, when applied to our perceptions, is opposed
to the conception of surface as the continuous boundary
of a body.   We have here an important example of
what is not an uncommon occurrence in science, namely,
two conceptions which cannot both correspond to realities
in the perceptual world.   Either perceptual bodies have
continuous boundaries, and the atomic theory has no
perceptual validity ; or, conversely, bodies have an atomic
structure, and geometrical surfaces are perceptually impossible.   At first sight this result might appear to the
reader to involve a contradiction between geometry and
physics ; it might seem that either physical or geometrical
conceptions must be false.   But the whole difficulty really
lies in the habit we have formed of considering bodies as
objective realities unconditioned by our perceptive faculty.
We cannot too often recall the fact that bodies are for us
more or less permanent, more or less clearly defined
groups of sense-impressions, and that the relationships and
sequences among the sense-impressions are largely conditioned by the perceptive faculty.   At the present time
we have no sense-impressions corresponding to geometrical
surface or to atom ; we may legitimately doubt whether
our perceptive faculty is of such a nature that it could
present impressions in any way corresponding to these
conceptions.   It is impossible, therefore, to say that one
of these conceptions must be real and the other unreal,

[1] *Popular Lectures and Addresses*, vol. i., " The Size of Atoms," p. 217.

for neither at present has perceptual validity—that is, exists in the world of real things. As conceptions both are equally valid ; both are equally ideals, not involved in our sense-impressions themselves, but which the reasoning faculty has discovered and developed as a means of classifying different types of sense-impressions and of resuming in brief formulæ their relationships and sequences.

Thus geometrical truths apply with absolute accuracy to no group whatever of our sense-impressions ; but they enable us to classify very wide ranges of phenomena by aid of the notions of position, size, and shape. Geometry enables us to predict with absolute certainty a variety of relations between sense-impressions, when these impressions do not involve more than a certain keenness in our senses, more than a certain degree of exactness in our measuring instruments. The absolute sameness and continuity demanded by geometrical conceptions do not exist as *limits* in the world of perceptual experience, but only as approximations or averages.[1] In precisely the same way the theory of atoms treats of ideal conceptions ; it enables us to classify another and different range of sense-impressions, and to formulate their mutual relations to a certain degree of keenness again in our senses, or of exactness in our scientific apparatus. Should the atom become a perception as well as a conception, this would not invalidate the usefulness of geometry. Very probably, however, if we could magnify a football up to the size of the earth, so that the perceptual atom, if it existed, would have a size between small shot and a football, we should find that the sense-impressions which the atom was conceived to distinguish and resume, had themselves disappeared under the new conditions.[2] In other words, our scientific conceptions are valid for the world as we know

[1] Geometry might almost be termed a branch of statistics, and the definition of the circle has much the same character as that of Quetelet's *l'homme moyen.*

[2] The visibility and tangibility of bodies may possibly be described by the motion of atoms, but we cannot predict that a *single* atom would be either visible or tangible, still less " bounded by a surface."

it, but we cannot in the least predict how they would be
related to a world which is at present beyond perception.

§ 10.—*Conceptual Continuity.   Ether*

The reader will now be prepared to appreciate scientific conceptions, which, if they corresponded to realities
of the phenomenal world, would contradict each other.
Having destroyed the continuity of bodies by the idea of
atom, it might at first sight appear as if our conceptual
space were fundamentally different from perceptual space.
The latter, as we have seen, is our mode of distinguishing
groups of sense-impressions, and where there is nothing
to distinguish, there there is no space.   The perceptive
faculty rather than nature may be said "to abhor a
vacuum."   On the other hand, having destroyed the continuity of bodies by the atomic hypothesis, we seem at
first sight to be postulating a void in conceptual space.
But here the physicist compels us to introduce a new
continuity.   This new continuity is that of the *ether*, a
medium which physicists conceive to fill up the interstices
between bodies and between the atoms of bodies.   By
aid of this concept, the ether (to which we shall return
later), we are able to classify and resume other wide
groups of sense-impressions.   With regard to the perceptual existence of the ether, it now stands, some physicists would assert, on a rather different footing from that
of the atom.   By the *real* existence of anything we mean
(p. 70) that it forms a more or less permanent group of
sense-impressions.   Now this can hardly be asserted of
the ether ; we conceive it rather as a conduit for the
motions by which we interpret sense-impression.   The
nerves seem to us conduits of the like kind, but then the
nerves also appear to us as permanent groups of sense-
impressions apart from their function of conductivity.
There are no sense-impressions which we class together
and term ether, and on this account it seems far better
to consider the ether as a conception rather than a perception.   It is true that to some minds the ether may

appear as real a perception as the air, and the matter is, perhaps, largely one of definition. Still even wireless telegraphy, for example, does not seem to me to have logically demonstrated the perceptual existence of the ether, but to have immensely increased the validity of the scientific concept, ether, by showing that a wider range of perceptual experience may be described in terms of it, than had hitherto been demonstrated before Hertz's experiment.[1] Further, many of the properties which we associate with the ether are not such as our past experience shows us are likely to become matter for direct sense-impression. I shall therefore continue to speak of the ether as a scientific concept on the same footing as geometrical surface and atom.

§ 11.—On the General Nature of Scientific Conceptions

Our discussion of these spacial conceptions will the better have enabled the reader to appreciate the nature of scientific conceptions in general. Geometrical surface, atom, ether, exist only in the human mind, and they are "shorthand" methods of distinguishing, classifying, and resuming phases of sense-impression. They do not exist in or beyond the world of sense-impressions, but are the pure product of our reasoning faculty. The universe is not to be thought of as a real complex of atoms floating in ether, both atom and ether being to us unknowable "things-in-themselves," producing or enforcing upon us the world of sense-impressions. This would indeed be for science to repeat the dogmas of the metaphysicians, the crassest paradoxes of a short-sighted materialism. On the contrary, the scientist postulates nothing of the world beyond sense ; for him the atom and the ether are —like the geometrical surface—models by aid of which he resumes the world of sense. The ghostly world of "things-in-themselves" behind sense he leaves as a play-

---

[1] Nay, in the nineteen years that have elapsed since the first edition of this book appeared, a perceptual ether has grown less and less possible. Little remains of the "ether" to-day but the conceptions involved in a set of differential equations !

ground to the metaphysician and the materialist. There these gymnasts, released from the dreary bondage of space and time, can play all sorts of tricks with the unknowable, and explain to the few who can comprehend them how the universe is "created" out of will, or out of atom and ether, and how a knowledge of things beyond perception, *i.e.* beyond the knowable, may be attained by the favoured few. The scientist bravely asserts that it is impossible to know what there is behind sense-impression, if indeed there can "be" anything ; [1] he therefore refuses to project his conceptions, atom and ether, into the real world of perception until he has perceived them there. They remain for him valid ideals so long as they continue to economise his thought.

That the conceptions of geometry and physics immensely economise thought is an instance of that wonderful power to which I have previously referred in this work (p. 104), namely, the power the reasoning faculty possesses of resuming in conceptions and brief formulæ the relationships and sequences it finds in the material presented to it by the perceptive faculty. As our knowledge grows, as our sense becomes keener under the action of evolution and with the guidance of science, so we are compelled to widen our concepts, or to add additional ones. This process does not as a rule signify that the original concepts are invalid, but merely that they form a basis, which is only sufficient for classifying and describing certain phases of sense-impression, certain aspects of phenomena. As we grow cognisant of other phases and aspects, we are forced to adopt new concepts, or to modify and extend the old. We may ultimately reach perceptions of space which cannot be described by the geometry of Euclid, but none the less that geometry will remain perfectly valid as an analysis and classification of the wide range of perceptions to which it at present applies. (See p. 97 and footnote.) If the reader will bear in mind the views here

---

[1] Our notion of "being" is essentially associated with space and time, and it may well be questioned whether it is intelligible to use the word except in association with these modes of perception.

expressed with regard to the concepts of science, he will never consider that science reduces the universe to a "dead mechanism" by asserting a reality for atom or ether or force as the basis of sense-impression. Science, as I have so often reiterated, takes the universe of perceptions as it finds it, and endeavours briefly to describe it. It asserts no perceptual reality for its own shorthand.

One word more before we leave this space of conception, separated by continuous boundaries in the eye of the geometrician, peopled with atoms and ether by the mind of the physicist. How, if geometrical surface, if atom and ether have no perceptual reality, has the mind of man historically reached them? I believe by carrying to a limit in conception processes which have no such limit in perception. Preliminary stages in comparison show apparent sameness and continuity, where more exact and final stages show no such limit; hence arises the conception of continuous boundaries. The atom again is a conceptual limit to the "moving bodies" of perception; while the ether possesses properties, which we have never met with in the physical media of our perceptual experience, but which are purely conceptual limits to the types of media with which we are directly acquainted. These concepts themselves are a product of the imagination, but they are suggested, almost insensibly suggested, by what we perceive in the world of phenomena.

§ 12.—*Time as a Mode of Perception*

I have dealt at greater length with space than it will be necessary to deal with *time*, for much that has been said in the former case as to perception and conception will directly apply to the latter. Space and time are so similar in character, that if space be termed the breadth, time may be termed the length of the field of perception. As space is one mode in which the perceptive faculty distinguishes objects, so time is a second mode. As space marks the coexistence of perceptions at an epoch of time—we measure the breadth of our field—so time marks the progression of perceptions at a position in space—we measure the length of our field. The combination of the two modes, or change of position with change of time, is *motion*, the fundamental manner in which phenomena are in conception presented to us.

If we had solely the power of perceiving coexisting things, our perception might be wide, but it would fall far short of its actuality. The power of "perceiving things apart" by progression or sequence is an essential feature of conscious life, if not of existence. Without this time-mode of perception the only sciences possible would be those which deal with the order or relationship of coexisting things, with number, position, and measurement — in other words, the sciences of Arithmetic, Algebra, and Geometry. Bodies might have size and shape and locality, but science would be unable to deal with colour, warmth, weight, hardness, etc., all of which sense-impressions we conceive to depend upon our appreciation of sequence. In short, the physical, biological, and historical sciences, which have for their essential topics change, or sequence in perception, would be impossible.

I have spoken of certain branches of science being possible or impossible without the time-mode of perception. I ought rather to say that the *material* for these branches of science can or cannot be conceived to exist without time. For in truth all scientific knowledge would be impossible without time ; thought undoubtedly involves an association of immediate and stored sense-impressions (p. 46) ; every conception, geometrical as well as physical, is ultimately based on perceptual experience, and the very word experience connotes the time-mode of perceiving things. This leads us to what at first sight appears a fundamental distinction between the modes space and time. Space as our method of perceiving coexisting things, of distinguishing groups of immediate sense-impressions, is associated with the world of actual phenomena which we project *outside* ourselves

(p. 61). For this reason it has been termed an *external* mode of perception. On the other hand, time is the perception of sequence in stored sense-impressions—the relationship of past perceptions with the immediate perception. Thus time involves in its essence memory and thought—in other words, *consciousness*.[1] Consciousness might indeed be defined as the power of perceiving things apart by *succession*. It may perhaps be possible to conceive consciousness as existing without the space-mode of perception, but we cannot conceive it to exist without the time-mode. On this account, time has been termed an *internal* mode of perception. A little consideration, however, soon shows us that this distinction is not a very valid one—as, indeed, no distinction based on the words *external* and *internal* can ever be (p. 65). Perception in space is, as a matter of fact, as largely dependent on the association of immediate and stored sense-impressions as perception in time. As we have seen, every object is for us largely a construct (p. 41), and the coexisting objects which we can perceive apart are indeed very limited. I distinguish the papers, the books, the inkstand, the candlesticks on my table as separate objects by the mode space; but at any *instant of time*, it is only a very small element of this complex of sense-impressions which is *immediate*, the rest are stored sense-impressions, capable of becoming immediate sense-impressions in the next instant, but not so in actuality. Thus in the case of both time and space the " perceiving apart " is the perception of an order existing between a very small element of sense-impression and a much larger range of stored sense-impressions. We do not therefore gain by terming space and time external and internal modes of perception. Both modes of perception are so habitual and yet so difficult of analysis, so commonplace and yet so mysterious, that, although we recognise a

---

[1] For a new-born infant time cannot be said to exist—it is without consciousness (p. 44). Only as stored sense-impresses result from immediate sense-impression does the faculty of memory, and so the time-mode of perception, become developed. The rest is reflex action, the product of inherited and unconscious association.

distinction between the two, we are often hardly certain
whether we are distinguishing things by time or by space.
Why we perceive things under these modes, the scientist
is content to classify with all other *whys* as an idle and
irrational question ; but clearer views as to the *how* of
these modes of perception will undoubtedly come with
the growth of physiological psychology, and with increased observation of the manner in which the lower
forms of life and young children discriminate perceptions.

Of time as of space we cannot assert a real existence ;
it is not in things, but in our mode of perceiving them.
As we cannot postulate anything of the beyond of sense-
impression, so we cannot attribute time directly or indirectly to the supersensuous. Like space, it appears
to us as one of the plans on which that great sorting-
machine, the human perceptive faculty, arranges its
material. Through the doorways of perception, through
the senses of man, crowd, in our waking state, sense-
impression upon sense-impression ; sound and taste,
colour and warmth, hardness and weight—all the various
elements of an infinite variety of phenomena, all that
forms for us reality—crush through the open gateways.
The perceptive faculty, sharpened by long centuries of
natural selection,[1] sorts and sifts all this mass of sense-
impressions, giving to each a place and an instant. Thus
the magnitude of space and time depends upon no
external world independent of ourselves, but on the complexity of our sense-impressions, immediate and stored.
Infinity of space or eternity of time has no meaning in
the field of perception, because the association and
sequence of our perceptions, wide as both undoubtedly
are, do not require these enormous frames to exhibit
them. Where the senses perceive no object, there there
is no space, for there no groups of sense-impressions are
to be distinguished. Where I can no longer carry back

[1] We cannot infer the time and space-modes of perception except for perceptive faculties, more or less similar to our own. The order of phenomena
in both space and time is essentially conditioned by the intensity and quality
of the consciousness (p. 83).

the sequence of phenomena, there time ceases for me because I no longer require it to distinguish an order of events. Let the reader endeavour to realise empty time, or time with no sequence of events, and he will soon be ready to grant that time is a mode of his own perception and is limited by the contents of his experience.[1] Thus the moments devoted to wonder over the eternities of time are as ill-spent as those consumed in pondering on the immensities of space (p. 187). They are like moments employed in examining the frame of a picture and not its contents, in admiring the constitution of the artist's canvas and not his genius. The frame is just large and strong enough to support the picture, the canvas is just wide and stout enough to sustain the artist's colours. But frame and canvas are only modes by which the artist brings home his idea to us, and our wonder should not be for them, but for the contents of the picture and its author. So it is with time and space —these are but the frame and the canvas by aid of which the perceptive faculty displays our experience. Our admiration is due not to them, but to the complex contents of perception, to the extraordinary discriminating power of the human perceptive faculty. The complexity of nature is conditioned by our perceptive faculty ; the comprehensive character of natural law is due to the ingenuity of the human mind. Here, in the human powers of perception and reason, lie the mystery and the grandeur of nature and its laws. Those, whether poets or materialists, who do homage to nature as the sovereign of man, too often forget that the order and complexity they admire are at least as much a product of man's perceptive and reasoning faculties as are their own memories and thoughts.

[1] It may well be questioned whether anything that falls outside human experience can be said to have existed in *perceptual* time. Such time is essentially the mode by which we distinguish an *immediate* sense-impression from a succession of stored sense-impresses (p. 41). That the world has existed for many million years is a *conception*, and the period referred to a conceptual rather than a perceptual one. The *future* also is a notion attaching rather to conceptual than to perceptual time. The full discussion of these points cannot, however, be entered upon at this stage.

§ 13.—*Conceptual Time and its Measurement*

Time as a mode of perception is limited, we have seen, to the extent to which sequences of stored sense-impressions can be carried back ; it marks that order of perceptions which is the history of our consciousness.   From this it is clear that perceptual time has no future and has no eternity in the past.   That consciousness in the future will continue as it has done in the past is a conception, but not a perception.   We perceive the past, but we only conceive the future.   How, then, we may ask, do we pass from perceptual to conceptual time, from our actual sequences of sense-impressions to a scientific mode of describing and measuring them ?   Clearly it would be extremely cumbersome to measure time by a detailed account of the changes in our sense-impressions.   Imagine the labour of describing all the stages of consciousness between breakfast and dinner as a means of determining the period which has elapsed between the two meals ! Yet this method of considering time brings out clearly how time is a relative order of sense-impressions, and how there is no such thing as *absolute* time.   Every stage in sense-impression marks in itself an epoch of time, and may form the basis of a measurement of time for an individual.   " I am sleepy, it is time to go to bed," says the child ; " I am hungry, it is time to eat," says the savage, and both without thinking of the clock or the sun.   Fortunately for us we are not compelled to measure time by a description of the sequence of states of consciousness.   There are certain sense-impressions which experience has shown us repeat themselves, and which, on the average, correspond to the same routine of consciousness.   In the first place, the recurrence of night and day are observed very early in the natural history of man to mark off approximately like sequences of sense-impressions ; a day and night becomes a measure of a certain interval of consciousness.   That the same amount of consciousness can, at any rate approximately, be got into *each* day and night by the normal human being is a matter rather of experience than of demonstration ; it cannot be proved,—it can only be felt.

Very much the same holds for the smaller intervals of time. When we say it is four hours since breakfast, we mean in the first place that the large hand of our clock or watch has gone round the dial-face four times—a repeated sense-impression which we could, if we please, have observed. But how shall we decide whether each of these four hours represents equal amounts of consciousness, and the same amount to-day as yesterday ? It may possibly be that our time-keeper has been compared with a standard clock, regulated perhaps from Greenwich Observatory. But what regulates the Greenwich clock ? Briefly, without entering into details, it is ultimately regulated by the motion of the earth round its axis, and the motion of the earth round the sun. Assuming, however, as a result of astronomical experience, that the intervals day and year have a constant relation, we can throw back the regulation of our clock on the motion of the earth about its axis. We may regulate what is termed the "mean solar time" of an ordinary clock by "astronomical time" of which the day corresponds to a complete turn of the earth on its axis. Now if an observer watches a so-called circumpolar star, or one that remains all day and night above the horizon, it will appear, like the end of his astronomical clock-hand, to describe a circle ; the star ought to appear to the observer to describe equal parts of its circle in equal times by his clock, or while the end of the clock-hand describes equal parts of its circle. In this manner the hours on the Greenwich astronomical clock, and ultimately on all ordinary watches and clocks regulated by it, will correspond to the earth turning through equal angles on its axis. We thus throw back our measurement of time on the earth as a time-keeper ; we assume that equal turns of the earth on its axis correspond to equal intervals of consciousness. But, all clocks being set by the earth, how shall we be certain that the earth itself is a regular time-keeper ? If the earth were gradually to turn more slowly upon its axis how should we know it was losing time, and how measure the amount? It might be replied that we should find that the year had fewer days in it; but then how could we settle that it was the day that was growing longer and not the year that was growing shorter? Again, it may be objected that we know a great number of astronomical periods relating to the motion of the planets expressed in terms of days, and that we should be able to tell by comparison with these periods. To this we must answer that the relation of these periods expressed in days, and in terms of each other, appears now indeed invariable; but what if all these relations are found to have slightly changed a thousand or five thousand years hence? Which body shall we say has been moving uniformly, which bodies have been gaining or losing? Or, what if, the ratios of their periods remaining the same, they were *all* to have lost or gained? How shall we, with such a possibility in view, assert that the hour to-day is the " same " interval as it was a thousand, or better perhaps a million, years back? Now certain investigations with regard to the frictional action of the tides make it highly probable that the earth is not a perfect time-keeper, nor are we able to postulate that regularity of motion, by which alone we could reach absolute time, of any body in our perceptual experience.

Astronomy says it is not in me, nor do we get a more definite answer from physics. Suppose an observer to measure the distance traversed by light in one second; can this be for all time a permanent record of the length of a second? Another observer a thousand years after measures again the distance for one of *his* seconds, and finds its differs from the old determination. What shall he infer? Is the speed of light really variable, has the planetary system reached a denser portion of the ether, has the second changed its value, or does the fault lie with one or other observer? No more than the astronomer can the physicist provide us with an *absolute* measure of time. So soon as we grasp this we appear to lose our hold on time. The earth, the sole clock by which we can measure millions of years, fails us when we once doubt its regularity.   Why should a year now represent the same amount of consciousness as it might have done a few million years back?   The absolutely uniform motion by which alone we could reach an absolute measurement of time fails us in perceptual experience.   It is, like the geometrical surface, reached in conception, and in conception only, by carrying to a limit there the approximate sameness and uniformity which we observe in certain perceptual motions.   Absolute intervals of time are the conceptual means by which we describe the sequence of our sense-impressions, the frame into which we fit the successive stages of the sequence, but in the world of sense-impression itself they have no existence.

Newton, defining what we term here conceptual time tells us :—

"That absolute, true, and mathematical time is conceived as flowing at a constant rate, unaffected by the speed or slowness of the motions of material things."

Clearly such time is a pure ideal, for how can we measure it if there be nothing in the sphere of perception which we are certain flows at a constant rate?   "Uniform flow," like any other scientific concept, is a limit drawn in imagination—in this case, from the actual "speed or slowness of the motions of material things."   But, like other scientific concepts, it is invaluable as a shorthand method of description.   Perceptual time is the pure order in succession of our sense-impressions and involves no idea of absolute interval.   Conceptual time is like a piece of blank paper ruled with lines at equal distances, upon which we may inscribe the sequence of our perceptions, both the known sequence of the past and the predicted sequence of the future.   The fact that upon the ruled lines we have inscribed some standard recurring sense-impression (as the daily transit of a heavenly body over the meridian of Greenwich), must not be taken as signifying that states of consciousness succeed each other uniformly, or that a "uniform flow" of consciousness is in some way a measure of absolute time.   It denotes no

more than this : that from noon to noon the average
human being experiences much the same sequence of
sense-impressions, and thus the same space in our conceptual time-log may be conveniently allotted for their in-
scription.   Above all, it must not lead us to project the
absolute time of conception into a reality of perception ;
the blank divisions at the top and bottom of our conceptual
time-log are no justification for rhapsodies on past or
future eternities of time.   Such rhapsodies, only by confusing conception and perception, can attribute to these
eternities meaning in the actual world of phenomena, in
the field of sense-impression.

§ 14.—*Concluding Remarks on Space and Time*

The reader who has recognised in perceptual space and
time the modes in which we distinguish groups of sense-
impressions, who has grasped that infinities and eternities
are products of conception, not actualities of the real world
of phenomena, will be prepared to admit the important
conclusions which flow from these views for both practical
and mental life.   If the individual carries space and time
about with him as his modes of perception, we see that
the field of miracle is transferred from an external
mechanical world of phenomena to the individual perceptive faculty.   The knowledge of this in itself is no small
gain to clearing up our ideas with regard to such recrudes-
cences of superstition as spiritualism and theosophy.   If
space and time are to be annihilated, it cannot be done
once for all, but it must be done for each individual
perceptive faculty.   When, for example, theosophists tell
us that, putting aside the bondages of space and time,
they can communicate with adepts from Central Asia in
London drawing-rooms, they are really saying that *their
own* perceptive faculties can distinguish groups of sense-
impressions in other than those modes of space and time
which are characteristic of the normal perceptive faculty.
They have not abrogated *our* space and time, only their
own.   They are merely declaring that their modes of

perception are different from ours. If we find from long experience that there is in man a normal perceptive faculty which co-ordinates sense-impressions in space and time in the same uniform manner, then we are justified in classifying the infinitesimal minority who suffer from abnormal modes of perception with the ecstatic and the insane. Through sickness they have lost, or through atavistic tendencies they have failed to develop, the normal perceptive faculty of a healthy man—the *mens sana in corpore sano*.

No less valuable is the conclusion that it is idle to speak of anything as existing in space or as happening in time which cannot be the material of perception. Whatever by its nature lies beyond sense-impression, beyond the sphere of perception, can neither exist in space nor happen in time. Thus the scientific conception of causation, or that of uniform antecedence cannot with any meaning be postulated of it—a result we have already reached from a slightly different standpoint (pp. 127 and 183). Indeed, it seems to me that, with a clear appreciation of space and time as modes of perception, most phases of superstition and obscurity fade into nothingness, while the field to which the category of knowledge applies is seen to be sharply defined.

SUMMARY

1. Space and Time are not realities of the phenomenal world, but the modes under which we perceive things apart. They are not infinitely large nor infinitely divisible, but are essentially limited by the contents of our perception.

2. Scientific concepts are, as a rule, limits drawn in conception to processes which can be started but not carried to a conclusion in perception. The historical origin of the concepts of geometry and physics can thus be traced. Concepts such as geometrical surface, atom, and ether, are not asserted by science to have a real existence in or behind phenomena, but are valid as shorthand methods of describing the correlation and sequence of phenomena. From this standpoint conceptual space and time can be easily appreciated, and the danger avoided of projecting their ideal infinites and eternities into the real world of perceptions.

LITERATURE

HUME, DAVID.—A Treatise on Human Nature (1739), book i. part ii. Of the Ideas of Space and Time. Green and Grose: Works of Hume, vol. i. pp. 334-371.

KANT, IMMANUEL.—Kritik der reinen Vernunft (1781). Elementarlehre, i. Teil. Sämmtliche Werke, Ausgabe v. Hartenstein, Bd. iii. S. 58-80.

A good account of Kant's views will be found in Kuno Fischer's Geschichte der Philosophie, Bd. iii. S. 312-349. A brief description is given on pp. 218-20 of Schwegler's Handbook of the History of Philosophy, translated by J. H. Stirling, Edinburgh, 1879.

None of the geometrical or physical text-book writers have hitherto ventured to discuss how the conceptual space and time which are at the basis of their investigations are related to perceptual experience. The reader will, however, find much that is valuable in Clifford's Philosophy of the Pure Sciences (1873), Lectures and Essays, vol. i. pp. 254-340, and in his "Of Boundaries in General," Seeing and Thinking (1880), pp. 127-156.

A criticism of Hume's views will be found on pp. 230-254 of Green's "General Introduction" to Hume's Works, vol. i., while Kant's doctrines have been attacked by both Trendelenburg and Ueberweg. References are given in vol. ii. pp. 158, 330 and 525 of the latter writer's History of Philosophy, London, 1874.

A good deal that is suggestive with regard not only to space and time, but position and motion, may still with caution be extracted from the Physics of Aristotle. See especially E. Zeller, Die Philosophie der Griechen, ii. Teil, 2. Abt. S. 384-408, Ueberweg, loc. cit. vol. i. pp. 163-6. The reader must not be discouraged by the unwarranted contempt expressed for Aristotle's ideas of space and motion in George Henry Lewes's Aristotle: a Chapter from the History of Science, London, 1864 (p. 128 et seq.).

CHAPTER VII

THE GEOMETRY OF MOTION

§ 1.—*Motion as the Mixed Mode of Perception*

WE have seen in the previous chapter that there are two modes under which the perceptive faculty discriminates between the contents of perception, namely, those of space and time. The combination of these two modes, to which we give the various names of change, motion, growth, evolution, may be said to be the *mixed* mode under which all perception takes place.[1] Science, accordingly, if we except special branches treating of the modes under which we perceive and think, is essentially, as a description of the contents of perception, a description of change or variation. In order to draw a mental picture of the universe, to map out in broad outline its characteristics, science has introduced the conception of geometrical forms ; in order to describe the sequence of perceptions, to form a sort of historical atlas of the universe, science has introduced the conception of geometrical forms changing with absolute time. The analysis of this conception is what we term the *Geometry of Motion*. The geometry of motion is thus the conceptual mode in which we classify and describe perceptual change. Its validity

---

[1] Trendelenburg sees in real or constructive motion the basis of all perception and conception. He tries to show that the conception of motion does not require the notions of space and time, which he asserts flows from the conception of motion itself. I do not think he is successful in this, but his attempt is instructive as showing how essentially perception and conception involve motion. (See his *Logische Untersuchungen*, 2nd edition, Bd. i. chaps. v.-viii. Leipzig, 1862.)

depends not upon its absolute correspondence with anything in the real world—a correspondence at once
rebutted by the ideal character of geometrical forms—but
upon the power it gives us of briefly resuming the facts
of perception or of economising thought.[1]   The geometry
of motion has been technically termed *kinematics*, from
the Greek word κίνημα, signifying a *movement*.   It teaches
us how to represent and measure motion in the abstract,
with reference to those particular types of motion which
a long series of experiments, and much careful observation
of the world of phenomena, have shown us are best fitted
to exhibit the special changes in the sphere of perception.
When we apply what we have learnt in the geometry
of motion to those particular types of motion—*natural*
types, as they may be conveniently called—and investigate how they are related, then we are led to the
so-called *Laws of Motion* and to those conceptions of *Mass*
and *Force*[2] upon which our physical description of the
universe depends.   These will form the topics of succeed-
ing chapters, but, in order to see our way more clearly
through that maze of metaphysics which at present
obstructs the entry of physics, we must devote some space
to a discussion of the elementary notions of kinematics.

---

[1] The term *economy of thought*, originally due, I think, to Professor Mach
of Vienna, embraces in itself a very important series of ideas.   Its value is
rendered more significant if we remember how thought depends on stored
sense-impressions, and that it is difficult to deny to these and to their nexus—
association—a physical or kinetic aspect, the *impress* of our terminology (p. 42).
The economy of thought thus becomes closely associated with an economy of
energy.   The range of perceptions is so wide, their sequence so varied and
complex, that no single brain could retain a clear picture of the relationship
of the smallest group but for the shorthand descriptions provided by the conceptions of science.   Dr. Wallace, in his *Darwinism*, declares that he can
find no ground for the existence of pure scientists, especially mathematicians,
on the hypothesis of natural selection.   If we put aside the fact that great
power in theoretical science is correlated with other developments of increasing
brain-activity, we may, I think, still account for the existence of pure
scientists as Dr. Wallace would himself account for that of worker-bees.
Their functions may not fit them individually to survive in the struggle for
existence, but they are a source of strength and efficiency to the society
which produces them.   The solution of Dr. Wallace's difficulty lies, I
think, in the social profit to be derived from science as an economy of
intellectual energy.

[2] Not force as the *cause* of motion, but force as a measure of motion.

§ 2.—*Conceptual Analysis of a Case of Perceptual Motion.*
Point-Motion

We shall, I think, best obtain clear ideas of motion by
examining some familiar case of physical change of
position and endeavouring to analyse it into simple types
which may easily be discussed by the aid of geometrical
ideals.   Let us take, for instance, the case of a man
ascending a staircase which may have several landings and
turns in its course.   The changes in our sense-impressions
during the man's ascent are of an extremely complex
character, and we see at once how difficult, if not
impossible, it would be to describe all that we perceive.
Not only the position of the man on the staircase changes,
but his hands and his legs are perpetually varying their
position with regard to his trunk, while his trunk itself
turns and oscillates, bends and alters its shape.   For
simplification let us, in the first place, fix our attention on
some small element of his person ; let us follow with our
eye, for example, the top button of his waistcoat.   Now
the first observation that we make is that this button
takes up a series of positions which are perfectly continuous from the start to the finish of the ascent.   There
can be no break in this series of positions anywhere
throughout the whole extent of the staircase ; for, if there
were any, the button must, in accurate language, have
ceased to be a permanent group of sense-impressions, and
to be distinguished from other groups under the mode
space.   In ordinary parlance, it must " have left our space
and come back to it again "—a phenomenon totally contrary to the experience of the normal human perceptive
faculty.   If we cut the button off the waistcoat, we could
still conceive it to move up the staircase in precisely the
same manner as when the man wore it,—carried up,
let us suppose, by an invisible spirit hand.   It will be
obvious that this motion of the button, if fully known to
us, would tell us a good deal about the motion of the
man.   It would not describe, of course, how he moved his
legs and arms about, but it would indicate very fairly

how long the man took to go from one landing to another
and when he was going quickly, when slowly.   But it is
still far from clear how we are to describe the motion of
the button, so that we could conceive its motion repeated
by aid of our description.   The button, like the man, has
many elements, and the question again arises how we are
to describe the motions of them all.

Let us now stretch our imaginations a little further ;
let us suppose the staircase to be embedded in a great
mass of soft wax, and suppose the button, guided still by
the spirit hand, to move up the staircase precisely as it
did on the man's waistcoat, but now pushing its way
through the wax.   The passage of the button would now
form a long tube-like hollow in our mass of wax extending from the bottom to the top of the staircase.   This
tube would not necessarily be of equal bore throughout,
because, owing to the motion of the man, the button
might occasionally move more or less sideways.   Still, the
smaller the button the smaller would be the bore of the
tube cut through the wax.   We will now suppose a long
piece of stiff wire passed through the tube and firmly fixed
at its ends.   The wax, and even the staircase, may now
be removed, and then, if a small bead be slung on the
wire and move up the wire in the same manner as the
button moved up the tube, we shall be able to describe a
good deal of the motion of the button from that of the
bead.   Now in conception we may suppose the wire to
get thinner and thinner, and the bead smaller and smaller,
till in conception the wire ends in a geometrical line
or curve, and the bead in a geometrical point.   The
motion of the ideal point along the ideal curve will represent with a great degree of accuracy the motion of an
extremely small button up a tube of an extremely small
bore through the wax.   The reader may feel inclined to
ask why we did not commence by saying : " Consider a
point of the man ; the motion must give a curve passing
from top to bottom of the staircase."   The answer lies in
this : that we cannot *perceive* a point.   In conception we
reach a point by carrying to a limit the perceptual process

of taking a smaller and smaller element of the man, and the stages we have indicated from man to button, bead and geometrical point, indicate how certain elements of the perceptual motion are dropped at each stage, till in conception we reach as a limit an ideal motion capable of being fairly easy described.

The motion of a point along a curve is the simplest ideal motion we can discuss. Obviously, however, it will enable us to classify and describe with considerable exactness a number of our perceptions with regard to the man's motion. Harness the button to the point, and the man to the button; then if the point move along its path, carrying button and man with it, we shall have a means of describing a good deal of the real motion of the man. When he starts, when he stops, when he goes fast, when he goes slowly, what time he takes from one landing to another will be deducible from the motion of the point. Of course this point-motion does not enable us to *fully* describe the motion of the man. For instance it is conceivable that he may have turned several somersaults· in going upstairs. About such eccentricities in the man's motion the motion of the point may tell us nothing at all. Even had the man been incapable of moving his arms, legs, head, etc.,—had he been a *rigid* body—the point-motion would have been incapable of fully describing his motion. As a rigid body the man might have been turned round and about the point without changing its motion. Did he go upstairs backwards or forwards, head or feet uppermost, or partly in one, partly in another of these modes? Clearly the motion of the point can tell us nothing of all this. The motion of the point can tell us nothing of how the man as a rigid body might have turned about the point; we should want to know at each instant of the motion which way the man was facing, what was his *aspect*, and further how he was changing his aspect or rotating about the point. The description of the ideal point-motion would have to be supplemented, even if the man were supposed to be a rigid body, by a description of the rotating or spinning motion. The first type of motion, corresponding to change of position, is termed *motion of translation* ; the second type, corresponding to the change of aspect of a rigid body, is termed *motion of rotation.*

§ 3.—*Rigid Bodies as Geometrical Ideals*

Just as the former motion is described by the purely ideal conception of a point moving along a curve, so the latter is also made to depend on geometrical notions, namely, those of a *rigid* body turning about a *line* passing through a *point.* What, in the first place, do we mean by using the term *rigid* body ? The real man is moving his limbs and bending his body, and generally changing his form at each instant of the motion. Now the reader may feel inclined to say : Replace the man by a wooden table or chair, and we shall have a rigid body. But this is only popular language, and what we are seeking is an accurate or scientific definition of rigidity. Such a definition is usually given in the following words :—

A body is said to remain rigid during any given motion when the distances between all pairs of its points remain unaltered throughout the whole duration of the motion.

But we see at once from this definition that we have replaced the real body, the group of sense-impressions which forms part of the picture constructed by our perceptive faculty, by an ideal geometrical body possessing " points," and that it is a property of this body—existing only on the ideal map on which conception plots out perception—that we are defining. It is quite true that the geometrical ideal of a rigid body is a better description of a wooden chair than of the flexible body of a man ; yet what is a " point " on the chair, and what is the " distance " between a pair of points ? How, again, am I to ascertain accurately that such distances remain unaltered during the motion ? The very idea of distance, when clearly appreciated, involves the geometrical conception of points and does not correspond to anything in our perceptual experience.[1]   Rigidity is thus seen to be a conceptual limit, which by concentrating our attention on a special group of perceptions forms a valuable method of classification.

Although for the description of some types of motion it may be useful to replace the wooden chair by a body of ideal rigidity in our conceptual map, still the physicist tells us that for the purpose of classifying other phases of sense-impression, he is bound to consider that the chair is *not* rigid, and that he is perceptually able to measure changes in the relative position of its parts.   He cannot describe the mechanical action between different parts of the chair without supposing it elastic, and this elasticity involves changes of form in its parts.   For example, the action between the parts of the chair changes, when it is supported on its back instead of its legs, and thus the chair changes its form in these two positions.   A like change of form will take place even if the chair be only rotating.   Nor does this variation in shape merely result from the chair being of wood—it would be equally true if the chair were of iron, or any other material.   Change of form is in many cases perceptually appreciable, and in most cases we can determine its conceptual value.   Thus, so far from the rigid body being a limit which might be reached in perception, our whole perceptual experience seems to indicate that the conception rigidity corresponds to nothing whatever in the real world of phenomena.   We perceive that most bodies do change their form, and where we do not perceive it physics compels us to conceive it.   Thus

---

[1] We speak, for example, of the "distance" from London to Cambridge being fifty-five miles, and this is a practical method of describing the sense-impressions of a journey from one place to the other, and distinguishing it from a journey of fifty-six or fifty-four miles.   But what do we exactly mean?   From Stepney Church to St. Mary's?   If so, from which part of one church to which part of the other?   Or, again, is it from the stone near the gateway of Stepney Church to the last milestone by St. Mary's?   If so, from which side of the one stone to which side of the other?   In the end we find ourselves driven to the conception of a point on either stone—no *perceptual* mark gets over the difficulty of the *where* to the *where*.   We are forced to conclude that the idea of distance is a conception reached as a *limit* to the perceptual, invaluable for classifying our experience but not accurately corresponding to a perceptual reality.

rigidity is very much like the spherical surfaces of geometry. The latter do not correspond accurately to anything whatever in our perceptual experience, and we cannot even conceive a continuous surface as a limit to be reached in perception. Both, however, are alike valuable bases of classification. By replacing real bodies by ideal rigid bodies we are able, although neglecting their changes of form, to classify and describe a wide range of our perceptions of motion. To classify other perceptions, however, we conceive the same bodies not to be rigid, but to be varying in form ; we actually measure the very changes in shape, which we purposely neglected in another branch of our survey of the physical universe.

§ 4.—*On Change of Aspect or Rotation*

Even when we have transferred our moving body from the perceptual to the conceptual sphere by postulating its rigidity, we shall still find the notions of aspect and spin involve further geometrical conceptions. Let us consider our rigid body capable of turning about a point, the question then arises, How can we distinguish one aspect from a second ? Clearly, the notion of direction involves that of a line, but the change in direction in *one* line will not be sufficient to describe change of aspect. For if C (Fig. 4) represent the fixed point about which the body rotates, and A be another definite point of the body, the line CA may take up a new position CA'; but the change in position of CA to CA' does not fully determine the aspect of the body, for there is nothing to fix how much the body may have been turned about the line CA while it was moving into the position CA'. We are compelled, therefore, to take a second point B, and a second direction CB ; then if we state the new position CB' taken by CB as well as the new position CA' of CA, we shall have absolutely determined the change of aspect of the body. The reader will very easily convince himself that in giving the new positions of two definite points A and B of the rigid body we have absolutely fixed its position. It is easy to show that this turning of two lines CA and CB into new positions CA′ and CB′ may also be attained by turning the body about a certain line of direction CO through a certain angle.[1] Thus the manner in which we conceive change of aspect to be described and measured

[1] This may be proved by the aid of elementary geometry in the following manner :—

Let the triangle CBA be displaced into the position CB′A′. Join the points A, A′ and B, B′, and let the mid-points of AA′ and BB′ be M and N respectively. Through C and M draw a plane perpendicular to AA′ and through C and N a plane perpendicular to BB′. These two planes meet in a line passing through C, since C is common to them both. Let O be any point in this line, and join it to M and N, then OM and ON are respectively perpendicular to AA′ and BB′. In the triangles AOM, A′OM, AM and

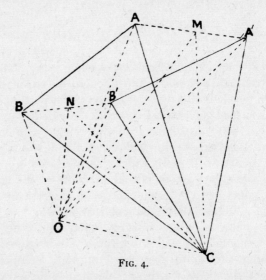

Fig. 4.

A′M are equal, OM is common, and the angles at M are right, hence it follows by *Euclid* i. 4 that the third sides OA and OA′ are equal. For precisely similar reasons it follows that OB and OB′ are equal. Hence the three distances of O from the angles of the triangle ABC are equal to its distances from the three angles of the triangle A′B′C respectively. Thus the two tetrahedrons with summits at O and having bases ABC and A′B′C respectively are equal in every respect, for all their edges are equal each to each. One of them may thus be looked upon as the other in a changed position. They have, however, the same edge OC. Hence one tetrahedron may be moved into the position of the other by rotating it through a certain angle about the edge OC. That is to say, the triangle CBA may be turned into the position CB′A′ by rotating it through a certain angle—the angle between the planes BOC and B′OC—about the line OC.

is essentially geometrical, or ideal. It depends on the conception of a straight line fixed in the body and fixed in space about which the body turns. It further involves the conception of the body turning through a certain angle, but an angle, Euclid tells us, is the inclination of two lines. Thus our description of change of aspect depends upon the conception of lines existing in the rigid body. It is entirely a *conceptual* description, but like the idea of point-motion, it again serves as a powerful means of discriminating and classifying our experiences of perceptual motion.

§ 5:—*On Change of Form, or Strain*

Thus far we have analysed the motion of our man ascending the staircase by considering the motion of an ideal point of him, and then treating him as a rigid body turning about this point, or changing its aspect. It only remains for us to consider how, when the point is in any given position and the man has any given aspect, we may remove the condition of rigidity, and describe how he can move his limbs about, change his form, or alter the relative distances of his parts. This change of form is technically termed *strain*, and its description and measurement forms the third great division in the conceptual motion of bodies. Now we cannot in this work enter into a technical discussion of how strain is scientifically described and measured, but for our present purposes we must ascertain whether the theory of strain deals, like that of the translation of a point and that of the rotation of a rigid body, with conceptual ideas.

There are two fundamental aspects of strain which most of us consciously or unconsciously recognise. These are change of size without change of shape, and change of shape without change of size. Take a thin hollow india-rubber ball and blow more air into its interior. This will increase its size without necessarily changing its shape. It was spherical in shape and remains spherical in shape, only it is larger. We conceive the ball represented by a sphere, and the change in size will depend upon the change in diameter. The ratio of the extension to the original length of the diameter may be taken as a proper basis for the measurement of the strain. Such a ratio is termed a *stretch*, and it may be shown that for a small increase of size the ratio of the increase of volume to the original volume is very nearly three times the stretch of the diameter.[1] This ratio is termed the *dilatation*, and is a proper measure of the change in size. Now it is clear that in order to measure this change of size, we require to measure the diameters in the two conditions of the body. But a diameter, although in the conceptual body definite enough as a straight line termin-

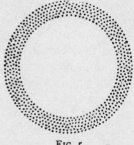

FIG. 5.

ated by two points, is, in this accurate sense of the word, a meaningless term when we are dealing with a perceptual body. If the body has no continuous boundary, but, according to the physicist, is a mass of discrete atoms (Fig. 5), none of which we can individually feel, and the mutual distance of which we cannot measure, it is clear that the only diameter we can be talking about is that of a conceptual sphere by which we have replaced the perceptual ball.

[1] The volumes of bodies of similar shape are as the cubes of corresponding lengths. Hence if V and V' be the old and new volumes, d and d' the old and new lengths, $V'/V = d'^3/d^3$, but if s be the stretch $(d' - d)/d = s$, or $d' = d(1 + s)$. A little elementary algebra gives us for the dilatation δ :—

$$\delta = \frac{V' - V}{V} = \frac{d'^3 - d^3}{d^3} = (1 + s)^3 - 1 = 3s + 3s^2 + s^3 = 3s, \text{ nearly,}$$

if s, as in most practical cases, be very small. For example, in metal $s = \frac{1}{1000}$ would be a rather large value; but taking $\delta = 3s$, we should only be neglecting about $\frac{1}{1000}$ of the value of δ.

As it is with change of size, so it is with change of
shape : we are really basing our system of measurement
upon conceptions, which enable us to describe and classify
perceptions, but are not real limits to perception.   Change
of shape without change of size can be realised in the
following manner : Take a piece of woven silk or other
slightly elastic material, and draw a rectangle upon it
with sides a few inches long parallel to the warp and
woof.   Then if such a rectangle be held firmly top and
bottom between two pairs of parallel pieces of wood, or
even between the two thumbs and their respective fore-

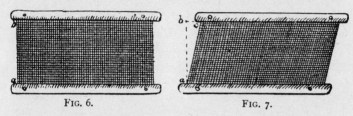

FIG. 6.   FIG. 7.

fingers, a *slide* of the holders parallel to each other will
produce a change of form without change of size.   Now
the extent of such a strain will depend on the amount by
which the warp and woof have changed their inclination
to each other,—that is to say, on the amount after strain
by which the angle between them differs from a right-
angle.   But this change in angle only becomes of meaning
if we suppose the warp and woof to be straight lines.
In other words, to get a measure of the strain we replace
the perceptual warp and woof by a geometrical network.
Such a type of strain is termed a *slide* or *shearing* strain,
and all changes of shape without change of size can in
conception be analysed into slides.[1]   Further, it may be
shown that all changes of form whatever can be analysed
into stretches and slides,[2] or into changes of length and

[1] Technically the slide is not measured by the change in angle or by the angle
bac in Fig. 7, but by the trigonometrical tangent of this angle, or by the ratio
of the length *bc* to the length *ba*—in other words, by the ratio of the amount
the woof has been slid to the length of the warp.

[2] An elementary discussion of strain will be found in Clifford's *Elements
of Dynamic*, part i. pp. 158-90 ; or in Macgregor's *Kinematics and
Dynamics*, pp. 166-84.   The reader may also consult §§ 8 and 13, con-

changes of angle.   But in the cases of both slide and stretch
we are thrown back on geometrical notions, when we
come to consider their measurement ; in both cases we
replace the perceptual body by a conceptual body built
up of points, lines, and angles.   Thus the whole theory of
strain deals with a conceptual means of distinguishing and
describing perceptions, and not with something actually
inherent in those perceptions themselves.

§ 6.—*Factors of Conceptual Motion*

We started with a man ascending a staircase, and we
have seen by our analysis that the conceptual description
of his motion requires us to discuss : (*a*) The Motion of a
Point, (*b*) the Motion of a Rigid Body about a Fixed
Point, (*c*) the Relative Motion of the Parts of a Body or
its Strain.   These are the three great divisions of Kinematics, or the Geometry of Motion.   But in the case of
all these divisions we find that we are thrown back on the
ideal conceptions of geometry ; we measure distances
between points and angles between lines, which are not
true limits to our perceptual experience.   Thus our ideas
of motion appear as ideal modes, in terms of which we
describe and classify the sequences of our sense-impressions : they are purely symbols by aid of which we resume
and index the various and continual changes undergone
by the picture our perceptive faculty presents to us.   The
more fully and clearly the reader grasps this fact, the more
readily will he admit that science is a conceptual *description*
and classification of our perceptions, a theory of symbols
which economises thought.   It is not an explanation of
anything.   It is not a *plan* which lies in phenomena themselves.   Science may be described as a classified index
to the successive pages of sense-impression which enables
us readily to find what we want, but it in nowise accounts
for the peculiar contents of that strange book of life.[1]

tributed by the present writer to chapter iii. of Clifford's *Common Sense of
the Exact Sciences*.
    [1] The extremely complex results which flow from the simple basis of the
planetary theory have often been taken as an evidence of "design" in the

Of the three types of motion just introduced to the notice of the reader, the first, or point-motion, is that which for our present purposes is most important. The remainder of the present chapter will therefore be devoted to its discussion. The reader will, I trust, pardon its somewhat technical character, for without this investigation of point-motion it would be impossible to analyse the fundamental notions of *Matter* and *Force*, or to rightly interpret the Laws of Motion.

§ 7.—*Point-Motion. Relative Character of Position and Motion*

Motion has been looked upon as change of position, but if we try to represent the position of a point we must do so *with regard to something else*. If space be a mode of distinguishing things, we must have at least two things to distinguish before we can talk about position in space. Position of a point is therefore relative, relative to something else, which for the moment we will suppose to be a second point. Absolute position in space, just as absolute space itself (p. 183), is meaningless. Let the letter P (Fig. 8) represent a point, and the letter O a point termed the " origin of reference," from which we are to measure P's relative position. Now the distance from O to P would indicate for us the position of P relative to O, but in our conceptual space we have in general a variety of other points or geometrical bodies besides O which we

universe. The universe has been with much confusion spoken of as the *conception* of an infinite mind. But the *conceptual* basis of the planetary theory lies in geometrical notions, no ultimate evidence of which can be discovered in the perceptual world. Thus, while the planetary theory answers our purposes of *description*, it could never have been the *conception* upon which the universe was " designed," for the conception is nowhere found perceptually realised. *Starting* with his material endowed with all its peculiar properties, the carpenter makes for us a box according to our geometrical description, but in reality not ultimately geometrical. Starting with *nothing* but the absolute power of realising conception in perception, he would have produced from our geometrical plan a geometrical box. Geometrical notions could flow as limits from the material universe, but the latter could not flow from the former. Material sensations must certainly have antedated geometrical conceptions, or, at any rate, planetary theory was not the conception upon which the universe was created out of nothing.

wish to distinguish from P, and to do this we must give what is termed direction to the distance OP, we must determine, as it were, whether it runs north and south, south-west and north-east, or upwards and downwards.[1] But even this is not enough. We must be also told the *sense* of this direction, whether, for example, it be *op* or *op'* (Fig. 8), or, say, runs from south-west to north-east or north-east to south-west. Thus, if we want to plot our position in space about a point O, we must do this by

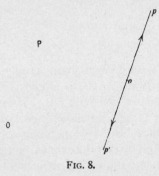

FIG. 8.

measuring distances from O in given directions and with given senses. We must know distance and *bearing*[2] from O to determine fully a point P. To represent geometric-ally the position of P with regard to O, we may draw a piece of a straight line (*op*) having as many units of length on our scale as there are units of distance from O to P, the line having the same direction as this distance, and having an arrow-head upon it to mark the sense. Such a line marking the magnitude, direction, and sense of P's position relative to O is termed a *step*. Such a step tells

[1] In the conceptual space which corresponds most closely to perceptual space—so-called space of *three* dimensions—we require, in order to mark the relative position of all possible bodies, to start from *three* standard points (which must not be in the same straight line) in order to fix direction. Throughout this chapter we shall understand by the position of a point P relative to another point O, the *directed* step OP, and by the motion of P relative to O change in this directed step. A fuller account of *Position* will be found in the chapter under that title contributed by the author to Clifford's *Common Sense of the Exact Sciences.*

[2] With the signification in which the words are here used, a line has *direction* but not *bearing*. We must add to direction the conception of *sense* before we form the idea of bearing.

us how to shift our position from O to P.   Step so many
feet with such and such a bearing, and we shall pass from
O to P.

The conception of *bearing* is so important that we must
say a few words more about it.   The statement merely of
P's distance from O would carry us to any point whatever
on a sphere about O as centre.   To fix a point on this
sphere we require the knowledge of at least two additional
independent points or elements.   For example, a point
which we may term the " pole," Z, of the sphere would
serve for one.   The opposite pole to Z would not serve
for the other, for it is not independent, but obtained by
producing ZO to cut the sphere again.   Neither would
the " equator " corresponding to the polar line OZ serve
our purpose, for it again is not independent of OZ.   But
a point X on this equator is independent of OZ and will
do very well.   The plane through the lines OX and OZ
cuts the sphere in a " meridian," and if we take XOZ as
the meridian to help us determine " bearing," we may speak
of it as a prime meridian.   If we take a line OX perpendicular to this prime meridian, it will cut the circle in
a point Y, and the system of lines OX, OY, OZ, each at
right-angles to the other two, is conveniently termed a
" frame of reference."   There are many other ways of
determining bearing, but they can all be reduced to the
consideration of a frame of reference.   Before, then, we
picture to ourselves any motion of a point P, we must
have selected an " origin of reference " O to give the
distance and a " frame of reference " OX, OY, OZ to give
the bearing.

Thus if P be in motion and we know what is the step
from O to P at each instant of the motion, we shall have
a complete picture of the sequences of positions, the
motion of P relative to O and its frame.   The reader
must be careful to notice the relativity of the motion ;
absolute motion, like absolute position, is inconceivable :
a point P is conceived as describing a path relatively to
something else.   Thus the button on the man's waistcoat
moved relatively to the staircase which serves as a frame,

but the staircase is rushing perhaps 1000 miles an hour round the axis of the earth, while the earth itself may be bowling 66,000 miles an hour round the sun. The sun itself is moving towards the constellation of Lyra at some 20,000 miles an hour, while Lyra itself is doubtless in rapid motion with regard to other stars, which, so far from being " fixed," may be travelling thousands of miles an hour relatively to each other. Clearly it is not only impossible to tell how many thousand miles an hour we are each one of us to be conceived as speeding through space, but the expression itself is meaningless. We can only say how fast one thing is moving *relatively* to another, since all things whatsoever are in motion, and no one can be taken as the standard thing, which is definitely "at rest."

Is it correct to say that the earth actually goes round the sun, or that the sun goes round the earth? Either or neither; both are conceptions which describe phases of our perception. Relatively to the earth the sun describes approximately an ellipse round the earth in a focus, relatively to the sun the earth describes approximately an ellipse about the sun in a focus. Relatively to Jupiter neither statement is correct. Why, then, do we say that it is more scientific to suppose the earth to go round the sun? Simply for this reason : the sun as centre of the planetary system enables us to describe in conception the routine of our perceptions far more clearly and briefly than the earth as centre. Neither of these systems is the description of an absolute motion actually occurring in the world of phenomena. Once realise the relativity of motion and the symmetry of the planetary system is seen to depend largely on the standpoint from which we perceive it : the theory of planetary ellipses can thus be easily recognised as a mode of description peculiar to an inhabitant of a solar system.

§ 8.—*Position.   The Map of the Path*

Relatively to O and its frame, then, our point P describes a continuous curve or path, and its position at

any instant of the motion is given by the step OP. In
order that the reader may have a clearer conception of
what we are considering, we will suppose the motion to
take place in one plane, and conceptualise certain everyday perceptions. We will suppose O to be a point taken
as the conceptual limit of Charing Cross, P to be the point
which marks the conceptual motion of translation of a
train on the Metropolitan Railway, and the curve in Fig. 9
to be a conceptual map of the same railway to the scale
of about one furlong to the $\frac{1}{20}$th of an inch. The points
P_1, P_2, P_3, . . . P_{16} mark the successive stations between
Aldgate and South Kensington. Any step like OP_6 will

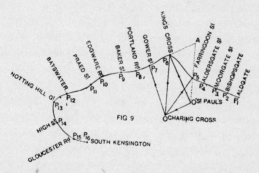

FIG 9

accurately determine a certain position of the train
relative to Charing Cross. The reader must notice an
important result about these steps. Suppose we had
been determining the position of P_6 relative to O'—say
St. Paul's—instead of O. We see at once that there are
two ways of describing the position of P_6 relative to O'.
We might either say, step the directed step $O'P_6$, or,
again, step first from O' to O, and then step from O to
P_6. These two latter steps lead to exactly the same final
position as the former single step. Now science is not
only an economy of thought, but, what is almost the
same thing, an economy of language. Hence we require
a shorthand mode of expressing this equivalence in final
result of two stepping operations. This is done as
follows :—

$$O'O + OP_6 = O'P_6,$$

which, put into words, reads : Step from O′ the directed
step O′O, and then take the directed step OP$_6$, and the
spot finally reached will be the same as if the directed
step O′P$_6$ had been taken from O′. The reader must be
careful not to confuse this geometrical addition with
ordinary arithmetical addition. For example, if OO′
were eight furlongs, O′P$_6$ ten furlongs, and OP$_6$ twelve
furlongs, then we appear at first sight to have :—

$$8 + 12 = 10,$$

and this is deemed absurd. But it is only absurd to the
arithmetician. For the geometrician 8, 12, and 10 may
be the lengths of *directed* steps, and he knows that, if he
follows a directed step of 8 furlongs by one of 12, he
may really have got only ten furlongs from his original
position. How, then, is the arithmetician limited ?
Why, obviously we must suppose him incapable of
stepping out in all directions in space, we must tie him
down to motion along one and the same straight line.
In this case a step of 8 followed by one of 12 will
always make a step of 20, as arithmetic teaches us it
should do. Briefly, the freedom of the geometrician consists in his power of *turning corners.*

Let us now go back a little and note that the
geometrical addition of steps, O′O + OP$_6$ = O′P$_6$, may
be represented in a slightly different manner. Let
us draw the line O′A parallel to OP$_6$ and P$_6$A parallel to
OO′, then we are said to complete the parallelogram on
O′O and OP$_6$, the line O′P$_6$ joining two opposite angles is
termed a diagonal, and we have the following rule :
Complete the parallelogram on two steps, and its diagonal
will measure a single step equivalent to the sum of the
other two. This rule is termed addition by the *parallelogram law,* and we see that the steps by which we measure
relative position, or displacements, obey this law. In
itself it is the same thing as geometrical addition. Its
importance lies in the fact that all the conceptions of the
geometry of motion, displacements, velocities, spins, and
accelerations may be represented as steps and can be

shown to obey the parallelogram law : that is to say, we add together velocities, spins, or accelerations *geometrically* and not arithmetically. Although the space at our disposal may not admit of our demonstrating this result for all the conceptions of kinematics,[1] the reader will do well to bear it in mind, as it is an important principle to which we shall have occasion again to refer.

§ 9.—*The Time-Chart*

Hitherto we have been considering how the position of the point P relative to O might be determined at each instant of time. We want, however, to know how the position changes, and how this change is to be described and measured. In order to do this we must consider how the displacement OP_6, for example, changes to the displacement OP_7. In our geometrical shorthand : $OP_7 = OP_6 + P_6P_7$, and the step P_6P_7 measures the change of position. We want, then, to ascertain a fitting measure of the manner in which this change varies with the time. To enable the reader better to conceive our purpose we will try to turn into geometry a column of *Bradshaw*, or, more definitely, a portion of a time-table of the Metropolitan Railway, corresponding to the stations marked in Fig. 9. Down the left-hand side of Fig. 10 are placed the names of the stations represented in Fig. 9 by the points $P_1, P_2, P_3, P_4, \ldots P_{16}$. These are placed, as in *Bradshaw*, against a vertical line, but we will somewhat improve on his arrangement. He puts the stations at equal distances below each other, and gives no hint as to the distance between each pair of them. Now we will place them at such distances along the vertical from each other that every $\frac{1}{20}$th of an inch represents a furlong, or $\frac{2}{5}$ths of an inch represents a mile, so that an inch-scale applied to the vertical ought theoretically to determine the parliamentary fare between any two stations. In the next place, we will place off (or *plot off*, as it is termed)

---

[1] For proofs see Clifford's *Elements of Dynamic*, "Velocities," p. 59, "Spins," pp. 123-4.

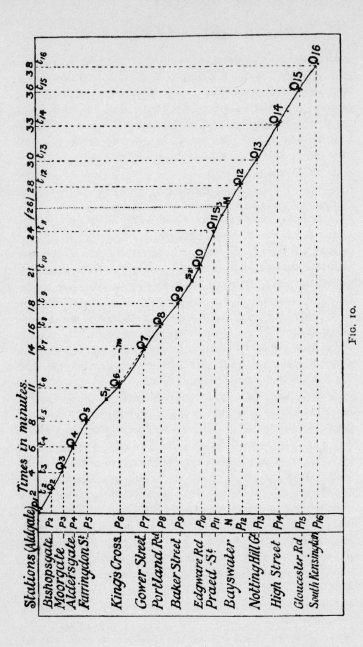

FIG. 10.

240

on the horizontal line through P_1 the number of minutes that the train takes from Aldgate to each of the other stations. Thus the times of a vertical column of *Bradshaw* are in our case ranged horizontally. But we will place these times at such distances that $\frac{1}{8}$th of an inch shall represent a minute, or the minutes between any pair of stations may be at once read off by aid of an inch-scale. To connect each station with its corresponding time we will draw a horizontal line PQ through the station, and vertical line tQ through the corresponding time. These meet in a point Q, and we obtain a series of points Q_1, Q_2, . . . Q_{16}, in our diagram, corresponding to the sixteen stations. Now at first sight it may seem rather an inconvenient form of *Bradshaw*, when each train takes up an entire page.[1] The reader, however, must wait till we have seen whether our page may not be made to convey a great deal more information as to the motion of the train than *Bradshaw's* single column.

Now it is clear that what we have done for the stations may be done for every signal-box, S_1, S_2, S_3, etc., on the line, and not only for every signal-box, but for every position along the whole line at which we choose to observe the time at which the train passes. We thus obtain a series of points : Q_1, Q_2, Q_3, Q_4, Q_5, S_1, Q_6, Q_7, Q_8, Q_9, S_2, etc., which are seen to take more and more the form of a curve as we increase their number. We will join this series of points by a continuous curve, and to simplify matters we will suppose our train to be a luggage train running from Aldgate to South Kensington without stopping, otherwise our curve would have a small straight horizontal piece at each station. This curve must be carefully distinguished from the map of the path in Fig. 9 ; it tells us nothing about the *direction* in which the train is moving at a given time—that is to say, whether it is going northwards, or southwards, or what. But with

[1] Such geometrical *Bradshaws* with, however, many train-curves on a page are used by the traffic managers of several French railways. I possess a facsimile of that for the Paris-Lyons route containing between 30 and 40 train-curves, and showing the passing places, stoppages and speeds of the corresponding trains.

the help of Fig. 9 it tells us the exact time the train takes
to reach, not only every station, but every position whatever between either terminus ; or, on the other hand, it
tells us the exact position for every time up to 38 minutes
after leaving Aldgate. How far has the train got in 26
minutes, for example ? To answer this we must scale off
along the horizontal line, or *time-axis*, 26 eighths of an
inch ; we must then draw a vertical line, striking our curve
in the point M ; a horizontal through M strikes the vertical line of stations, or *distance-axis*, at the point N between
Praed Street and Bayswater, and a scale divided into $\frac{2}{5}$ths
of an inch applied to $P_{11}N$ tells us how many miles the
train is beyond Praed Street. An inverse process will show
us the time to any chosen position on the distance-axis.
Our geometrical time-table, or *time-chart*, as we shall call
it, thus gives us a good deal more information than
Bradshaw. It is further clear that such a time-chart can
be drawn in conception for every point-motion, and that,
taken in conjunction with a map of the path, it fully
describes the most complex point-motion. Hence the
fundamental problem in such motions is to ascertain the
map and the time-chart.[1]

§ 10.—*Steepness and Slope*

If we examine the time-chart we see that there is a
considerable difference in its steepness at different points,
and other motions would give us curves with still greater
variations in this respect. We observe that if we lessen
the time between two stations, say P_{10} and P_{11}, we must
shift the line $Q_{11}t_{11}$ towards $Q_{10}t_{10}$, and the result is that
the curve becomes steeper between Q_{10} and Q_{11}. On the
other hand, if we lessen the space traversed in a given
time the curve becomes less steep and ultimately quite
horizontal if the train stops at a station. Tnus *the
steepness of the time-chart curve corresponds in some manner*

---

[1] The time-chart has been generally attributed to Galilei ; I do not know
on what authority. A *speed-chart* occurs in his *Discorsi*, but I do not think
there is anything that could be called a time-chart.

to the speed of the train.   We thus reach two new conceptions which need definition and measurement, namely,
those of *steepness* and *speed.*   In Fig. 11 we have a
horizontal straight line AB, and a sloping line AC.

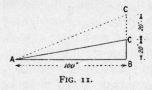

FIG. 11.

Clearly the greater the angle
BAC the steeper AC will be,
and the greater will be the
height we shall ascend for the
horizontal distance AB.   If AB
be 100 feet and CB the vertical
through B be 20 feet, we shall have ascended 20 feet for
a horizontal 100, or since the steepness of AC is the same
at all points, we shall ascend 2 feet in 10 feet, or 200 feet
in 1000 feet, or $\frac{1}{5}$ of a foot in 1 foot.[1]   Now, by
elementary arithmetic the ratios of 20 to 100, 2 to 10,
200 to 1000, and $\frac{1}{5}$ to 1 are all equal and may be
expressed by the fraction $\frac{1}{5}$.   This is termed the *slope* of
the straight line AC, and is a fitting measure of its steepness.   The slope is clearly the number of units or the
fraction of a unit we have risen vertically for a unit of
horizontal distance.   If slope be a fit measure of steepness for a straight line, we have next to inquire how we
can measure the steepness of a curved line.   Let A and C
in Fig. 12 be two points on a
curved line, the curve showing
no abrupt change of direction
at the point A.[2]   Now draw
the line, or so-called chord,
AC; then, whether we go
up the curve from A to
C or along the chord
from A to C, we shall

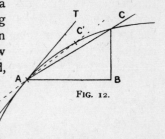

FIG. 12.

have ascended the same vertical piece CB for the same
horizontal distance AB.   The slope of the chord AC

[1] This statement depends on the proportionality of the corresponding sides
of similar triangles (see *Euclid* vi. 4).

[2] A must be in the "middle of continuous curvature," as Newton expresses
it.   This condition is important, but for a full discussion of the steepness of
curves we must refer the reader to pp. 44-7 of Clifford's *Elements of Dynamic*,
part i.

is then termed the *mean* slope of the portion AC of the curve, because, however the steepness may vary from A to C, the final result CB in AB could have been attained by the uniform average slope of AC.

But this idea of mean slope does not settle the actual steepness of the curve, say, at the point A. Now let the reader imagine that the curve AC is a bent piece of wire, and the chord AC a straight piece of wire; further, he must suppose small rings placed about both wires at A and C. In conception we will suppose the wires to be indefinitely thin, so that they approach as closely as we please to the geometrical ideals of curve and line. Then the ring A being held firmly at A on the curved wire, let the ring C be moved along the curved wire towards A. As it moves, the straight wire slips first into the position AC', and ultimately, when the ring C reaches A, takes up the position AT. In this position the straight line is termed the *tangent* to the curved line at the point A. As the slope of AC or AC' measures the mean steepness of the curve from A to C, or from A to C', so does the slope of the chord in its limiting position of touching line, or *tangent*, measure the mean steepness of an indefinitely small part of the curve about A. The slope of the tangent is then said to measure the steepness of the curve *at* A. It is clear that in this notion of measuring the mean for a vanishingly small length of curve we are dealing with a conception which is invaluable as a method of description. It represents, however, a limit which, no more than a curve or line, can be attained in perceptual experience.

§ 11.—*Speed as a Slope.   Velocity*

Having now reached a conception by aid of which we can measure the steepness of a curve at any point—namely, by the slope of the tangent at that point—we may return to the curve of our time-chart and ask what we are to understand by its slope. Turning to Fig. 10, we observe that the mean slope of the portion Q_6Q_7 of

the curve corresponding to the transit from King's Cross
to Gower street is Q_7m in Q_6m, or since Q_7m is equal to
P_6P_7, and Q_6m to t_6t_7, it is P_6P_7 in t_6t_7.   But P_6B_7 is, in a
certain scale, the number of miles between the two
stations, and t_6t_7 is, in another scale, the number of
minutes between the two stations.   Thus the slope, which
with one interpretation is a certain rise in a certain
horizontal length, is with another interpretation a certain
number of miles in a certain number of minutes.   Now a
certain number of miles in a certain number of minutes
is exactly what we understand by the mean or average
speed of the train between King's Cross and Gower
Street ; the train has increased its distance from Aldgate
by so many miles in so many minutes.   The manner
in which change of distance is taking place during any
finite time is thus determined by the slope of the corresponding chord of the time-chart.   The average rate of
change of distance, or the *mean speed* for any given interval,
is thus recorded by the slopes of these chords.

It is clear, however, that by varying the length of the
chord Q_6Q_7—by bringing Q_7 nearer to Q_6, for example—
we shall obtain different mean speeds for different lengths
of the journey after passing King's Cross.   The shorter
we take the time the steeper becomes in this case the
chord, the greater the mean speed.   The conception of a
limit to this mean speed is then formed ; namely, the
mean speed for a vanishingly small time after leaving
King's Cross, and this mean speed is defined as the *actual
speed* of passing King's Cross.   We see at once that the
actual speed will be measured by the slope of the tangent
to the time-chart at Q_6, for this tangent is, according to
our definition, the limit to the chord.   Thus the actual
speed at each instant of the motion is determined by the
steepness at the corresponding point of the time-chart, and
it is measured in miles per minute by the slope of the
tangent at that point.   We thus find that our time-chart
is not only like *Bradshaw*, a time-table, but is also a
diagram of the varying speed of the train throughout its
journey.

There are one or two points about speed which the reader will find it useful to bear in mind. In the first place, speed is a numerical quantity, it is equal to a slope, the unit of which is one vertical unit in or *per* one horizontal unit ; thus the speed unit is one space unit in or *per* one time unit—for example, one mile per minute. Secondly, unless the time-chart has a straight line for its curve, the speed must continually change its magnitude from one point to another of the path. If the curve of the time-chart be a straight line the speed is said to be *uniform*, otherwise it is called *variable*. Lastly, looking back at the map of the path (Fig. 9, p. 237), we see that the *bearing* of the motion as well as the speed varies from point to point of the path. Remembering our definition of tangent we see that the direction of the motion at P is along the tangent at P, and further it has a *sense*—for example, the motion is from P_6 to P_7 and not from P_7 to P_6. Now we see that the change in the motion is of two kinds : change in magnitude, or change in speed, and change in bearing. In order to trace this change still more clearly we form a new conception, namely, that of speed with a certain bearing, and this combination of speed and bearing we term *velocity*. To fully describe the velocity, say at the position P_6, we must therefore combine speed and bearing ; the speed is the slope of the tangent at Q_6 (Fig. 10, p. 240), and, when the units of time and space have been chosen, it is solely a number ; the bearing is the direction of the tangent to the path at P_6 (Fig. 9) together with the sense, namely, from P_6 to P_7. Like displacement, velocity can accordingly be represented by a step, the magnitude of the step measures the speed, the direction of the step shows the direction of the motion, and the arrow-head gives the sense of the motion.

§ 12.—*The Velocity Diagram or Hodograph. Acceleration*

Now, as it is awkward to have to turn to two different figures—the map of the path and the time-chart—in order to determine velocity, we construct a new figure in the following manner : From any point I we draw a series of rays, IV_1, IV_2, IV_3, IV_4, . . . IV_{16}, parallel to the tangents at the successive points P_1, P_2, P_3, . . . P_{16}, and we measure off along the rays in the sense of the motion as many units of length as there are units of speed in the motion at these points.   Each of these rays will, by what precedes, be a step representing the velocity at the corresponding point of the path.   If this be done for a very great

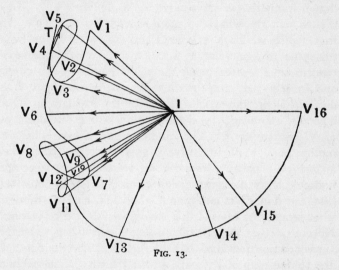

FIG. 13.

number of positions the points V_1, V_2, V_3, etc., will be a series approaching more and more closely to a curve. This curve is termed the *hodograph*, from two Greek words signifying a " description of the path." The name has been somewhat unfortunately chosen, as the curve is not a " description of the path," but a " description of the motion in the path," rather a *kinesigraph* than a hodograph. Fig. 13 is supposed to represent the hodograph of the motion dealt with in our Figs. 9 and 10.[1]   Thus while

[1] The true hodograph would require a great number of points, such as V, to determine its shape at all accurately.   The constant changes in the direction of the railway (see Fig. 9, p. 237) cause the hodograph curve to bend backwards and forwards, while the slight variations of the speed produce the tangles in the curve.

the rays of the map of the path (Fig. 9, p. 237) give the position of P relative to O, the rays of the hodograph give the velocities of P relative to O. So soon as we are in possession of the time–chart and the map of the path we can construct this diagram of the velocities. When constructed it forms an accurate picture of how the motion is changing in both magnitude and direction.

Let us now examine the hodograph a little more closely. It consists of a point or *pole* I and rays IV drawn from this pole to a curve $V_1 V_2 V_3 \ldots V_{16}$. Now this is exactly what the map in Fig. 9 consists of. In that figure we have a pole O and rays OP drawn from this pole to a curve $P_1 P_2 P_3 \ldots P_{16}$. In the course of the motion P passes along the whole length of this curve, and in just the same manner we may look upon V as moving along the whole length of the hodograph-curve. The ray IV would in each position be the displacement of V relative to I. The question now arises : Has the motion of V round its curve any meaning for the motion of P in the path? Suppose we were now to treat the hodograph as the map of a new motion, and to construct first the time-chart and then the hodograph of this motion, what would the rays of this second hodograph represent ? Now a sort of logical rule-of-three sum will give us the answer to this question. As the rays of the first hodograph are to the map of the path, so are the rays of the second hodograph to the map of V's motion. But we have seen that the rays of the first hodograph measure the velocities of P in its path, and that these velocities are a fitting measure of how the ray OP, or the position of P relative to O, is changing. Hence it follows that the rays of the second hodograph would measure the velocities of V in the first hodograph, and that these velocities are a fitting measure of how the ray IV or the velocity of P relative to O is changing. Thus the velocity of V along the hodograph is the measure of how the velocity of P relative to O is changing. This velocity of V, or change in the velocity of P, is termed *acceleration*, and we see that a diagram of accelerations may be obtained by drawing the hodograph of the velocity-diagram, treated as if it were itself the map of an independent motion. Acceleration therefore stands in just the same relation to velocity as velocity stands to the position-step. As change of position is represented by the steps drawn as rays of the velocity-diagram or first hodograph, so change of velocity is represented by the steps drawn as rays of the acceleration-diagram or second hodograph.[1] Whatever may be demonstrated of the position-step and velocity will still hold good if the words position-step and velocity be replaced by the words velocity and acceleration respectively.

§ 13.—*Acceleration as a Spurt and a Shunt*

We must now investigate somewhat more closely this notion of acceleration as a proper measure of the change in velocity. In a certain interval of time the speed of the point P (Fig. 9, 237) changes from a number of miles per minute represented by the number of linear units in IV_4 to the number of miles per minute represented by the linear units in IV_5, the speed has in this case (see Fig. 13) quickened, or there has been what we may term a *spurt* in the speed. Further, the bearing of the motion has changed ; instead of the point P moving in the direction IV_4, it now moves in the direction IV_5 that is to say, the direction of the motion has received a *shunt*. Thus the total change in the velocity of P as it moves from P_4 to P_5 consists of a spurt and a shunt. When a train quickens its speed from 40 to 60 miles an hour, and instead of running due north runs north-east, we may describe its motion as spurted and shunted ; technically, we say that its velocity has been *accelerated*. Acceleration has thus two fundamental factors—the spurt and the shunt.[2] If we consider the perceptual world around us, it is clear

[1] We might proceed in the same manner to measure the change in acceleration by drawing a third hodograph. Fortunately this third hodograph is rarely, if ever, wanted. The concepts which practically suffice to describe our perceptual experiences of change are position, velocity and acceleration.

[2] Spurt in scientific language includes a retardation or slackening of speed as a negative spurt.

that the spurting and shunting of motion are conceptions as important for describing our everyday experience as those of the speed and direction of motion itself.

We have seen that the speed changes from the length IV_4 to the length IV_5 in a certain time—namely the time represented by the length t_4t_5 of our time-chart (Fig. 10). The increase of speed per unit of time (or the ratio of the difference of IV_5 and IV_4 to t_4t_5) is termed the *mean speed-acceleration* or the *mean spurt* between P_4 and P_5. Further, the ray IV has been turned from IV_4 to IV_5, or through the angle V_4IV_5 in time t_4t_5. This increase of angle per unit time (or the ratio of the angle V_4IV_5 to t_4t_5) is termed the *mean shunt*, or *mean spin of direction* between the positions P_4 and P_5. The two combined, or the mean rate of spurting and shunting, form what is termed the *mean acceleration* during the given change of position, or for the given time (t_4t_5). What we measure, therefore, in acceleration is the *rate* at which spurting and shunting take place. Turning to Fig. 13 the reader must notice that there are two processes by aid of which we can conceive the velocity IV_4 converted into IV_5. In the first process we follow the method just discussed : we stretch IV_4 till it is as long as IV_5, that is, we increase the speed from its value in the position P_4 to its value in the position P_5; then we spin the stretched length round I till it takes up the position IV_5. This is the spurt and shunt conception of acceleration. In the second process we say add the step V_4V_5 to the step IV_4 and we shall reach the step IV_5 (pp. 237-238)—that is to say, we can consider the new velocity IV_5 obtained from the old velocity IV_4 by adding the step or velocity V_4V_5 by the parallelogram law. The mean acceleration is in this case expressed by the step V_4V_5 added in the given interval t_4t_5. But if we compare Figs. 9 and 13 as maps for the motions of P and V we shall see that adding V_4V_5 in time t_4t_5 corresponds to adding P_4P_5 in time t_4t_5. The latter operation, however, led us, by aid of the time-chart, from the idea of mean speed or mean change in OP to the idea of actual speed or instantaneous change in OP at

P_4; the instantaneous change in OP_4 was in the direction of the tangent at P_4, and was measured by the slope of the time-chart at Q_4 (see Fig. 10). In precisely the same manner the instantaneous change in IV_4 will be along the tangent at V_4, and will be measured by the slope of the time-chart *for V's motion* at the corresponding point. Thus actual acceleration appears, as in our first discussion of the matter, as the velocity of V along the hodograph. Now, however close V_5 is to V_4, whether we give a stretch and a spin or add the small step V_4V_5, the final result of the two processes will be the same. Hence we can either look upon actual acceleration as the velocity of V along the hodograph, or as the combined mode in which IV is being actually stretched and spun.[1] Either method of treating acceleration leads to the same result, and both possess special advantages for describing various phases of motion.

In the first case actual acceleration is represented by a step ; the bearing of this step denotes the direction and sense in which V is moving, or the velocity with which IV is changing ; the number of units of length in this step denotes the number of units of speed with which V is moving, or the number of units of speed being actually added per unit of time in the given direction to the velocity IV of P. By "added in the given direction" we are to understand that the increments of velocity are to be added geometrically or by the parallelogram law (*e.g.* $IV_5 = IV_4 + V_4V_5$, and this however small V_4V_5 may be in conception).

§ 14.—*Curvature*

In the spurt and shunt method of regarding acceleration, on the other hand, actual acceleration will be specified by two factors : (1) the rate at which velocity is being spurted or IV being stretched ; (2) the rate at which velocity is being shunted or IV being spun about I (Fig.

[1] What we have here stated of acceleration applies just as much to change of position. Turning to Fig. 9, we may look upon the change of position of OP as measured by the velocity of P along its path, or by the manner in which OP is being actually stretched and spun.

13, p. 247). As in the first case the direction of actual acceleration at V_4 is that of V_4T or the tangent at V_4, it is clear that as a rule acceleration will not be in the direction of velocity,[1] but will act partly in the direction of velocity and partly at right-angles to it. This result is so important that the reader will, I hope, pardon me for considering it from a slightly different standpoint. Let us imagine the acceleration to be such that throughout it never stretches IV, and let us try to analyse this case a little more closely. Obviously if IV be never stretched, if the speed be never spurted, the point V can only describe

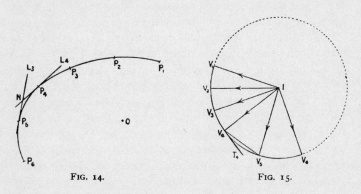

FIG. 14.   FIG. 15.

a circle, for IV remains uniform in length. Uniform speed can, however, be conceived associated with a point moving in any curved path whatever. Let Fig. 14 represent this path, and let Fig. 15 be the circular hodograph, corresponding points of the two curves being denoted by the same subscript numerals attached to the letters P and V.

Now, since all the acceleration in this case depends upon the change in the direction of motion, or the change in the direction of the tangent to the path, we must stay for a moment to consider how this change in direction, or the *bending* of the path may be scientifically described and measured. Now if we pass, for example, from the

---

[1] At V_3, for example, IV_3 appears to coincide with the direction of the tangent at V_3. In this case the whole effect of acceleration is instantaneously to spurt without shunting.

point P_4 to P_5 on the path, and P_4L_4, P_5L_5 be the tangents (p. 252) at P_4, P_5 respectively, then the direction of the curve has continuously altered from P_4L_4 to P_5L_5 as we traverse the length P_4P_5 of the curve. The angle between these directions is L_4NL_5, and clearly the greater this angle for a given length of curve P_4P_5, the greater will be the amount of bending.[1] The amount of angle through which the tangent has been turned for a given length of curve

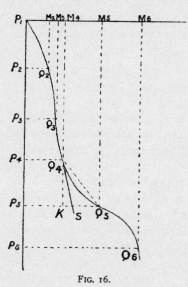

FIG. 16.

forms a fit measure of the total amount of bending in that length. Accordingly we define the mean bending or *mean curvature* of the element of curve P_4P_5 as the ratio of the number of units of angle in L_4NL_5 to the number of units of length in the element of curve P_4P_5. Thus the mean curvature of any portion of a curve is the average turn of its tangent per unit length of the curve. From the mean curvature we can reach a conception of *actual curvature* as a limit when the element of arc P_4P_5 is very small in just

---

[1] We are supposing here that the sense of the bending between P_4 and P_5 does not change, that the curve is not like this : ∽. We can always ensure that no such change takes place by taking a sufficiently small length of arc.

the same manner as from mean speed we reached a conception of actual speed. This process of reaching a limit in conception, which cannot be really attained in perception, is so important that we will again consider it for this special case, in order that the reader may have little difficulty henceforth in discovering and discussing such limits for himself. Let us accordingly suppose the distances between the points P_1, P_2, P_3, . . . P_6 plotted off (Fig. 16) down a vertical line as in the time-chart of Fig. 10 (p. 240). Along the horizontal line P_1M_6 instead of assuming units of length to represent units of time, let them represent units of angle,[1] and let the number of units taken from P_1 represent successively the number of units of angle between the tangents P_2L_2, P_3L_3, P_4L_4, etc., in Fig. 14 (p. 252), and the tangent to the curve at P_1. Thus let P_1M_4 represent the angle between the tangents at P_1 and at P_4; P_1M_5 that between the tangents at P_1 and at P_5, and so on. Now draw in Fig. 16 vertical lines through the points M_2, M_3, etc., and horizontal lines through the points P_2, P_3, etc., and suppose these lines pair and pair to meet in the points Q_2, Q_3, etc. We have then a series of points Q, which increase in number as we increase the points P in Fig. 14, and in conception ultimately give us the curve marked in Fig. 16 by the continuous line. The diagram thus obtained is a chart of the bending or curvature in Fig. 14. For, the mean curvature in the length P_4P_5 is the ratio of the angle L_4NL_5 to the length P_4P_5 in Fig. 14, or, what is the same thing, the ratio of the number of

---

[1] According to *Euclid* iii. 29 and vi. 33, the angles at the centre of a circle which stand on equal arcs are themselves equal; if we double or treble the arc we must double or treble the angle; the arc is thus seen to be a fit measure of the angle. Further (Clifford's *Common Sense of the Exact Sciences*, pp. 123-5), the arcs of different circles subtending equal angles at their respective centres are easily shown to be in the ratio of their radii. If, therefore, we take as our standard circle for measuring angles the circle whose radius is the unit of length, its arc c for any given angle will be to the arc a of a circle of radius r subtending the same angle in the ratio of 1 to r, or in the form of a proportion, $c : a :: 1 : r$, whence it follows that $c = a/r$, or the *circular measure* c of any angle, is the ratio of the arc a subtended by this angle at the centre of any circle to the radius r of this circle. The unit of angle in circular measure will therefore be one for which a equals r, or which subtends an arc equal to the radius. This unit is termed a *radian*, and is generally used in theoretical investigations.

units in M_4M_5 to the number in P_4P_5 in Fig. 16. But if Q_4K be drawn parallel to M_5Q_5 to meet P_5Q_5 in K, this ratio is that of KQ_5 to Q_4K, or is the *slope* of the chord Q_4Q_5 to the *vertical* line P_1P_6. Thus the slope of any chord of the curvative-chart to the vertical measures the mean curvature of the corresponding portion of the curve in Fig. 14. When we make the chord Q_4Q_5 smaller and smaller by causing Q_5 to move towards Q_4, the mean curvature becomes more and more nearly the mean curvature at and about P_4; but as on p. 243 the chord becomes more and more nearly the tangent at Q_4. As we have defined actual curvature to be the limit to the mean curvature in a vanishingly small length of curve beyond P_4 (see Fig. 14), we see that the actual curvature at P_4 is the slope to the vertical of the tangent Q_4S at the corresponding point Q_4 of the curvature-chart. This slope, and accordingly the actual curvature, is therefore a measurable quantity at each point of any curve.[1]

§ 15.—*The Relation between Curvature and Normal Acceleration*

Returning again to Figs. 14 and 15, we note that the mean curvature over the length P_4P_5 is the ratio of the number of angle units in L_4NL_5 to the number of length units in the element of curve P_4P_5. Now the speed in

[1] The mean curvature over any arc *ab* of a circle centre O is the ratio of the angle between the tangents at its extremities, or—what is the same thing, since the tangents are perpendicular to the radii O*a* and O*b*—of the angle *aOb* at the centre to the arc *ab*. But we have seen in the footnote, p. 254, that the measure of this angle in *radians* is the ratio of the arc *ab* to the radius. Hence it follows that the mean curvature of a circle is equal to the inverse of the radius (or unity divided by the radius). As this mean curvature is therefore independent of the length of the arc, it follows that the actual curvature at each point must be the same and be equal

FIG. 17.

to the inverse of the radius. Since the radius of a circle can take every value from zero to infinity, a circle can always be found which has the same amount of bending as a curve at a given point, and thus fits it more closely at that point than a circle of any other radius. The radius of this circle is termed the *radius of curvature* of the curve at the given point. Hence the curvature of a curve is the inverse of its radius of curvature.

the length P_4P_5 is constant and equal to IV_4; hence if the point P traverse this length in a number of minutes, which we will represent by the letter t, we must have, since speed is the number of units of length per minute, the length P_4P_5 equal to the product of IV_4 and t (or in symbols $P_4P_5 = IV_4 \times t$). Further, since the angle L_4NL_5 is turned through by the tangent also in time t, the ratio of the angle L_4NL_5 to t is the mean rate at which the tangent is turning round in the time t, or is the *mean spin* of the tangent (or, if the mean spin be denoted by the letter S, we have in symbols $\angle L_4NL_5 = S \times t$). From these results it follows at once that the mean curvature which is the ratio of L_4NL_5 to P_4P_5 must be equally the ratio of the mean spin S to the mean speed IV_4. Thus we have directly connected motion with curvature.

Proceeding in conception to the limit we have the important kinematic result that : *If a point moves along a curve the ratio of the spin of the tangent to the speed of the point is the actual curvature at each situation of the point.*

It remains to connect this result with the acceleration. The acceleration in the case we are dealing with is the velocity of V along its circle (Fig. 15). This acceleration at V_4, for example is along the tangent V_4T_4 to the circle, or at right-angles to IV_4 the direction of the velocity of P (Fig. 14) ; it has thus, as we have seen, purely a shunting and no spurting effect. Now, since IV_4 and IV_5 were drawn parallel to the directions of motion L_4P_4, L_5P_5 at P_4 and P_5 respectively, it follows that the angles L_4NL_5 and V_4IV_5—between two pairs of parallel lines—must be equal. Hence the mean spin of the tangent from P_4 to P_5 must be the ratio of the angle V_4IV_5 to the time t in which P passes from P_4 to P_5, or, what is the same thing, in which V passes from V_4 to V_5. But the magnitude of the angle V_4IV_5 is (see the footnote, p. 254) the ratio of the arc V_4V_5 to the radius IV_4. Further, the ratio of the arc V_4V_5 to the time t is the mean speed of V from V_4 to V_5 (p. 245). Thus it follows that the mean spin of the tangent (Fig. 14) is the ratio of the mean speed of V to the radius IV_4. If we take P_5 closer and closer to P_4, and therefore V_5 to V_4, mean values become the actual values at P_4 and V_4; we therefore conclude that the actual spin of the tangent at P_4 is the ratio of the actual speed of V at V_4 to IV_4, or, in other words, to the speed of P. Thus the spin of the tangent is the ratio of the speed of V to the speed of P. But the speed of V is the magnitude of the acceleration, which in this case is all shunt. Hence we conclude that the rate of shunting at P is properly measured by the product of the spin of the tangent and the speed of P (or in symbols, shunt acceleration $= S \times U$, U being the speed of P). But we have seen above that the curvature is the ratio of the spin of the tangent to the speed of P (or in symbols curvature $= S/U$). Combining, accordingly, these two results we see that the shunt acceleration in this case is properly measured by the product of curvature and the square of the speed.[1] This acceleration takes place in the direction $V_4 T_4$, or is perpendicular to the direction of motion at P.

A little consideration will show the reader that the expression we have deduced for the acceleration perpendicular to the motion would not be altered were the speed to vary between P_4 and P_5. For, returning to Fig. 13, we note that IV_4 is to be changed to IV_5. This can be conceived as accomplished in the following two stages (p. 250): (i.) rotate IV_4 round I without changing its length into the position IV_5; (ii.) stretch IV_4 in its new position into IV_5. The first stage corresponds to the type of motion we have just dealt with, or shunt acceleration without spurt; the second stage to the case of spurt acceleration without shunt. In the limit when IV_5 is indefinitely close to IV_4, the first stage gives us the element of acceleration *perpendicular* to the direction of motion, and the second stage the element of acceleration in the direction of motion. By the above reasoning the former

---

[1] If r be the radius of curvature (see the footnote, p. 255), then $1/r$ will be the curvature, and if we term this element of acceleration *normal acceleration*, we have, by the above results, the three equivalent values : normal acceleration $= \dfrac{U^2}{r} = S \times U = rS^2$.

is seen to be measured by the product of the square of the speed and the curvature.

§ 16.—*Fundamental Propositions in the Geometry of Motion*

We are now in a position, after restating our results, to draw one or two important conclusions.

Acceleration has spurt and shunt components.

The spurt acceleration takes place in the direction of motion, and is measured by the rate at which speed is being increased (or, it may be, decreased).

The shunt acceleration takes place perpendicular to the direction of motion, and is measured by the product of the curvature and the square of the speed.

These two kinds of acceleration are usually spoken of as *speed acceleration* and *normal acceleration*.

From these results we conclude that :—

1. If a point be not accelerated it will describe, with regard to the given frame of reference for which the acceleration is measured, a straight line with uniform speed. For there will be no spurt, and therefore the speed must be uniform, and there will be no shunt, and therefore the path must have zero curvature, but the only path without bending is a straight line. Neither uniform speed nor zero curvature *alone* denotes an absence of acceleration.

2. When a point is constrained to move in a given path the normal acceleration may be determined in each position from the speed and the form of the path, *i.e.* from its curvature of bending. In this case the problem is to find the speed from the speed acceleration.

3. When a point is free to move in a given plane, then its motion can be theoretically determined, if we know its velocity in any one position, and its acceleration for all positions. For from the normal acceleration and the speed we can calculate the initial amount of bending of the path ; thus the initial form of the path is known. For a closely adjacent position on this initial form, we

can determine from the speed acceleration the change in speed due to this change of position. Hence we obtain the speed in the new position. From the speed in the new position and the normal acceleration in this position, the bending in the next little element of path may be deduced. This process may be repeated as often as we please, till the whole path of the motion is constructed. The succession of positions may be taken so close together that we obtain the form of the path to any degree of accuracy required. Knowing the path and the speed at each point of it we are able to construct a time-chart like that of our Fig. 10 (p. 240). For we know from the speeds the slope at each point of the Q-curve. Hence we commence by drawing a little element, say P_1Q_2, at the slope given by the initial speed; this element by aid of the horizontal Q_2P_2, through its terminal Q_2, gives a new position at distance P_1P_2 from the initial position; the speed in this new position determines the slope of the next little element Q_2Q_3 of the curve; Q_3 by aid of the horizontal Q_3P_3 gives a third position with a third speed and so a slope for the third element, and this process can be continued till we have constructed the time-chart by a succession of little elements. By taking these elements sufficiently small, we make the resulting polygonal line differ as little from the true curve of the time-chart as we please. Now we have seen that when the map of the path and the time-chart are known, the motion has been fully described. Thus we conclude that : *Given the velocity of a point in any position and the acceleration of the point in all positions, the motion of the point is fully determined.*[1]

This proposition really indicates the basis of the whole of our mechanical description of the universe. Rightly interpreted, it contains all that we can assert of the

---

[1] The methods by which we have shown that the initial velocity and position, together with the acceleration in all positions, determine the map of the path and the time-chart, are only theoretical methods of construction. The practical methods of constructing these curves involve the highest refinements of mathematical analysis. Our object here is only to show that the motion is theoretically determined by a knowledge of the above quantities.

" mechanical determinism " of nature ; wrongly interpreted, it is the foundation of that crude materialism which pictures the universe as an aggregate of objective material bodies, enforcing for all eternity certain motions on each other, and a perception of those motions upon us.   What the proposition exactly tells us is this : that a motion is fully determined, that is, can be conceptually described, either by giving the path and the time to each position of the path, or by giving the velocity in any one position and the acceleration in all positions.   We are really dealing with two different modes of *describing* motion, either of which can be deduced from the other, but neither of which *explains* why the motion takes place, or can be said to " determine " it in the sense of the materialists.

§ 17.—*The Relativity of Motion.   Its Synthesis from Simple Components*

There still remains a matter to which it is needful to draw the reader's attention.   The whole motion of our point P (Fig 9, p. 237) has been considered relative to a point O and a particular frame.   We started with a position relative to O, and it follows that the velocity and acceleration we have been discussing describe changes of motion relative to O and its frame also.   The *absolute* velocity and *absolute* acceleration are seen to be as meaningless as absolute position.   If the points O and P were *both* to have their motions accelerated in the same manner the relative path would not be changed—any more than the map (Fig. 9) is changed by our moving about, in any manner we please, the page on which it is printed.   But the fact that all motion is relative leads us at once to the very natural question : How are we to pass from the motion of a point relative to one pole O to motion relative to a second pole O′, the bearing being measured with regard to the same frame.   We must look at this point somewhat closely, for it involves some important consequences.

Let us suppose the motion of P relative to O known,

and the motion of O' relative to O known, we require to find the motion of P relative to O'. Let P_1, P_2 (Fig. 18) be two successive positions of P relative to O, and O'_1, O'_2 the corresponding positions of O'. Then $O'_1 P_1$ is the first and $O'_2 P_2$ is the second step, measuring the position of P relative to O'. From O'_1 draw $O'_1 P'_2$ parallel and equal to $O'_2 P_2$, then $O'_1 P_1$ and $O'_1 P_2$ give the relative motion of P with regard to O_1, and the relative displacement in the given interval is $P_1 P'_2$. Now draw $O'_1 O_2$ parallel and equal to $O'_2 O$, then $O'_1 O$, and $O'_2 O$, or $O'_1 O_2$, give the relative positions of O with regard to O'.

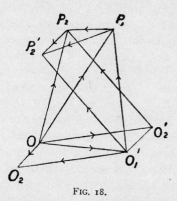

FIG. 18.

But by the equality of opposite sides of parallelograms OO_2 equals $O'_2 O'_1$, equals $P_2 P'_2$. Hence $P_2 P'_2$ is equal to the displacement of O relative to O'. But in the geometry of steps (p. 237) :—

$$P_1 P'_2 = P_1 P_2 + P_2 P'_2,$$

or in words: the displacement of P relative to O' is equal to the displacement of P relative to O added *geometrically* to the displacement of O relative to O'. Now this result is true, however large or small these displacements may be, and these displacements divided by the number of units in the interval of time which is the same for all of them, represent the mean velocites in this interval. Hence we conclude that: the mean velocity of P relative to O' is equal to the mean velocity of P relative to O added *geometrically* to the mean velocity of O relative to O'. If we take the interval of time, and consequently the displacements, smaller and smaller, mean velocities become in the limit the actual velocities. These actual velocities have always the direction of the displacements $P_1P'_2$, P_1P_2, and OO_2, which ultimately from chords become tangents to the corresponding paths; further, since the interval of time is the same for all the displacements, the magnitudes or speed of these velocities are always proportional to the sides $P_1P'_2$, P_1P_2, and $P_2P'_2$ (or OO_2) of the triangle $P_1P'_2P_2$. Hence the mean velocities and ultimately the actual velocities always form the three sides of a triangle which has its sides parallel and proportional to the sides of the triangle $P_1P'_2P_2$, and this however small the latter triangle becomes. The actual velocity of P relative to O' thus forms one side of a triangle of which the actual velocities of P relative to O and of O relative to O' form the other two sides. In other words, the actual velocity of P relative to O' is obtained from the actual velocities of P relative to O and of O relative to O' by adding them geometrically, or by the *parallelogram law*. Just as the position of P relative to O' was found by applying the parallelogram law to the steps $O'O$ and OP (p. 238), so we obtain the velocity of P relative to O' by applying the same law to the velocities of P relative to O and of O relative to O'. A very similar proof shows us that the acceleration of P relative to O' may be obtained in the same way from the accelerations of P relative to O and O relative to O'. We thus obtain an easy rule—that of the parallelogram law—for passing from the motion of P relative to O to that of P relative to O'.

The whole of this discussion may be looked at from a somewhat different standpoint. We may suppose the plane of the paper in which the motion of P about O takes place to be always moved as a whole so that the point O' remains stationary. In order to do this we must always be shifting the paper so that O'_2 falls back on O'

and $O'_2O'_1$ will measure the fitting shift of the paper. This carries P_2 clearly forward to P'_2 and O to O_2. Thus the motion of P relative to O' may be looked at as the motion of P due to two sources—a movement of P about O, and a movement of the plane containing P and O ; this later motion is the motion of O about O', or is equal and opposite to the perfectly arbitrary motion of O' about O. Thus we conclude that if a point P has two independent velocities (corresponding to the limits of the displacements P_1P_2 and $P_2P'_2$) then the actual velocity of P will be found by adding these velocities geometrically. This statement is usually termed the *parallelogram of velocities*. A precisely similar statement holds for independent accelerations (p. 239), and is called the *parallelogram of accelerations*. To these important results we shall have occasion again to refer. We conclude, therefore, with the general statement that the independent displacements, the independent velocities, and the independent accelerations of a moving point are respectively added geometrically as we add steps, or by the so-called parallelogram law.

The value of this rule of combination lies in the power it gives us of building up complex cases of motion from simple cases. If we find as a result of experience that the perceptual antecedents[1] of a motion we describe by one acceleration may be superposed on the perceptual antecedents of a motion we describe by a second acceleration—without it being necessary to alter the values of these accelerations (at any rate to our degree of refinement in appreciating change) when describing the motion corresponding to the combined antecedents,—then the parallelogram of accelerations will be invaluable as a mode of *synthesis*, or of constructing the complex from the simple. The law of gravitation applied to the

---

[1] By " perceptual antecedents of motion " we are to understand *cause* in the scientific sense, but the word has not been used in the above paragraph, because the reader might have supposed the cause of motion to be the metaphysical (and imperceptible) entity *force*, whereas it really lies in a *perceptible* relationship, *i.e.* the relativity in perceptual space (Chap. VIII. § 5).

planetary theory is a striking example of the value of such a synthesis.

In this chapter we have seen how the relative position, velocity, and acceleration of points may be defined, described, and measured. We have been gleaning wholly in the conceptual field of geometrical ideals. We have next to ask how these conceptions may be applied to describe our perceptual experience of change in the world of phenomena. How are these three factors, position, velocity, and acceleration, related to each other in that ideal dance of corpuscles to which we reduce the physical universe, in that atomic waltz by aid of which we describe and resume our sense-impressions? How do we conceive the relative position of these corpuscles to change? How are their speeds and directions of motion varying? Does experience show us that relative position produces a definite speed, or a definite spurt and shunt? The answer to these questions lies in the so-called properties of matter and in the laws of motion which will be the topics of our two following chapters.

SUMMARY

1. All the notions by aid of which we describe and measure change are *geometrical*, and thus are not real perceptual limits. They are forms distinguishing and classifying the contents of our perceptual experience under the mixed mode of motion. The principal of these forms are point-motion, spin of a rigid body and strain. Motion is found to be relative, never absolute ; for example, it is meaningless to speak of the motion of a point without reference to what system the motion of the point is considered with regard to.

2. An analysis of point-motion leads us to the conceptions of velocity and acceleration, the first as a proper measure of the manner in which position is instantaneously changing, the second as a proper measure of how velocity itself is changing. It is found that a motion is fully determined, or theoretically a complete description of the path and position at each instant of time may be deduced, when the velocity in any one position and the acceleration for all positions are given.

3. The parallelogram law as the general rule for combining motions is the foundation of the synthesis by which complex motions are constructed out of simple motions.

LITERATURE

CLERK-MAXWELL, J.—Matter and Motion, chaps. i. and ii.   London, 1876.

CLIFFORD, W. K.—The Common Sense of the Exact Sciences, chap. iv. "Position," and chap. v. "Motion"; London, 1885.   Also for a more advanced treatment the same writer's Elements of Dynamic, part i. book i. chaps. i. and ii.; book ii. chaps. i. and ii.; book iii. chap. i.; London, 1878.

MACGREGOR, J. G.—An elementary Treatise on Kinematics and Dynamics, part i. "Kinematics," chaps. i.-iii., v. and vii. ; London, 1887.

CHAPTER VIII

MATTER

§ 1.—"*All things move*"—*but only in Conception*

AN old Greek philosopher, who lived perhaps some five hundred years B.C., chose as the dictum in which he summed up his teaching the phrase: "*All things flow.*" After-ages, not understanding what Heraclitus meant—it is doubtful whether he understood himself—dubbed him "Heraclitus the Obscure." But to-day we find modern science almost repeating Heraclitus' dictum when it says: "*All things are in motion.*" Like all dicta which briefly resume wide truths, this dictum of modern science requires expanding and explaining if it is not to be misinterpreted. By the words "All things are in motion" we are to understand that, step by step, science has found it possible to describe our experience of perceptual changes by types of relative motion: this motion being that of the ideal points, the ideal rigid bodies, or the ideal strainable media which stand for us as the signs or symbols of the real world of sense-impressions. We interpret, describe, and resume the sequences of this real world of sense-impressions by discussing the relative positions, velocities, accelerations, rotations, spins, and strains of an ideal geometrical world which stands for us as a conceptual representation of the perceptual world. In our Chapter V. we saw that space and time did not themselves correspond to actual perceptions, but were *modes* under which we perceived, and by which we discriminated, groups of sense-impressions. So motion as the combination of space with time is essentially a *mode* of perception, and not in itself a perception (p. 193). The more clearly this is realised the better able the reader will be to appreciate that the " motion of bodies " is not a reality of perception, but is the conceptual manner in which we represent this mode of perception and by aid of which we describe changes in groups of sense-impressions ; the perceptual reality is the complexity and variety of the sense-impressions which crowd into the telephonic brain-exchange. That the results which flow from the conceptual world of geometrical motions agree so closely with our perceptual experience of the outside world of phenomena (p. 65) is a phase of that accordance between the perceptive and reasoning faculties upon which I have laid stress in an earlier part of this volume (p. 103).

Wherein lies the advance from Heraclitus to the modern scientist ? Why was the dictum of one not unjustly termed obscure, while the other claims—and rightly claims—to find in the development of his dictum the sole basis for our knowledge of the physical universe ? The difference lies in this : Heraclitus left his flow undescribed and unmeasured, while modern science devotes its best energies to the accurate investigation and analysis of each and every type of motion which can possibly be used as a means of describing and resuming any sequence of sense - impressions. The whole object of physical science is the discovery of ideal elementary motions which will enable us to describe in the simplest language the widest ranges of phenomena ; it lies in the symbolisation of the physical universe by aid of the geometrical motions of a group of geometrical forms. To do this is to construct the world mechanically;[1] but this mechanism, be it noted, is a product of conception, and does not lie in our perceptions themselves (p. 115). Startling as it may appear to the reader, when first stated, it is nevertheless true that the mind struggles in vain to clearly realise the motion of anything which is neither a geo-

[1] This word is here used in the scientific sense of Kirchhoff, and not in the popular sense of Mr. Gladstone : see pp. 114 and 116.

metrical point nor a body bounded by continuous surfaces ; the mind absolutely rebels against the notion of anything moving but these conceptual creations, which are limits, unrealisable, as we have seen, in the field of perception. If the world of phenomena be, as the materialists would have us to believe, a world of moving bodies like the conceptual world by which science symbolises it, if we are to assert the perceptual existence of atom and ether, then in both cases we are incapable of considering the ultimate element which moves as anything but a perceptual realisation of geometrical ideals. Yet, so far as our *sensible* experience goes, these geometrical ideals have no phenomenal existence ! We have clearly, then, no right to infer as a basis of perception things which our whole experience up to the present shows us exist solely in the field of conception. It is absolutely illogical to fill up a void in our perceptual experience by projecting into it a load of conceptions utterly unlike the adjacent perceptual strata. It is " a profound psychological mistake," says George Henry Lewes, " to assert that whenever we can form clear ideas, not in themselves contradictory, these ideas must of necessity represent truths of nature."[1] The reader will, we feel certain, find it impossible to conceive anything other than geometrical ideals as the moving element at the basis of phenomena. The attempt, however, to conceive something else is worth the making, for it inevitably leads us to the conclusion that the term " moving body " is not scientific when applied to perceptual experience. In external perception (p. 183) we have sense-impressions and more or less permanent groupings of sense-impressions. These sense-impressions vary, dissolve, form new groups—that is, they *change*. Of the universe as contained in messages received at the brain telephonic exchange, or of groups of sense-impressions, we cannot assert motion—objects appear, disappear, and reappear ; sense-impressions alter and modify their grouping. Change is the right word to apply to them rather

[1] See especially §§ 69, 69a, and 108 of his *Aristotle : a Chapter from the History of Science*. London, 1864.

than motion. It is in the field of conception solely that we can properly talk of the motion of bodies ; it is there, and there only, that geometrical forms change their position in absolute time—that is, *move*. In the field of perception motion is but a popular expression to describe the mixed mode in which we discriminate and distinguish groups of sense-impressions.

§ 2.—*The Three Problems*

That we speak of the motion of bodies as a fact of perceptual experience is largely due to the constructive elements associated with immediate sense-impression [1] (p. 41). These constructive elements are drawn from our conceptual notions of change, which again flow very naturally from a limited perception ; a deeper perceptual experience is required to demonstrate their purely ideal character (p. 197). But the reader will, perhaps, hardly be prepared to accept the conclusion that change is perceptual, motion conceptual, without closer analysis. This analysis may be summed up in the three questions : *What is it that moves ? Why does it move ? How does it move ?*

In the first place we must settle whether we are asking these questions of the conceptual or of the perceptual sphere. If it be of the former, the world of symbolic motions by aid of which science describes the sequences of our sense-impressions, then these questions are easy to answer. The things which move are points, rigid bodies and strainable media, geometrical concepts one and all. To ask why they move is to ask why we form conceptions at all, and ultimately to question why science exists. Finally, the manner in which they move is that which enables us most effectually to describe the results of our perceptual experience.

[1] The writer is not objecting to the current use of such expressions as "the sun moves" or "the train moves." Both do move—in conception ; in perception there is a change of sense-impressions. So soon as space is recognised as a mode of perception, and not itself a phenomenon, this conclusion cannot be avoided.

If we turn to the perceptual sphere and ask what it is that moves and why it moves, we are compelled to confess ourselves utterly incapable of finding any answers whatever. *Ignorabimus*, we shall always be ignorant, say some scientists. That we are really ignorant will be the theme of the present chapter, but I believe that this ignorance does not arise from the limitation of our perceptive or reasoning faculties. It is rather due to our having asked unanswerable questions. We may legitimately ask why the complex of our sense-impressions changes, but, according to the views expressed above, motion is not a reality of perception, and it is therefore, for the sphere of perception, idle to ask what moves and why it moves. With the growth of more accurate insight into the conceptual nature of motion these questions will, I believe, be dismissed like the older questions as to the blue milk of the witches and the influence of the stars (p. 22). With their dismissal, however, physical science will be for ever relieved of the metaphysical difficulties as to matter and force which it has inherited from the old scholastic traditions. *Ignorabimus*, therefore, does not seem the true answer to the first two questions ; it may be a true answer to the problem of changes in sense-impression (see our pp. 107 and 268). The third question—How do things move ?—also wants restating to be of any real value, and when restated it merges in the same question asked of the conceptual sphere. What, we must ask, are the conceptual types of motion best suited to describe the stages of our perceptual experience ? The answer to this question forms the subject-matter of our next chapter.

Some of my readers may feel inclined to consider that in this discussion we are entirely deserting the plane of common sense. What moves ? Why, natural bodies move, they will say, is the common-sense answer. But common sense is often a name for intellectual apathy. Being inquisitive, we naturally ask what these bodies consist in, and probably shall be told that they are quantities of *matter*. Still persisting with our questions we ask : What, then, is matter ? It will not do to put us off with the reply that matter is that which moves. All we should, then, have done would be to give a name to the moving thing, but in doing so we should not have succeeded in defining or describing it. The reader may, perhaps, imagine that insight into the nature of matter will be gained by consulting the accepted text-books of science. Let us accordingly examine the statements of one or two.

§ 3.—*How the Physicists define Matter*

A first writer says: "*Matter is a primary conception of the human mind,*" and more than one elementary text-book provides us with practically the same definition. Now the obscurity and paralogism of this statement can only be equalled by the perversities of the metaphysicians.[1] Matter, we are told, is what moves in the phenomenal world, and if it were asserted that matter is a primary *perception* of the human mind we might be no wiser, but at any rate the statement would not be without sense. But perhaps the phrase is not to be taken literally as signifying that a primary conception actually moves among perceptions, but only that we can form intuitively a conception of what moves perceptually—that the perceptual actually corresponds to the conceptual. In this case we are again thrown back on the fact that conceptual motion is a motion of geometrical ideals, and that these correspond in no accurate sense to our perceptions. Indeed, if matter be a conception at all, like the conception of a circle it ought to be a clear and definite idea, whereas the reader

---

[1] "Matter," says Hegel, "is the mere abstract or indeterminate reflection-into-something-else, or reflection-into-self at the same time as determinate ; it is consequently Thinghood which then and there is,—the subsistence or substratum of the thing. By this means the thing finds in the matters its reflection-into-self ; it subsists not in its own self, but in the matters, and is only a superficial association between them, or an external bond over them " (*The Logic of Hegel*, translated by W. Wallace, Oxford, 1874, p. 202). We may smile over such absurdities, but that they should be taught in the last decade of the nineteenth century in our universities, and this to immature minds, and largely at the public expense, is a cause for sorrow rather than amusement. The much-abused schoolmen never rivalled these Hegelian quagmires even before they were transferred to English soil.

who will honestly ask himself what he *conceives* by matter will find that an answer is impossible, or that in attempting one he is sinking deeper and deeper into the metaphysical quagmire.

Proceeding further, we naturally turn to the little work termed *Matter and Motion* by Clerk-Maxwell, one of the greatest British physicists of our generation. This is what he writes of matter :—

" *We are acquainted with matter only as that which may have energy communicated to it from other matter, and which may in its turn communicate energy to other matter.*"

Now this appears something definite ; the only way in which we can understand matter is through the energy which it transfers. What, then, is energy? Here is Clerk-Maxwell's answer :—

" *Energy, on the other hand, we know only as that which in all natural phenomena is continually passing from one portion of matter to another.*"

All our hopes are shattered ! The only way to understand energy is through matter. Matter has been defined in terms of energy, and energy again in terms of matter. Now Clerk-Maxwell's statements are extremely valuable as expressing concisely the nature of certain conceptual processes, by aid of which we describe certain phases of our perceptual experience, but as defining matter they carry us no further than the statement that matter is that which moves.

We will now turn to the famous *Treatise on Natural Philosophy* of Sir William Thomson (afterwards Lord Kelvin) and Professor Tait—the standard work in the English language on its own branches of physical science. These writers, in § 207, tell us :—

" We cannot, of course, give a definition of *matter* which will satisfy the metaphysician, but the naturalist may be content to know matter as *that which can be perceived by the senses*, or as *that which can be acted upon by, or can exert, force.* The latter, and indeed the former also, of these definitions involves the idea of *force*, which, in point of fact, is a direct object of sense ; probably of all our senses, and certainly of the 'muscular sense.' To our chapter on 'Properties of Matter' we must refer for further discussion of the question, *What is matter?*"

That the naturalist nowadays is not bound to satisfy the metaphysician—any more than he is bound to satisfy the theologian — will be admitted at once by the sympathetic reader of my own volume. But the naturalist is bound in the spirit of science to probe and question every statement, however high the authority on which it is made; and he is further bound to inquire whether a statement as to a physical fact is also in accord with his psychological experience. Science cannot be separated into compartments which have no mutual relationship, no mutual dependence, and no inter-communication. Science and its method form a whole, and if a physical definition be not psychologically true, it is not physically true. Now we have seen that the contents of perception are sense-impressions and stored sense-impresses, and that which can be perceived by the senses are these and these only. Do our authors mean to define all sense-impressions as matter? Would they call colour, hardness, pain, matter? We think this is hardly likely; they would probably tell us that the *source* of certain groups of sense-impressions is what they term matter; but this is not what they say. Had they said it they must themselves have recognised that they were passing beyond the veil of sense-impression and postulating a "thing-in-itself" (p. 72) behind the world of phenomena. They would then have seen that they were unconsciously endeavouring to satisfy the metaphysician, whom they had so properly disowned. This unconscious attempt to satisfy the "metaphysician within themselves" is further evidenced by their second statement, which throws back matter upon *force*. But *force* for these authors is the cause of motion (§ 217), not in the import of an antecedent or accompanying sense-impression—as, for example, relative position as cause—but in the metaphysical sense of a moving agent. They do not, indeed, place this moving agent behind sense-impression ; they even describe it as a "direct object of sense," but from the psychological standpoint force must either be a sense-impression or a group of sense - impressions, for as source or object of sense-impressions it would be purely metaphysical. But as a group of sense-impressions in us, force cannot be that which *causes* motion in an objective world. As to our muscular appreciation of force, that is a point to which we shall find occasion to return later. We ought not, however, to lay much stress on these authors' remarks as to matter, for they expressly tell us that what matter is will be further discussed in another chapter of their work. Unfortunately, this portion of their great treatise has never been published, although they wrote the above remarks more than twenty-five years before this criticism appeared. Perhaps, had they returned to the subject, they would have recognised that, if the word matter had not appeared more frequently in their text than it does in their index, their volumes would have lost not an iota of their inestimable value to the physicist.

One of the two authors of the *Treatise on Natural Philosophy* did, however, publish a separate work, entitled, *The Properties of Matter*. On pp. 12-13 of that work we have no less than nine, and on pp. 287-91 we have no less than twenty-five definitions or descriptions of matter, yet so far from matter being rendered intelligible by all these statements with regard to it, Professor Tait himself writes :—

" *We do not know, and are probably incapable of discovering, what matter is.*" And again : " *The discovery of the ultimate nature of matter is probably beyond the range of human intelligence.*"

Now these statements mark a considerable advance on the standpoint of the *Treatise on Natural Philosophy.* They will at least suggest to the reader that it is no mere whim on my part to question the right of matter to appear *at all* in scientific treatises. When one author tells us it is a primary conception of the human mind, and another that it is probably beyond the range of human intelligence, we feel an uncomfortable sense of the metaphysician smiling somewhere round the corner. If our leading scientists either fail to tell us what matter is, or even go as far as to assert that we are probably incapable of knowing, it is surely time to question whether this fetish of the metaphysicians need be preserved in the temple of science.

§ 4.—*Does Matter occupy Space?*

But to return to Professor Tait; he called his book *The Properties of Matter*, and this the reader will say means something, and something very definite. Now, for the purposes of classifying our sense-impressions, it is undoubtedly useful to term particular groups of them which have certain distinguishing characteristics " material sense-impressions," and these material sense-impressions are what Professor Tait dealt with under the properties of matter. It was Professor Tait, the unconscious metaphysician, who grouped this class of sense-impressions together and supposed them to flow as properties from something beyond the sphere of perception, namely, matter.[1] As a working definition of matter, Professor Tait considered that we might say: " *Matter is whatever can occupy space.*" Now this definition will lead us to a number of ideas which it is instructive to follow up. In the first place, is it perceptual or conceptual space to which the definition applies? If the latter, then matter must be a geometrical form—a result which we think our author does not intend. We think it more probable that Professor Tait looked upon space as itself objective, although he avoided any definite statement on this really important issue (see his p. 47). From the standpoint of

[1] The unconscious metaphysics of Professor Tait occur on nearly every page of his treatment of the fundamental concepts of physical science. Thus he asserted the " objectivity of matter," while force is not objective, we are told, but subjective. Notwithstanding this assertion, "matter is, as it were, the plaything of force." How this nothing, this " mere phantom suggestion of our muscular sense," this force, can have an objective plaything it would puzzle a metaphysician to explain. The metaphysical physicist of the present day would replace " matter " by " electricity," but he would probably offer even less definition for this substitute as a perceptual entity than Professor Tait.

our present volume, however, space is the mode by which we distinguish coexisting groups of sense-impressions, and therefore only groups of sense-impressions can be said to "occupy" space. This definition would therefore lead us to identify matter with groups of sense-impressions, and in practical everyday life the things which we term matter are certainly more or less permanent groups of sense-impressions, not unknowable "things-in-themselves" beyond sense-impression. Now there can be no scientific objection to our classifying certain more or less permanent groups of sense-impressions together and terming them matter,—to do so indeed leads us very near to John Stuart Mill's definition of matter as a "permanent possibility of sensation" [1]—but this definition of matter then leads us entirely away from matter as the thing which moves. It can hardly be said that weight, hardness, impenetrability *move*; these are sense-impressions in the brain telephonic exchange; their grouping, their variation and succession may lead us to the *conception* of motion, but a sense-impression in itself cannot be said to move; it is there at the brain terminal or not there. In order to bring motion into the sphere of sense-impression, we are compelled to associate colour, hardness, weight, etc., with geometrical forms, and in making such constructs (p. 41) we pass from the plane of perception to that of conception. I move my hand; my power to realise this motion depends on my conceiving my hand bounded by a continuous surface. If the physicist tells me that my hand is an aggregation of discrete molecules, then my idea of the motion of the hand is thrown back on the motion of the swarm of molecules. But the same difficulty arises about the individual molecule. I may surmount it by supposing the molecule to be in itself a corporation of atoms, but I cannot conceive the atom's motion unless it be bounded by a continuous surface or else be a point. The only

---

[1] *System of Logic*, bk. i. chap. iii. That groups of sense-impressions recur in a more or less permanent form is an experience we have every moment of our lives. There is a "permanent possibility of sense-impressions." We are not forced to assert anything about this possibility residing in a *supersensuous* entity matter.

other way out of the difficulty is to construct the atom of
still smaller atoms——(and there are certain phenomena
presented partly by the spectrum analysis of the gaseous
elements, and partly by modern electrical investigations,
that might well induce us to believe that the atom cannot
be conceived as the ultimate or "prime element of
matter ")——but what about these smaller atoms, are they
geometrical ideals or are they built up of tinier atoms
still, and if so where are we to stop? The process
reminds us of the lines of Swift :——

> "So naturalists observe, a flea
> Has smaller fleas that on him prey ;
> And these have smaller still to bite 'em,
> And so proceed *ad infinitum*."

I am unable to verify Swift's statement as to the fleas, but
I feel quite sure that to assert the real existence in the
world of phenomena of all the concepts by aid of which
we scientifically describe phenomena——molecule, atom,
prime-atom——even if it be *ad infinitum*, will not save us
from having ultimately to consider the moving thing to
be a geometrical ideal, from having to postulate the
phenomenal existence of what is contrary to our perceptual experience. This point brings out very clearly
what the present writer holds to be a fundamental canon
of scientific method, namely : *To no concept, however
invaluable it may be as a means of describing the routine
of perceptions, ought phenomenal existence to be ascribed until
its perceptual equivalent has been actually disclosed.*

Whenever we disregard this canon, when, for example,
we assert reality for the mechanisms by aid of which we
describe our physical experience, then we are more likely
than not to conclude with an *antinomy*, or a conflict of
rules. For such mechanisms are constructs largely based
on conceptual limits, which are unattainable in the field
of perception. When we consider space as objective and
matter as that which occupies it, we are forming a construct largely based on the geometrical symbols by aid of
which we analyse motion conceptually. We are projecting the form and volume of conception into perception,

and so accustomed have we got to this conceptual element in the construct that we confuse it with a reality of perception itself. When we go a stage further in the phenomenalising of conceptions, and postulate the reality of atoms, the antinomy becomes clear. If bodies are made up of swarms of atoms, how can they have a real volume or form? What is the volume or form of a swarm of bees or a cloud of dust? Obviously we can only give them shape and size by enclosing them conceptually in an ideal geometrical surface. Just as in a swarm of bees or a cloud of dust odd members of the community near this imaginary surface are continually passing in and out, so—if we phenomenalise conception—we must assert that at the surface of water or of iron odd molecules or atoms are perpetually leaving or, it may be, re-entering the swarm. Condensation and evaporation go on at the surface of the water and the iron gives a metallic smell. Now if the swarm be in this continual state of flow at the surface we can only speak of it as having volume or form *ideally*, or as a mode of conceptually distinguishing one group of sense-impressions from another (p. 192). It is the conceptual volume or form which occupies space, and it is this form, and not the sense-impressions, which we conceive to move. If we throw back the occupancy of space on the individual members of the swarm, it is certainly not the volumes or forms of the individuals, which we consider as the volume or form of the material body, for the former we treat as imperceptible and the latter as perceptible. Further, we must then infer that the unknown is ultimately unlike the known, that geometrical ideals can be realised in the imperceptible. This, however, is a distinct breach of the second canon of logical inference (p. 60).

So far, then, our analysis of the physicist's definitions of matter irresistibly forces upon us the following conclusions : That matter as the unknowable cause of sense-impression is a metaphysical entity [1] as meaningless for

[1] The scientific reader must for the present have at least sufficient confidence in the author to believe that the essential facts as to *mass* are not thrown overboard with the fetish matter.

science as any other postulating of causation in the beyond of sense-impression ; it is as idle as any other *thing-in-itself*, as any other projection into the supersensuous, be it the force of the materialists or the infinite mind of the philosophers.   The classification of certain groups of sense-impressions as material groups is, on the other hand, scientifically of value ; it throws no light, however, on matter as that which perceptually moves.

Conceptually all motion is the motion of geometrical ideals, which are so chosen as best to describe those changes of sense-impression which in ordinary language we term perceptual motion.

§ 5.——*The " Common-sense " View of Matter as Impenetrable and Hard*

Now the reader may feel inclined, on the basis of his daily experience, to assert that both the physicists above referred to and the author are really quibbling about words, and that we can sufficiently describe matter by saying that it is *impenetrable* and *hard*.   Now these terms describe important classes of sense-impressions, and the sense-impressions of impenetrability and hardness are very frequently factors of what we have called material groups of sense-impressions.   But it is very doubtful whether we can consider them as invariably associated with these material groups.   At any rate, if we do, we shall find ourselves again involved in the antinomies which result when we pass incautiously to and fro from the field of perception to that of conception.   When we say a thing is impenetrable, we can only mean that something else will not pass through it, or that there are two groups of sense-impressions which, in our perceptual experience, we have always been able to distinguish under the mode space. Impenetrability, therefore, can only be a relative term ; one thing is impenetrable for a second.   When we say that matter is impenetrable we cannot mean that nothing whatever can pass through it.   A bird cannot fly through a sheet of plate glass, but a ray of light does penetrate it perfectly easily. A ray of light cannot pass through a brick wall, but a wave of electric oscillations can. In order to describe the motion of these luminous and electric waves the physicist conceives ether to penetrate all bodies and to act as a medium for the transit of energy through them. Matter cannot therefore be looked upon as the thing which is *absolutely* impenetrable.

Or, are we missing the point of what is meant, when it is asserted that matter is that which is impenetrable? Are we to postulate the real existence of atoms and then to suppose the individual members of the swarm impenetrable? Here again a difficulty arises. There is much that tends to convince physicists that the atom cannot be conceived as the simplest element of the conceptual analysis of material groups. Just as a bell when struck sets the air in motion and gives a note, so we conceive an atom capable of being struck, and of setting not the air but the ether in motion, of giving, as we might express it, an ether note. These notes produce in us certain optical sense-impressions—for example, the bright lines of the spectrum of an attenuated gas. As without seeing two bells we might, and indeed often do, distinguish them by their notes,[1] so the physicist distinguishes an atom of hydrogen from an atom of oxygen, although he has never seen either, by the different light notes which he conceives to arise from them. But as the bell to give a note must be considered as vibrating—changing its shape or undergoing strain—so the physicist practically finds himself compelled to conceive the atom as undergoing strain, or changing its shape. This conception forces us to suppose the atom built up of distinct parts capable of changing their relative position. What are these ultimate parts of the atom, by the relative motion of which we describe our sense-impressions of the bright lines in the spectrum? We are now beginning to form conceptions of the constitution of the atom. The ultimate parts of the atom are

---

[1] The householder is generally able to distinguish the sound of his back-door from that of the front-door bell, although, probably, in ninety-nine cases out of a hundred he may never have examined the bells in his house.

now spoken of as "electrons," and the ether is conceived as penetrating the atom. In the present state of our theories (see Chapter IX.) it is impossible to say definitely whether it would or would not simplify things to conceive the electron as " penetrable " or "impenetrable "; these terms become in themselves almost without meaning. Hence, even if we go so far as to give the concept atom a phenomenal existence, it will not help us to understand what is meant by the assertion that matter is impenetrable.

§ 6.—*Individuality does not denote Sameness in Substratum*

Shall we, however, be more dogmatic still, and, denying that ether is matter, assert that matter is impenetrable *relative* to matter ? In order to give any definite answer to this question we have again to pass from the perceptible material group to its supposed elementary basis, the atom, and to ask whether we have any reason for conceiving atoms as incapable of penetrating each other. In the first place, the physicist, although he has never caught an atom, yet conceives it as something which is incapable of disappearing—*it continues to be*. In the next place, if we conceive it as entering into combination with a second atom, although we have no reason for asserting that the two atoms do not mutually penetrate, we are still compelled, in order to describe by aid of atoms our perceptual experience, to conceive that, out of the combination, two separate atoms can again be obtained with the same individual characteristics as the original two possessed. What right have we to postulate these laws with regard to atoms when atoms are, even if " real," still absolutely imperceptible to us, when we are absolutely unable to observe their mutual actions ? We have exactly the same logical right as we have to lay down any scientific law whatever. Namely, we find that these laws as to the action of single atoms, when applied to large groups of atoms, enable us to describe with very great accuracy what occurs in those phenomenal bodies which we scientifically symbolise by groups of atoms ; they enable us to construct, without contradiction by perceptual experience, those routines of sense-impression which we term chemical reactions.

The hypotheses that the individual atom is both indestructible and impenetrable suffice to elucidate certain physical and chemical properties of the bodies we construct from atoms. But the continued existence of atoms under physical changes and the reproduction of their individuality on the dissolution of chemical combination might possibly be deduced from other hypotheses than those of the indestructibility and impenetrability of the individual atom. It does not follow of logical necessity that because we experience the same group of sense-impressions at different times and in different places, or even continuously, that there must be one and the same thing at the basis of these sense-impressions. An example will clearly show the reader what I mean and at the same time demonstrate that however useful as hypotheses the indestructibility and impenetrability of the atom may be, they are still not absolutely necessary conceptions; so that even if we do project our atom into an imperceptible of the phenomenal world, it will not follow that there must be an unchangeable individual something at all times and in all positions as the basal element of a permanent group of sense-impressions. The permanency and sameness of the phenomenal body may lie in the individual grouping of the sense-impressions and not in the sameness of an imperceptible something projected from conception into phenomena.

The example we will take is that of a wave on the surface of the sea. The wave forms for us a group of sense-impressions, and we look upon it, and speak of it, as if it were an individual thing. But we are compelled to conceive the wave when it is fifty yards off as consisting of quite different moving things from what it does when it reaches our feet—the substratum of the wave has changed. Throw a cork in; it rises and falls as the wave passes it, but is not carried along by it. The wave may retain its form and be for us exactly the same group of sense-impressions in different positions and at different times,

and yet its substratum may be continually changing.
We might even push the illustration further: we might
send two waves of different individual shapes (Fig. 19)
along the surface of still water in opposite directions (*a*),
or in the same direction if the pursuing wave had the
greater speed.   One of these waves would meet or over-
take the other (*b*); they would coalesce or combine (*c*),
producing in us for a time (which depends entirely on
their relative speeds) a new group of sense-impressions

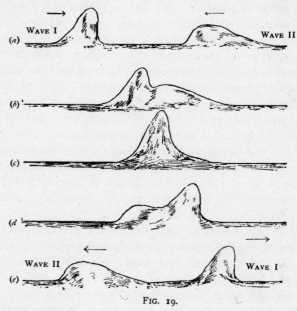

FIG. 19.

differing totally from either individual group; but they
would ultimately pass each other (*d*) and emerge with
their distinct individualities the same as of old (*e*).
Throughout the whole of this sequence the substrata of
the two individual waves are changing and for the time of
the combination their substratum is identical, and yet the
waves are able to preserve their individual characteristics,
so far as reappearing with them after combination is concerned.[1]   Thus sameness of sense-impressions before and

[1] If analogy were to be sought to the sameness of total weight before,

after a combination is seen from a perceptual example not to involve of necessity a sameness of substratum.

Now I have cited this example of the wave for two reasons. In the first place, it shows us that it is possible to conceive atoms as penetrable by atoms, and as varying from moment to moment in their substratum, without at the same time denying the possibility of their physical permanency and individual reproduction after chemical combination. To consider an atom as consisting always of the same substratum, and as impenetrable by other atoms, may help us to describe easily certain physical and chemical phenomena ; but it is quite conceivable that other hypotheses may equally well account for these phenomena, and this being so we have clearly no right first to project special conceptions into the world of real phenomena, and then to assert on the strength of this that matter, penetrable in itself, is impenetrable in its ultimate element, the atom. Clearly impenetrability is neither in perception nor conception a necessary factor of material groups of sense-impressions. Further, the permanence and sameness of such a group do not necessarily involve the conception of a permanent and the same substratum for the group.

My second reason for citing this wave example lies in the light it throws on the possibilities involved in the statement : " *Matter is that which moves.*" The wave consists of a particular form of motion in the substratum which for the time constitutes the wave. This form of motion itself moves along the surface of the water. Hence we see that besides the substratum something else can be conceived as moving, namely, *forms of motion.* What if, after all, matter as the moving thing could be best expressed in conception by a form of motion moving, and this whether the substratum remain the same or not ? To this suggestion we shall return later, as it is one extremely fruitful in its results.

during, and after combination, it might be found in the sameness of the volume of fluid raised above the sea-level before, during, and after coalition. Thus sameness of weight does not in conception necessarily involve sameness of substratum.

§ 7.—*Hardness not Characteristic of Matter*

It remains for us now to deal with the other characteristic, hardness, which is popularly attributed to matter.
There are certain persons who are content, when men's
ignorance as to the nature of matter is suggested to them,
to remark that one has only to knock one's head against a
stone wall in order to have a valid demonstration of the
existence and the nature of matter.   Now if this statement be of any value, it can only mean that the ·sense-
impression of hardness is the essential test of the presence
of matter in these persons' opinion.   But none of us doubt
the existence of the sense-impression hardness associated
with other sense-impressions in certain permanent groups ;
we have been aware of it from childhood's days, and do
not require its existence to be experimentally demonstrated now.   It is one of those muscular sense-impressions
which we shall see are conceived by science to be
describable in terms of the relative acceleration of certain
parts of our body and of external bodies.   But it is
difficult to grasp how the sense-impression of hardness
can tell us more of the nature of matter than the sense-
impression of softness might be supposed to do.   There
are clearly many things which are popularly termed
matter and are certainly not hard.   Further, there are
things which satisfy the definitions of matter as that
which moves or as that which fills space, but which are
very far indeed from producing any sense-impression of
the nature of hardness or softness ; nor would they even
satisfy our definition if we said that matter is that which
is heavy, heaviness being certainly a more widely-spread
factor of material groups of sense-impressions than hardness.   Between the sun and planets, between the atoms
of bodies, physicists conceive the ether to exist, a medium
whose vibrations constitute the channel by means of which
electro-magnetic and optical energy is transferred from
one body to another.   In the first place, the ether is a
pure conception by aid of which we correlate in conceptual
space various motions.   These motions are the symbols

by which we briefly describe the sequences and relationships we perceive between various groups of phenomena.
The ether is thus a mode of resuming our perceptual
experience ; but, like a good many other conceptions of
which we have no direct perception, physicists project
it into the phenomenal world and assert its real existence.
There seems to be just as much, or little, logic in this
assertion as in the postulate that there is a real substratum,
matter, at the back of groups of sense-impressions ; both
at present are metaphysical statements.   Now there is no
evidence forthcoming that the ether must be conceived as
either hard or heavy,[1] and yet it can be strained or its
parts put in relative motion.   Further, from Professor
Tait's standpoint, it occupies space.   Hence those who
associate matter with hardness and weight must be prepared to deny that the ether is matter, or be content to
call it non-matter.   It is worth noting, at the same time,
that the metaphysicians—whether they be materialists
asserting the phenomenal existence both of space and of
a permanent substratum of sense-impression, or " common-
sense " philosophers asking us to knock our heads against
stone walls—reach hopelessly divergent results when they
say that matter is that which moves, that matter occupies
space, and that matter is that which is heavy and hard.

§ 8.—*Matter as non-Matter in Motion*

There is, however, a still greater dilemma in store for
the " common-sense " philosophers.   We have not yet
reached a clear conception of what the ether, the non-
matter of our philosophers, consists in.   There are in fact
two, at first sight, completely divergent ways in which the
ether is reached as a conceptual limit to our perceptual
experience (see p. 208), but it is the great hope of science
at the present day that " hard and heavy matter " will be
shown to be ether in motion.   In other words, it is well

---

[1] I venture to think the late Lord Kelvin's attempt to *weigh* ether a
retrograde step (see his *Lectures on Molecular Dynamics*, pp. 206-8,
Baltimore, 1884).   If the ether be a sufficiently wide-embracing conception,
gravitation should flow from it, and this certainly was Lord Kelvin's view when
he propounded the vortex atom.

within the range of possibility that during the next quarter of a century science will have discovered that our symbolic description of the phenomenal universe will be immensely simplified, if we take as our symbolic basis for material groups of sense-impressions a type of motion of the conceptual ether ; in other, more expressive if less accurate, language, if we treat our friends' matter as their non-matter in motion. We shall then find that our sense-impressions of hardness, weight, colour, temperature, cohesion, and chemical constitution, may all be described by aid of the motions of a single medium, which itself is conceived to have no hardness, weight, colour, temperature, nor indeed elasticity of the ordinary perceptual type. This would mean an immeasurably great advance in our scientific power of description.[1] Yet if physicists even then persist in projecting the conceptual into the sphere of sense-impression, and in asserting a phenomenal existence for the ether, we should still be ignorant of what it is that moves, of what ether-matter may really consist in.

Our analysis, therefore, of the various statements made by physicists and common-sense philosophers with regard to the nature of matter shows us that they are one and all *metaphysical*—that is, they attempt to describe something beyond sense-impression, beyond perception, and appear, therefore, at best as dogmas, at worst as inconsistencies. If we confine ourselves to the field of logical inference, we see in the phenomenal universe, not matter in motion, but sense-impressions and changes of sense-impressions, coexistence and sequence, association and routine. This world of sense-impression science symbolises in conception by an infinitely extended medium, whose various types of motion correspond to diverse groups of sense-impressions, and enable us to describe the associations and sequences of these groups. The moving elements of this medium can in thought be conceived of only as geometrical ideals, as points or continuous surfaces. To

---

[1] We now seem to be groping towards an advance in this direction. Physicists are beginning to conceive " matter " as an aggregate of centres of electromagnetic action, and the differentiation of matter as lying in the grouping and motion of these centres.

make our symbolic chart or picture agree the better with perceptual experience, we find it necessary to endow these geometrical ideals with certain relative positions, velocities, and accelerations, the relationships of which are expressible in certain simple laws termed the laws of motion (see the following Chapter).   If we choose to term the moving things of the conceptual chart *matter*, there can be no objection to the term, provided we carefully distinguish this conceptual matter from any metaphysical ideas of matter as the substratum of sense-impression, as that which perceptually moves, as that which fills space, or as that which can be defined as heavy, hard, and impenetrable.   Conceptual matter is thus merely a name for the geometrical ideals endowed with certain associated motions by aid of which we describe the routine of our external perceptions.   It is in this sense that we shall use the term matter for the remainder of this work, unless we are expressly referring to the matter of the metaphysicians. " Heavy " matter will be a name for the conceptual symbol by which we represent what we have termed material groups of sense-impressions united in single individuals, while ether-matter will be a name for the symbol by which we describe other phases of sense-impression, especially the relationship in space and time of sense-impressions belonging to different material groups.   We shall not project our conceptions into imperceptibles [1] in the field of perception (!)——except in so far as it may be necessary in order to criticise current physical notions.   We shall try and preserve throughout the standpoint that science is a description of perceptual experience by aid of conceptual shorthand, the symbols of this shorthand being in general *ideal* limits to perceptual processes, and as such having no exact perceptual equivalents.

The reduction of " matter to non-matter in motion," of

[1] The reader may perhaps expect the words " unperceived things " rather than "imperceptibles."   But as every external perception is a group of sense-impressions, and as our senses are limited, the atom, if a real phenomena, could only appear sensible by colour, hardness, temperature, etc., the very sense-impressions it is conceived to describe.   Hence, if the ultimate atom is to be *not* these things but their source, it may be truly termed *imperceptible*.

heavy-matter to ether-matter in motion, is so important as a possible simplification of our scientific analysis of phenomena that we must devote a few pages to its discussion. We will term the fundamental element of heavy-matter, the element out of which, perhaps, chemical atoms themselves are to be conceived as built up, the *prime-atom*. We have, then, to ask what types of motion in the ether have been suggested as possible forms for the prime-atom. There are two suggestions to which reference may be made, both of which depend upon our postulating the same constitutior for the ether. We must here make a brief digression in order to throw some light on this constitution of the ether.

§ 9.—*The Ether as "Perfect Fluid" and " Perfect Jelly"*

The reader is certainly acquainted with two types of perceptual bodies which may be roughly described as liquid and elastic. As specimens of these two types we will take water and jelly. As substances water and jelly have a remarkable agreement in one respect and a remarkable divergence in another. If we put either water or jelly into a cylinder closed at the bottom and attempt to compress them by aid of a heavily-loaded piston, we shall find that the compression is either insensible or of very small amount indeed. Careful experiments with elaborate apparatus show that these substances are compressible, but the amount of compression, although measurable, is exceedingly minute as compared, for example, with the amount that air would be compressed by the same load. We express this result by saying that both water and jelly offer great resistance to one form of strain, namely, change of size (p. 229). But this resistance is only relative, relative to other substances, such as gases, and to the machinery of compression at our disposal. So far as our perceptive experience goes, there is no substance which resists absolutely all change of size, or for which change of size is impossible. Hence an incompressible substance is merely a conceptual limit which has not its equivalent in the world of phenomena, but which is reached in conception by carrying on indefinitely a process (or a classification of compressible bodies) starting in perception.

Turning from this agreement to the divergence between water and jelly, we remark that if a lath of wood or even a knife-blade be pressed downwards on a jelly it requires considerable effort to shear or separate the jelly into two parts ; on the other hand, the water is separated by the lath without any sensible resistance. Now the change of shape we are in this case concerned with is of the nature of a slide (p. 231), and we say that the water offers little and the jelly considerable resistance to sliding strain. Here, again, the question of the amount of resistance is relative. As far as our perceptual experience goes, all fluids offer some, however small, resistance to the sliding of their parts over each other. The fluid which offers absolute resistance to compression and no resistance at all to slide of its parts—or the parts of which slip over each other without anything of the nature of frictional action—is only a conceptual limit. Such a fluid is termed a *perfect fluid*. On the other hand, by proceeding to the opposite limit in the case of an incompressible jelly, that is, by supposing it to resist absolutely change of shape by sliding, we should obtain a body incapable of changing its form by either compression or slide, and thus reach that conceptual limit, the *rigid body*. If we suppose absolute resistance to compression and partial resistance to slide, we have in conception a medium which might perhaps be described as a *perfect jelly*.

Returning now to our ether, we note that physicists conceive it incompressible, but that for some purposes they appear to treat it as a *perfect fluid*, for other purposes as a *perfect jelly*.[1] This might at first sight appear a contradiction or conflict of conceptions, and it does undoubtedly involve difficulties which physicists are at present far from having thoroughly mastered. If we consider the ether as purely conceptual, then, in order to describe different phases of phenomena, we are certainly at

[1] For further purposes again scarcely as either.

liberty to first consider it as of one nature and then as of another. But in doing so it is evident that we are leaving room for a wider conception which will resume both phases of phenomena at once, will not lead us into logical contradictions if both phases have to be dealt with in the same investigation. Thus, if the ether as a perfect fluid enable us to describe atoms by its types of motion, and the ether as a perfect jelly enable us to describe the radiation of light, it is clear that when we treat the atom as a source of light-radiations, we may get into serious confusion by the conception that the ether is at the same time a perfect fluid *and* a perfect jelly. We are compelled, indeed, to try and find some reconciliation between these two conceptions. If we turn to perceptual experience for a suggestion, we may note that water is the principal component of jelly, and may, by the addition of more or less gelatinous material, be stiffened to a jelly of any consistency. In the like manner we can conceive a series of perfect jellies formed, ranging in their resistance to slide, from the perfect fluid, through all stages of viscosity, up to the perfectly rigid body. We might, then, out of this series of jellies choose one which, for sliding strains of a certain magnitude, was sensibly a perfect fluid, while for smaller strains, such as are involved in the theory of light-radiation, it would act as a perfect jelly. This is the solution propounded in 1845 by Sir George G. Stokes,[1] and it may be termed the jelly-theory of the ether. The jelly-theory of the ether has undoubtedly been of value in simplifying many of our conceptions of physical phenomena, but how far it can be reconciled with any system of ether-motion as a basis for the prime-atom yet awaits investigation.[2]

[1] *Mathematical and Physical Papers*, vol. i. pp. 125-29, and vol. ii. pp. 12-13. The present writer considers, however, that there is a difference in quality as well as in degree between a viscous fluid and an elastic medium. The complete difference in type between the equations of a plastic solid and a viscous fluid is sufficient evidence of this. In the former case, any shear *above a certain magnitude* produces set ; in the latter, any shear *whatever, if continued long enough.*

[2] For example, Lord Kelvin's vortex atom would hardly be a possibility.

There is another possibility to which I can only briefly refer here—namely, that the ether is to be conceived as a perfect fluid, but that just as a certain type of motion of this ether corresponds to the atom, so types of motion may be used to stiffen the ether, or to give it elastic rigidity. The ether may be a perfect fluid, but, owing to the turbulence of its motion, it may act for certain purposes as a perfect jelly. This hypothesis will be better appreciated when I have said a few words as to the ether-motions which may constitute the prime-atom.

§ 10.—*The Vortex-Ring Atom and the Ether-Squirt Atom*

In constructing an atom out of an ether-motion we have first to gain some idea of how it is possible that ether, not being itself hard or resisting change of shape, can yet be conceived to produce the sensations of hardness and resistance by its motion. Some general idea can easily be got of the sort of resistance produced by particular types of motion in the following manner : Take an ordinary spinning-top, and suppose we succeed by great care in balancing it on its peg. Clearly the least touch of the hand will upset it ; it offers no resistance to the motion of the hand. The same remark applies if the peg of the top were fixed by a ball-and-socket joint to the table. But, on the other hand, if the top be set spinning, we shall find the case entirely altered ; it will now present considerable resistance to being upset, and, if partially turned round its ball-and-socket joint, will tend to return to the old vertical position. A considerable number of such spinning-tops would offer a large amount of resistance to a hand passed over the table at a less distance than their height. This example may perhaps bring home to the reader how a certain type of motion may suffice to stiffen a body not otherwise stiff. Another example of motion stiffening a body is the smoke-ring, with which most devotees of tobacco are well acquainted. Two such smoke-rings will not coalesce ; they pass through or wriggle round each other, and round solid corners which come in their way, and, furthermore, their relative motion is easily seen to closely depend upon their relative position. Now we see smoke-rings because the moist particles in the smoke render the gaseous mixture visible, as similar particles render steam visible ; but we might blow air-rings in air, which would act precisely as the smoke-rings do, only they would be invisible.   Such rings are termed *vortex-rings* ; and if we study the action of such rings not in air or water but in our conceptual perfect fluid, we shall find that, like atoms, they retain their own individuality ; they enter into combination, but cannot be created or destroyed.   This is the basis of Lord Kelvin's vortex-ring theory of matter—a prime atom, according to his theory, is an ether vortex-ring.[1]   By the aid of vortex-motion, or spinning elements of liquid in a liquid, we are also able to conceive a liquid stiffened up to a required degree of resistance to sliding strain, and thus to replace the ether as a perfect jelly by the ether as a perfect fluid in a turbulent condition.[2]   This is the so-called *gyrostatic* ether, the properties of which have been developed by Sir. J. Larmor.   We can then dispense with Sir George Stokes' hypothesis of slight viscosity.   But however suggestive these ideas may be for the lines upon which we may in future work out our conceptions of ether and atom, they are very far indeed from being at present worked out, and there are many difficulties in the vortex-atom theory — notably that of deducing gravitation — which the present writer is not very hopeful will ever be surmounted.

While Lord Kelvin's theory supposes that the sub-stratum of an atom always consists of the same elements of moving ether, the author has ventured to put forward a theory in which, while the ether is still looked upon as a perfect fluid, the individual atom does not always

---

[1] For a fuller account of this theory see Clerk-Maxwell's article "Atom" in the *Encyclopædia Britannica*, or his *Scientific Papers*, vol. ii. pp. 445-84. See also as to spin producing elastic resistance Sir William Thomson's *Popular Lectures and Addresses*, vol. i. pp. 142-46 and 235-52.

[2] See G. F. Fitzgerald : "On an Electro-magnetic Interpretation of Turbulent Fluid Motion," *Nature*, vol. xl. pp. 32-4.

consist of the same elements of ether.   In this theory
an atom is conceived to be a point at which ether flows
in all directions into space ; such a point is termed
an *ether-squirt*.   An ether-squirt in the ether is thus
something like a tap turned on under water, except that
the machinery of the tap is dispensed with in the case of
the squirt.   Two such squirts, if placed in ether, move
relatively to each other, exactly like two gravitating
particles, the mass of either corresponding to the mean
rate at which ether is poured in at the squirt.   From
periodic variations of the rate of squirting, as influenced
by the mutual action of groups of squirts, we are able to
deduce many of the phenomena of chemical action,
cohesion, light, and electro-magnetism.   Indeed the ether-
squirt seems a conceptual mechanism capable of describing
a very considerable range of phenomena.   It involves, of
course, the conception of negative matter, or *ether-sinks* ;
for the amount squirted into an incompressible fluid must
be at least equalled by the amount which passes out.   As,
however, an ether-squirt and an ether-sink must be
conceived to repel each other, there need be no surprise
that we are compelled to consider our portion of the
universe as built up of positive matter ; the negative
matter, or ether-sinks, would long ago have passed out of
the range of the ether-squirts.[1]

§ 11.—*A Material Loophole into the Supersensuous*

Now the reader may naturally ask : Where can we
conceive the ether to come from when it pours in at the
squirt or prime-atom ?   In taking the ether-squirt as a
model dynamical system for the atom, we are not bound
to answer this question in order to demonstrate its validity,
any more than we are bound to explain why ether and

---

[1] Carnelley, however, demanded an element of negative atomic weight, and
a substance of negative weight is by no means inconceivable.   Should the
reader be interested in a mathematical account of this theory he may consult :
" Ether-squirts ; Being an Attempt to Specialise the Form of Ether-Motion
which forms an Atom in a Theory propounded in former Papers," *American
Journal of Mathematics*, vol. xiii. pp. 309-62.   See also *Camb. Phil. Trans.*
vol. xiv. p. 71 ; *London Math. Society*, vol. xx. pp. 38 and 297.

atom themselves come to be. From our standpoint, they are justified as conceptions if they enable us to resume our perceptual experience. But as there are many who will insist on projecting the conceptual into the phenomenal field, I will endeavour to answer the question by suggestion.

Suppose we had two opaque horizontal plane surfaces placed close together, and containing between them water in which lived a flat fish, say a flounder. Now it is clear that the perceptions of our fish would be limited to motion forwards or backwards, to right or to left, but vertically upwards or downwards would be an imperceptible, and therefore probably inconceivable, motion for him. Now let us pass in conception to a limit unrealisable in perception ; let us suppose our flounder to get flatter and flatter, and the film of water thinner and thinner, as the planes are pressed closer together. The motion of the flounder and the motion of the water may then, for conceptual purposes, be supposed to take place in one horizontal plane. Now if we were to make a hole in one of the planes and squirt water in, it is clear that our flounder would experience new sense-impressions when he came into the neighbourhood of the squirt. Indeed the pressure produced by the flow of water might compel the flounder to circumnavigate the squirt—that is, the squirt might be for him hard and impenetrable. Such squirts, although only water in motion, might form very *material* groups of sense-impressions for our fish. If, however, he were told that matter was formed of squirts, he would be quite unable to conceive where the squirting came from. It could be from neither forwards nor backwards, neither from right nor left, for it flows *in* in all these directions. The flounder would presume we were quite mad did we suggest that the water came vertically upwards or downwards ; that there was another direction in space—" upward and outward in the direction of his stomach," as the author of *Flatland*[1] felicitously expresses it. Could the flounder

---

[1] *Flatland : a Romance of Many Dimensions*, by A. Square. London, 1884.

get out of his space through the squirt—*through and out in the direction of matter*—he would reach a new world, wherein he would perceive what squirts were, and what his matter really consisted in.   Through the eye of the needle, out through the matter of flatland, the flounder would reach the heaven of our three-dimensioned space, where we go up and down, as well as forward and backward, and to right and left.   But for the flounder this "out through matter" would remain inconceivable, not to say ridiculous ; it would be to penetrate behind the surface of sense-impressions.

Now this parable of the flounder is specially intended for those minds which, strive as they will, cannot wholly repress their metaphysical tendencies, which *must* project

FIG. 20.

their conceptions into realities beyond perception.   The danger of this metaphysical speculation lies in the frequency with which it contradicts our perceptual experience when it passes from the "beyond" of sense-impression to the world of phenomena.   Now a happy conception as to how the prime-atom is to be constructed, fitting in with all our perceptual experience (that is, enabling us to describe it symbolically with great accuracy), *might* leave a loophole for the metaphysical mind to pass to something which does not symbolise the perceptual, and therefore might *dogmatically* be assumed to belong to the supersensuous.   Out from our space through the ether-squirt, out through matter we in conception pass, like the flounder, to another dimensioned space.   This space has for a number of years past formed the subject of elaborate investigations by some of our best mathematicians,[1] and it

[1] Riemann, Helmholtz, Beltrami, and Clifford.

possesses this great advantage : that when we pass from the conclusions drawn for this higher space to the space of our perceptual experience, then we are not involved in the contradictions which abound in the transition from the older metaphysics to our physical experience. Here in this new playroom, entered, perhaps, by the doorway of matter, metaphysician and theologian can for the present safely spin beyond the sensible the cobwebs, which have been swept away by the scientific broom whenever they encumbered the habitable apartments of knowledge. The necessary mathematical equipment required for genuine research in the field of higher-dimensioned space will at any rate act as a safeguard against over light-hearted expeditions " beyond the sensible " ! Should a time ever come, which may, perhaps, be doubted, when a happy conception as to the structure of the prime-atom is discovered to be a *perceptual* fact, then if such a conception involves the existence of four-dimensioned space,[1] our friends will have done yeoman service in preparing a way for a scientific theory of the supersensuous—*out through the doorway of matter* !

§ 1 2.—*The Difficulties of a Perceptual Ether*

But I have romanced enough for the sake of the meta-physically-minded. Returning to the solid ground of fact, we have to remember that no hypothesis as to the structure of the prime-atom from ether in motion is at present scientifically accepted ; no model dynamical system for the atom has as yet been shown to have such a wide-reaching power of describing our perceptual experience that it has passed from the field of imagination and

---

[1] The ether-squirt is not the only atomic theory which suggests a space beyond our own. Clifford imagined matter to be a *wrinkle* in our space, which suggests the idea of another space to bend it in. This notion of Clifford's may, perhaps, be brought home to our reader by imagining the flounder rigidly flat and a crumple or wrinkle in his plane of motion. The wrinkle would, like matter, be impenetrable to the fish ; he could not *fit* it ; either the wrinkle or he would have to get out of the way. This non-fitting of two kinds of space has not hitherto, however, been developed as a mode of describing any of our fundamental physical experiences.

become a current symbol of scientific shorthand.   Nor is
the reason far to seek ; we desire to construct, if possible,
the prime-atom from an ether-motion, but our conceptions
of the ether are at present very ill-defined.   We are
agreed that it must be conceived as a medium which
resists strain, but we are not certain how to represent best
the relative motions that follow on relative change in the
position of the ether-elements.   We are not yet satisfied
with a perfect fluid, a perfect jelly, or even a turbulent
perfect fluid conception of the ether.

Treating the ether not as a conception but as a
phenomenon, we find it difficult to realise how a *continuous* and *same* medium could offer any resistance to a
sliding motion of its parts, for the continuity and sameness would involve, after any displacement, everything
being the same as before displacement.   The idea of a
perfect jelly appears to involve some change in structure
as we magnify smaller and smaller elements larger and
larger.   Finally, any relative motion of translation as distinct from one of rotation seems excluded by the idea
of absolute incompressibility.[1]   It is not a metaphysical
quibble when we demand that two things shall not occupy
the same space, but that when motion begins there shall
be *somewhere* unoccupied for *something* to move into.
The obvious fact is that while in conception we can
represent the moving parts of the ether *as points*, and we
can endow these points with such relative velocities and
accelerations as will best describe our perceptual experience,
yet when we project the ether into the phenomenal world
it is at once recognised as a conceptual limit unparalleled
in perceptual experience, and we do not feel at home with
it.   The old problems as to "heavy matter" recur.
What is the ultimate element of the ether which moves ?
and why does it move ?   Build a perceptual matter out
of a phenomenal ether, and we have again thrust upon us
the question as to ether-matter's nature.   Is it also to be
a *terra incognita nunc et in æternum* ?   The mind again

---

[1] For absolutely incompressible elements (other than points) motion round
any closed curve other than a circle seems inconceivable.

fails to rest in peace until it reaches somewhere the motion
of a point, the sizeless ultimate element of matter postulated
by Boscovich.   We find ourselves again involved in the
contradictions which flow from asserting a reality for
motion in the phenomenal field.   We are again forced to
the conclusion that motion is a pure conception, which
may describe perceptual changes, but cannot be projected
into the phenomenal world without involving us in inexplicable difficulties.

§ 13.— *Why do Bodies move ?*

We have left but little space for the discussion of our
second question : Why do bodies move ?   But the
answer to this question must be clear after what precedes.
If we mean : Why do sense-impressions change in a
certain manner ?—then we have already seen what are
the possibilities of knowledge on this point when considering consciousness, the nature of the perceptive faculty
and the routine of perceptious (pp. 101-7).   If we mean :
Why do the geometrical symbols by which we conceptualise material groups of sense-impressions move in a
certain fashion ?—then the answer is, that after many
guesses we have found these types of motion to be best
capable of describing the past and predicting the future
routine of our perceptions.   If, however, any one persists
in phenomenalising our conceptual symbols of motion,
then science can only reply to this question : Why does
matter move ?   *We don't know*.   Let us suppose that
the earth actually moves in an ellipse round the sun in a
focus, and then let us attempt to analyse the *why* of it.
Well, conceptually we construct this motion out of a
certain relative motion of the elementary parts of sun and
earth.   We say that if these elementary parts have
certain relative accelerations when in each other's presence, then the earth will describe an ellipse about the
sun.   These elementary parts may be looked upon as
atoms or groups of atoms, but to save any hypothesis let
us simply term them *particles* of matter.   Now, why do

two particles when in each other's presence move relative to each other in a certain fashion? It will not do to answer: Owing to the *law* of gravitation. That merely describes how they move. Nor can we say: Owing to the *force* of gravitation. That is merely throwing the answer on the beyond of sense-impression—it is the metaphysical method of avoiding saying: We don't know.

When we see two persons dancing round each other we assume that they do it because they wish to, because they *will* to. They cannot be said, if one is not holding the other, to enforce each other's motion. To attribute the dance to their common will is the sole explanation we can give of it.[1] When we find the ultimate particles of matter dancing about each other, we can hardly, like Schopenhauer, attribute it to their common will to dance thus, because will denotes the presence of consciousness, and consciousness we cannot logically infer unless there be certain types of material sense-impressions associated with it. Thus will, if it had any meaning as a cause of motion—which we have seen it has not (p. 125)—could not help us with regard to our dance of material particles. All we can scientifically say is, that the *cause* of their motion is their relative position; but this is no explanation of why they move when in that position. The difficulty cannot be surmounted by appealing to the notion of force. Of the metaphysical conception of force we have said enough (p. 116 *et seq.*), and we need not reconsider it here. But force is sometimes said to be a sense-impression—we are said to have a " muscular sensation " of force. I *will* to push a thing with my hand, and on the will becoming action a " muscular sensation " occurs which is termed the exertion of force. But why is this more a sense-impression of force than a sense-impression of changes in the motion, or of relative accelerations in the particles of my finger-tips? Add to this that the so-called " muscular sensation " of force is associated with a conscious being, or is a subjective side of some changes of motion in his person, and we see that

[1] See Appendix, *Note V.*

ceuctst.

it can throw absolutely no light on the reason why material particles move. "Force is a direct *object* of sense," wrote Sir William Thomson and Professor Tait.[1] Force "is not a term for anything objective," wrote Professor Tait.[2] In the face of such contradictions, is it not better to cease supposing that any lucid explanation of the why of motion can be abstracted from the idea of force?

But may not our particles, like two dancers, *hold hands*, and so the one "enforce" the other's motion? We must not say that this holding hands is impossible, although the particles be 90,000,000 miles apart. We conceive light as easily traversing those 90,000,000 miles by aid of the ether, and may not our particles hold hands by means of the ether? All scientists hope that this may be so, at any rate conceptually, although they have not yet conceived how it can be so. But if we phenomenalised the ether and were able to describe by aid of it action at a distance of millions of miles, we should still be left with the problem: Why does the relative position of two adjacent parts of ether influence the motion of those parts? It might seem at first sight easier to explain why two adjacent ether elements "move each other" than why two distant particles of matter do. The common-sense philosopher is ready at once with an explanation: They *pull* or *push* each other. But what do we mean by these words? A tendency when a body is strained to resume its original form; a tendency in a certain relative position of its parts to a certain relative motion of its parts. But why does this motion follow on a particular position? It is the old problem over again, with the difference that relative position now involves small instead of large distances. It will not do to attribute it to the *elasticity* of the medium; this is merely giving the fact a *name*. We do indeed try to describe the phenomenon of elasticity conceptually, but this is solely by constructing elastic bodies out of *non-adjacent*

[1] *A Treatise on Natural Philosophy*, part i. p. 220. Cambridge, 1879.
[2] *The Properties of Matter*. Edinburgh, 1885.

particles, the changes of position of which we associate with certain relative motions. In other words, to appeal to the conception of elasticity is only to " explain " one " action at a distance " by a second " action at a distance." If the ether-elements owe their elasticity to such an arrangement, we shall want another ether to " explain " the motion of the first, and the process will have to be continued *ad infinitum*. Clearly the phenomenalisation of the ether is absolutely useless as a means of explaining why matter moves. It still leaves us with the same problem in another form : Why does ether-matter move ? And here no answer can be given. We cannot proceed for ever " explaining " mechanism by mechanism. Those who insist on phenomenalising mechanism must ultimately say : " *Here we are ignorant,*" or, what is the same thing, must take refuge in matter and force. According to Paul du Bois-Reymond, the problem of action at a distance is the third *Ignorabimus*,[1] but the problem is really identical with that of Emil du Bois-Reymond's first *Ignorabimus*, the nature of matter and force.

It seems to me that we are ignorant and shall be ignorant just as long as we project our conceptual chart, which symbolises but is not the world of phenomena, into that world ; just as long as we try to find realities corresponding to geometrical ideals and other purely conceptual limits. So long as we do this we mistake the object of science, which is not to explain but to describe by conceptual shorthand our perceptual experience. When we once clearly recognise that change of sense-impression is the reality, motion and mechanism the descriptive ideal, then the Brothers du Bois-Reymonds' first and third problems and their cry of *Ignorabimus* become meaningless. Matter and force and " action at a distance " are witch-and-blue-milk problems (p. 22), if mechanism be purely a conceptual description. What moves in conception is a geometrical ideal, and it moves because we conceive it to move. *How* it moves becomes the all-important question, for it is the means by which we

[1] See the work cited on our p. 38.

regulate our mechanism so as to describe our past and predict our future experience. This *how* of motion is the point to which we must next turn. The laws of motion in the widest sense embrace all physical science— perhaps it were not too much to say all science whatever. All laws, von Helmholtz tells us, must ultimately be merged in laws of motion. Even such a complex phenomenon as that of heredity is at bottom, Haeckel holds, a transference of motion. Strong in her power of describing *how* changes take place, Science can well afford to neglect the *why*. She may not, so long at least as psychology stands where it does, go as far as to fully accept even Emil du Bois-Reymond's second *Ignorabimus* ; but as to what consciousness is and why there is a routine of sense-impressions she is content for the present to say, "*Ignoramus.*"

SUMMARY

The notion of matter is found to be equally obscure whether we seek for definition in the writings of physicists or of "common-sense" philosophers. The difficulties with regard to it appear to arise from asserting the phenomenal but imperceptible existence of conceptual symbols. Change of sense-impression is the proper term for external perception, motion for our conceptual symbolisation of this change. Of perception the questions "what moves" and "why it moves" are seen to be idle. In the field of conception the moving bodies are geometrical ideals with merely descriptive motions.

Of the du Bois-Reymonds' three cries of *Ignorabimus*, only the second in a modified sense is scientifically valuable, the others are unintelligible, because we find that matter, force, and "action at a distance" are not terms which express real problems of the phenomenal world.

LITERATURE

BOIS-REYMOND, EMIL DU. — Über die Grenzen des Naturerkennens. Leipzig, 1876.

CLERK-MAXWELL, J.—Articles "Atom" and "Ether" in the Encyclopædia Britannica, reprinted in the Scientific Papers, vol. ii. pp. 445 and 763. The article on the "Constitution of Bodies" may also be consulted with advantage.

CLIFFORD, W. K.—Lectures and Essays, vol. i. ("Atoms" and "The Unseen Universe"). London, 1879.

TAIT, P. G.—Properties of Matter (especially chaps. i.-v.).   Edinburgh, 1885.

THOMSON, SIR WILLIAM (LORD KELVIN). — Popular Lectures and Addresses, vol. i. (especially pp. 142-52).   London, 1889.

A popular account of Larmor's gyrostatic ether and also of the ether-squirt will be found in a lecture, " Over Ether-Theorieën," given by W. H. Julius in 1899 before the Netherlands Natur- en Geneeskundig Congres, and published in its Proceedings.

CHAPTER IX

THE LAWS OF MOTION

§ 1.—*Corpuscles and their Structure*

IN the last chapter we have seen how the physicist conceptually constructs the universe by aid of a vast atomic dance. I use the word *atom* although it is most probably the ultimate element of the ether, which we ought to talk about as the fundamental unit of the dance. Let us term this latter unit the *ether-element*, without intending to assert by the use of this word that the ether is necessarily discontinuous.[1]   Two adjacent ether-elements will be the symbols, necessarily geometrical, by which we represent the relative motion of the parts of the ether. On the basis of the ether-element let us try and conceive how the physicist imagines his mechanical model of the universe constructed.   Perceptual experience gives us no hint as to what we ought to conceive the ether-element to consist of, or how we ought to imagine it to act, if it could be isolated.   But we are compelled to consider ether-elements when in each other's presence as moving in certain definite modes, as taking part in a regulated dance. Perceptually there is no reason for this dance, conceptually it enables us to describe the world of sense-impressions.

Probably, although this point is far from being definitely settled, one type of motion among the ether-elements may

---

[1] If we suppose the ether to be a conceptual limit to a perceptual fluid or jelly (pp. 289 and 301), then to conceptualise at all its transmission of stress or its elasticity we are, I think, compelled to suppose it discontinuous.

be conceived as constituting the prime-atom. These prime-atoms, the *protyle* of Crookes, are to be taken as symbols of the ultimate basis of material groups of sense-impressions, or, in ordinary language, of gross or sensible " matter." Prime-atoms in themselves, or, what is more likely, in groups, form the atom of the chemist, the conceptual substratum of the so-called simple elements such as hydrogen, oxygen, iron, carbon, etc., by aid of which the chemist classifies all the known heavy matter of the physical universe. If the prime-atom of the physicist is really the atom of the chemist, then the prime-atom must be conceived as having variations either in its structure or in its type of motion corresponding to the different chemical elements. There are certain perceptual facts, however, which suggest that we should describe phenomena best by conceiving the atom of the simple chemical element to be constructed from groups of prime-atoms, the disassociation of which corresponds to no definite perceptual results which the chemist has hitherto succeeded in attaining. Out of the atoms of the simple elements the chemist constructs *compounds* ; that is, by combining con-ceptually these atoms in certain groupings he forms the *molecule* of the compound. Thus two atoms of hydrogen and one of oxygen are united to form the molecule of water. Any portion of the compound substance itself is conceived as composed of an immense number of molecules. In order to describe the sense-impressions which we physically associate with a " piece of a given substance " we are bound to postulate that the smallest physical element of it is to be considered as containing millions of molecules.[1]

[1] The reasons for this statement are chiefly drawn from the Kinetic Theory of Gases. Clerk-Maxwell in his article " Atom " (*Encyclopædia Britannica*) considers that the *minimum visibile* of the present day may be conceived as containing sixty to one hundred million atoms of oxygen or nitrogen. He proceeds to draw from this result conclusions, which I think quite unwarranted, as to our power of describing by aid of molecular structure the physiological facts of heredity. He remarks that : " Since the molecules of organised substances contain on an average fifty of the more elementary atoms, we may assume that the smallest particle visible under the microscope contains about two million molecules of organic matter. At least half of every living organism consists of water, so that the smallest living being

If we take a piece of any substance, say a bit of chalk, and divide it into small fragments, these still possess the properties of chalk. Divide any fragment again and again, and so long as a divided fragment is perceptible by aid of the microscope it still appears chalk. Now the physicist is in the habit of defining the smallest portion of a substance which, he conceives, could possess the physical properties of the original substance as a *particle*. The particle is thus a purely conceptual notion, for we cannot say when we should reach the exact limit of subdivision at which the physical properties of the substance would cease to be. But the particle is of great value in our conceptual model of the universe, for we represent its motion by the motion of a geometrical point. In other words, we suppose it to have solely a motion of translation (pp. 225 and 232); we neglect its motions of rotation and of strain. The physicist has here reached a purely conceptual limit to perceptual experience ; he takes a smaller and smaller element of gross " matter," and supposing it always to be of the same substance (*i.e.* to produce the same sense-impressions although it

---

visible under the microscope does not contain more than about a million organic molecules. Some exceedingly simple organism may be supposed built up of not more than a million similar molecules. It is impossible, however, to conceive so small a number sufficient to form a being furnished with a whole system of specialised organs."

This reasoning is simply a form of special pleading based on the assumption that variations in physiological organs depend *solely* on chemical constitution and not on physical structure. Why are we to put on one side the facts that there are upwards of fifty atoms in the organic molecule, that there *is* a certain proportion of water, and that these organic molecules must be conceived as *closely* packed into a scarce visible germ ? Why are these one hundred million atoms not to be conceived as physically influencing each other's *motion* ? If this be so, then their relative position, the structure of the germ as a dynamical system, may be shown to involve no less than 10,000 million million periodic motions, having various relative positions in space, and apart from this relative position having in amplitude, relative phase, and "note," three hundred million variables at the disposal of the physiologist ! Whether heredity can or cannot be described by the influence of such a molecular structure on other molecules is quite beyond our present scientific knowledge to determine ; but we certainly cannot dogmatically assert with Maxwell that : "Molecular science sets us face to face with physiological theories. It forbids the physiologist from imagining that structural details of infinitely small dimensions can furnish an explanation of the infinite variety which exists in the properties and functions of the most minute organisms."

becomes imperceptible), he deals with it as a moving point. What right has the physicist to invent this ideal particle? He has never perceived the limiting quantity, the *minimum esse* of a substance, and therefore cannot assert that it would not produce in him sense-impressions which could only be described by aid of the concepts spin and strain. The logical right of the physicist is, however, exactly that on which all scientific conceptions are based. We have to ask whether postulating an ideal of this sort enables us to construct out of the motion of groups of particles those more complex motions by aid of which we describe the physical universe. Is the particle a symbol by aid of which we can describe our past and predict our future sequences of sense-impressions with a great and uniform degree of accuracy? If it be, then its use is justified as a scientific method of simplifying our ideas and of economising thought.

The reader must note that this hypothesis of the particle is made use of by Newton in the statement of his law of gravitation: " Every *particle* of matter in the universe attracts every other *particle*," he tells us, in such and such a manner. Yet Newton is here dealing with conceptual notions, for he never saw, nor has any physicist since his time ever seen, individual particles, or been able to examine how the motion of two such particles is related to their position. The justification of the law of gravitation lies in the power it gives us of constructing the motion of those groups of particles by aid of which we symbolise physical bodies and ultimately describe and predict the routine of our sense-impressions. The particle, therefore, as the symbolic unit of physical substance with its simple motion of translation is as valid as the law of gravitation, in the statement of which it is indeed involved.

Lastly, groups of particles bounded in conception by continuous surfaces are the symbols by which we represent those material groups of sense-impressions that are currently spoken of as physical bodies or objects. To find the simplest possible types of relative motion for these various concepts, and thence to construct the motion

of the geometrical forms by which we symbolise physical
bodies, so that the motion describes to any required degree
of accuracy our routine of sense-impressions, is the scope
of physical science. We find that by assuming certain
laws for the relative motion of these conceptual symbols
—the laws of motion in their widest sense—we are able
to construct a world of geometrical forms moving in
conceptual space and time, which describe with wonderful
exactness the complex phases of our perceptual experience.

§ 2.—*The Limits to Mechanism*

Let us now resume the elements of our conceptual
model of the physical universe in a purely *diagrammatic*
manner.[1] An asterisk shall represent the ether-element,

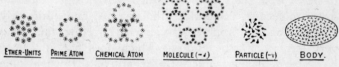

ETHER-UNITS   PRIME ATOM   CHEMICAL ATOM   MOLECULE (~⁴)   PARTICLE (~v)   BODY.

FIG. 21.

a ring of asterisks will suggest the prime-atom probably
constructed from a special ether-element motion — for
example, a vortex-ring. One, two, or more prime-atoms
form the chemical atom, and for its symbol we will take
three interlaced rings. Combinations of chemical atoms
form the molecule, in our diagram represented by two
chemical atoms of three and one of two prime-atoms.
Millions of these molecules, of which we can only represent
a few by the shorthand symbol ⁴, would form the particle
(shorthand symbol v), while millions of particles, here
merely suggested, conceptually enclosed by a continuous
surface, symbolise the physical bodies of our perceptual experience. These concepts, from ether-element to particle,
it must be borne in mind, have no perceptual equivalents, and it is only by experiments on the perceptual
equivalent of the last of the series, the conceptual body,

[1] The diagram is only to suggest the physical relationships to the reader,
and has no meaning from the standpoint of relative size or form.

that the physicist is able to test the truth of the laws of motion he propounds.

In the first place he postulated these laws for particles, and demonstrated their validity by showing that they enabled him to describe the routine of his sense-impressions with regard to physical " bodies." But with the growth of our ideas as to the nature of ether and gross " matter," we naturally begin to question whether the laws which describe the relative motion of two particles are to be conceived as holding for two molecules, two chemical atoms, two prime-atoms, and ultimately for two ether-elements. Or, what may possibly be still more important, are they to hold for the relative motion of a prime-atom and adjacent ether-elements ? How far are we to consider the laws of motion as applied to particles of gross " matter " to result from the manner in which particles are built up from molecules, molecules from atoms, and ultimately atoms probably from ether-elements ? Now this is a very important issue, and one which does not appear to have been always sufficiently regarded. If we assume that the particle is ultimately based on a certain type of ether-motion, then we must admit the existence of other types of ether-motion which do not constitute gross " matter." In this case it will by no means follow that the relative motion of two particles, or of two prime-atoms, will follow the same laws as the relative motion of two ether-elements. It is quite clear, of course, that modes of motion peculiar to gross " matter " must arise from its special structure, and not be assumed to flow from laws applying to *all* moving things. For example, gravitation, magnetisation, electrification, the absorption and emission of heat and light are all phases of sense-impression which we associate with gross " matter," and therefore they must be described by modes of motion characteristic of gross " matter," or modes which flow from its peculiar constitution. As kinetic formulæ or special laws of motion they cannot be extended to the ether in general. But there are still more general laws of motion, which we may describe as the Newtonian laws, and which certainly when applied to particles are confirmed by our perceptual experience of bodies. Ought we to assert that these laws hold in their entirety for all the downward scale from particle to ether-element? Shall we find our conceptual description of the universe simplified, or the reverse, by supposing complete *mechanism* to extend from particle to ether-element? Or will it be more advantageous to postulate that mechanism in whole or part flows from the ascending complexity of our structures, that the ether-element is largely the *source* of mechanism, but is not completely mechanical [1] in the sense of obeying the laws of motion as given in dynamical text-books? The question is undoubtedly an important one, but one which cannot be answered off-hand. Nor, indeed, till we have much clearer conceptions of the structure of the prime-atom than we have at present reached, will it be possible to say how far the mechanism we postulate of particles may be conceived to flow from its structure.

In order to remind the reader that the general laws of motion we are about to discuss may either entirely or only in part hold for the whole series of physical concepts from particle to ether-element, we will class the whole series together as *corpuscles*, a word simply signifying little elementary bodies. We shall then have to ask in each case to which of the ideal corpuscles we are to suppose our laws to apply. The test will always be the same, namely : How far is the assumption necessary in order to obtain a model which will enable us to describe briefly the routine of perception?

§ 3.—*The First Law of Motion*

Let us now return to our conception of the universe as the regulated dance of the elemental groups which we have termed prime-atoms, chemical atoms, molecules, and particles. Individual corpuscles dance in groups, groups

---

[1] For example, as will be shown in the sequel, the "mass" of a particle must be considered as in all probability very different from the "mass" of an ether-element (see § 11 of this chapter).

dance round groups, and groups of groups dance relatively to each other. *How*, we have next to ask, do two corpuscles dance with regard to each other? In the first place we must observe that, at least in the case of gross " matter," a corpuscle which is conceived as forming part of the sun must be considered as regulating its dance with due regard to a corpuscle forming part of the earth. We cannot assert that it would not be best to conceive this as really done through a chain of partners, namely, ether-elements intervening between the sun and earth corpuscles, but as we have not yet settled how this chain of partners is to act, we must content ourselves at present by the statement that sun and earth corpuscles do regard each other's presence. But if they can do this at 90 million miles, there is every reason for inferring no breach in continuity and supposing they would also do it at 90 billion miles. We note, however, at once that it is necessary to conceive a particle at the surface of the earth paying more attention in its dance to an earth particle than to a sun particle, and again the phenomenon of cohesion tells us that two adjacent particles of the same piece of substance pay more heed to each other than particles of different pieces. Hence we conclude that : (1) in general terms corpuscles must be conceived as moving with greater regard to their immediate partners in the dance than to their near neighbours, and with greater regard to near neighbours than to still more distant corpuscles ; but (2) there is no limit to the distance at which we conceive corpuscles can influence each other's motion. This influence may, however, be so small that even when summed for the bodies that we construct from corpuscles, there is no perceptual equivalent to be found for it by aid of any instrument at our disposal. We can now state a first general law of motion :—

Every corpuscle in the conceptual model of the universe must be conceived as moving with due regard to the presence of every other corpuscle, although for very distant corpuscles the regard paid is extremely small as compared with that paid to immediate neighbours.

If the reader once grasps that every corpuscle in the universe must be conceived as influencing the motion of every other corpuscle, he will then fully appreciate the complexity of the corpuscular dance by aid of which we symbolise the world of sense-impressions.   The law of motion just stated probably applies to prime-atoms, and through them to chemical atoms, molecules, and particles. Possibly it does not apply to distant ether-elements directly, but these, perhaps, influence each other's motion only indirectly by directly influencing the motion of their immediate neighbours.   In this case the "action at a distance" generally asserted of corpuscles of gross "matter" may very probably be conceived as due to the action between adjacent ether-elements.   We should then have to state the first law as follows :—

Every corpuscle, whether of ether or gross "matter," influences the motion of the adjacent ether corpuscles, and through them of every other corpuscle, however distant; the influence thus spread is nevertheless very insignificant at great as compared with small distances.

§ 4.—*The Second Law of Motion, or the Principle of Inertia*

Now, in constructing the universe conceptually from our corpuscles, it is impossible to take into account the influence of all the corpuscles upon each other at one and the same time.   Accordingly we neglect at once influences which even in the aggregate are beyond our powers of measurement.   Further, we purposely exclude from consideration slight, if measurable, variations of motion due to more distant groups.   We isolate a particular group of corpuscles, and this group which we deal with conceptually apart from the rest we term, for the purposes of some particular discussion, the *field*.

The most limited field that we can conceive is that of a single corpuscle.   If we could isolate such a corpuscle from the rest of the conceptual universe, how would it move?   At first sight the question is absurd, because in Chapter VII. (p. 233) we saw that motion is meaningless if it be not relative to something.   The moment, however, we introduce other corpuscles into the field in order to measure the motion of the first, they begin to pay regard to each other's presence, and we are no longer dealing with the motion of an isolated corpuscle.   But we have seen that the greater the distance between the corpuscles, the less this influence must be conceived to be ; hence we may take the conceptual limit by supposing that the corpuscles are so far off each other that their mutual influence is negligible, while their mutual presence will still suffice to provide the " frame " (see p. 235) necessary for describing a relative motion.[1]   Now in order that the laws which govern the motion of corpuscles shall lead to the construction of complex motions, fully describing the phases of our perceptual experience, we are compelled to suppose that the more and more completely we separate one corpuscle from the influence of other corpuscles, the more and more nearly does its motion relative to a suitable frame determined by these corpuscles cease to vary. The first corpuscle either remains at rest relatively to this frame or continues to move with the same speed—the same number of miles per minute—in the same direction. But this is what we term uniform motion, or motion without acceleration (pp. 258-9), and we are thus endowing our corpuscles with a very important property, namely, we assert that they will not dance, that is, alter their motion, unless they have partners to dance with.   This characteristic which we attribute to corpuscles, namely, that their uniform motion is not altered except in the presence of other corpuscles, is scientifically termed their *inertia.*

Now the reader must be very careful to note the essential features of this principle of inertia.   In the first place we consider that all corpuscles are going to in-fluence each other's motion, and in the second place we find it necessary, owing to the relativity of all motion, to

---

[1] The reader must remember that relative position is conceptualised by a *directed* step, and that it is a series of directed steps which forms the path of the relative motion (p. 237).   Each directed step is to be conceived as " fixed " in direction by a " frame," and the points of this frame are to be considered as having no accelerations relative to each other.   See Appendix, *Note I.*

introduce other corpuscles, in order to determine a " frame
of reference" (p. 235). Such a frame of reference can
be placed at once in conceptual space and all relative
motion referred to it, but what shall we take to correspond to it in perceptual space? In order to reach the
idea of such a frame, we have to fix it by corpuscles at
such a distance that their influence is insensible (see the
second part of the first law), and then seek in the perceptual sphere for something which approaches this conceptual limit. We find it for practical purposes in a frame
determined by the stars. Such a frame is open to several
theoretical and some few practical objections. In the
first place, although the mutual influences of the stars
upon each other must be very small, yet this very law of
inertia would allow them to be relatively in motion, and
we have so far no means of satisfactorily ascertaining the
straight lines we conceive them as relatively describing,
or even describing relative to our own system. Then, in
the next place, as we only know in the roughest way our
probable distances from the fixed stars, or theirs from
each other, it is impossible to plot our small changes of
distances here relative to a frame with its origin at a
fixed star. Accordingly, it is usual to take the origin of
reference in our own solar system and merely use the
stars to give directions by means of which " bearing " may
be defined (p. 234). This serves, in nearly all cases, as a
sufficient link to connect actual phenomena with our conceptual model, but for some refined astronomical purposes
we are compelled to pay heed to the slight variations in
direction of these lines to the stars. Practically these
variations are so slight, that the stars are spoken of as
" fixed " stars, but the reader must bear in mind that they
are not fixed, and that our frame of reference giving a fixed
bearing is only one of those ideal conceptions drawn as
a limit to conceptual experience, to which we have often
had occasion to refer (pp. 199, 203). Should we ever be
able to associate the conceptual ether with phenomena of
a persistent character in districts of perceptual space unoccupied by gross " matter," then possibly the ether itself

might be used to determine our frame of reference,[1] and there is little doubt that this would clear up many of our current difficulties as to inertia and absolute rotation. Meanwhile, we must bear in mind that while the frame of reference and the principle of inertia are quite clear ideas in the conceptual model of corpuscles, they have no exact perceptual equivalents. But no parts, indeed, of our mechanical models have, as we have before noted, exact perceptual equivalents ; all we must ask is : Are they valid as instruments for describing phenomena ? Here the answer must be : Most certainly, if we take our frame as determined by the so-called "fixed" stars.

With regard to this law of inertia it must probably be conceived as holding from the prime-atom to the particle, but a difficulty comes in when we consider ether-elements. If the prime-atom be a particular type of ether-motion, for example an ether vortex-ring or ether-squirt, then the very existence of the corpuscles of gross "matter" depends upon the presence of the ether-elements, not only in their own constitution, but in their immediate neighbourhood. It becomes, therefore, hopelessly absurd to consider what a corpuscle of gross "matter" would do if it were isolated from the influence of ether-elements. The law of inertia for gross "matter" must then flow from the peculiar structure of gross "matter." The mutual presence of ether-elements and of an isolated prime-atom will then be seen to involve the inertia of the latter, but the ether-elements themselves will, while the prime-atom moves uniformly, be varying their motion with due regard to the presence of the prime-atom.[2] What the law of inertia is to be considered as meaning when applied to isolated ether-elements, it is again difficult to say.

---

[1] Actually the ether is used ; it is the direction of a ray of light in the ether which gives the "fixed" direction, and this light may have left the star millions of years ago, and does not necessarily mark the present direction of the star. Unfortunately it does not *persist*. On the general subject of motion relative to the ether see Chapter X. §§ 9, 10.

[2] For example, it may be shown that an *isolated* vortex-ring in an infinite fluid moves without sensible change of size with uniform velocity perpendicular to its plane ; on the other hand, the ether-elements vary their velocity according to their position relative to the ring (see A. B. Basset, *A Treatise on Hydrodynamics*, vol. ii. pp. 59-62).

Possibly it is idle to inquire so long, at any rate, as the conceptual ether remains as little defined as at present. Our notions of the ether are so essentially bound up with the conception of its *continuity*, while our notions of gross " matter " are, on the other hand, so closely associated with the idea of the discontinuity of matter, that we are inclined to treat as fundamental for ether-elements the method in which they act in each other's presence, and for gross " matter " corpuscles the method in which they act when isolated. On this account the law of inertia, as we postulate it for gross " matter " corpuscles, may be considered as a feature of mechanism very probably flowing from the structure of the prime-atom itself.

§ 5.—*The Third Law of Motion.   Mutual Acceleration is determined by Relative Position*

Let us now proceed a stage further and postulate the next simplest field ; let us suppose two corpuscles taken and their motions determined relatively (p. 235) to a frame through a third corpuscle, which, however, like that on p. 314, we will consider to be at such a distance as to be quite isolated from their influence. What must we conceive as happening ? In the first place, because two corpuscles are in the same field must we consider them as having a certain definite position relative to each other ? Certainly not. We find ourselves compelled to consider them as capable of taking up a great variety of positions with regard to each other. Does, then, the fact that they are in the same field, or in a certain relative position in that field, determine with what velocities we are to consider them as moving ? Again we must answer : No —at any rate for particles. In order to construct motions which will effectively describe our sequences of sense-impressions we are forced to suppose that particles may move through the same relative position with every variety of velocity. What, then, must we consider as determined when we know the relative position of two corpuscles ? It is their accelerations, the rates at which they are changing their relative position. *Two corpuscles may be moving through the same position with any velocities, but they will spurt and shunt each other's motions in a perfectly definite manner, depending on their relative position.*

If A and B represent two corpuscles moving relative to the "frame" in the directions AT and BT′ with the velocities V and V′ given by the steps OQ and O′Q′ of their respective hodographs (p. 247), then the spurt and shunt of V and V′, or, as we have seen (p. 248), the velocities of Q and Q′ along their hodograph paths, will be determined at each instant by the relative position of A and B.   Let these velocities of Q and Q′, or the accelerations of A and B, be represented by the steps Q*t*

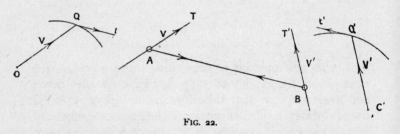

FIG. 22.

and Q′*t* taken along the tangents at Q and Q′ (pp. 243 and 251).   Then the question naturally arises, How are we to consider the spurts and shunts given by Q*t* and Q′*t*′ (p. 249) to depend on the relative position of A and B? In the first place we conceive Q*t* and Q′*t*′ to be *parallel, but in opposite senses* (p. 234).   We find it needful to suppose universally that the mutual accelerations of corpuscles have the same direction but opposite senses.[1]   In the next place it is usually assumed that this direction is that of the line joining the points which represent the corpuscles A and B.   Now this assumption is possibly correct enough[2] when we are dealing with particles of gross "matter," at any rate when we are discussing the motion of non-adjacent particles, or those for which we

---

[1] That is, if A spurts B in the direction from B toward A, then B will spurt A in the direction from A to B and *vice versa*.

[2] See Appendix, *Note II.*

are not compelled to consider the distance AB vanishingly small like the dimensions of the particles themselves.[1] On the other hand, there appear to be many physical and even chemical phenomena which cannot be described by replacing the motion of a prime-atom, chemical atom, or molecule by the motion of a point. In this case the line joining the two corpuscles becomes a meaningless term, and we have really to deal with the relative motion of groups of elements, constructed very probably from the motion of simple ether-elements.

When, however, we ask of ether-elements whether we are to consider them as mutually accelerating each other in the line joining them, we are at once stopped by the difficulty that we have reason for supposing non-adjacent ether-elements do not influence each other's motion at all (p. 313). But if we turn to adjacent ether-elements, the line joining them vanishes with the dimensions of the elements when we try to conceive the ether as absolutely continuous (pp. 205, 298, and 317). Discontinuity of the ether may carry us over this difficulty and allow us to consider ether-elements as mutually accelerating each other's motion in the direction of the line joining them, but such discontinuity reintroduces one of the problems which the conception of the ether was invented to solve (pp. 205 and 301). We may be quite safe in postulating that when an ideal geometrical surface is supposed drawn and fixed in the ether its *points* will have a motion relative to each other upon its form being changed ; the points of the surface will tend to return to their original positions with accelerations depending on their change of relative position. But when we assert that this is due to ether-elements mutually accelerating each other's motion in the line joining them, we may, after all, be postulating

---

[1] It will be noticed in this case that if we take the motion of A relative to B, the ray and tangent to the path or orbit of A are respectively parallel to the tangent and ray to the hodograph or path of Q. This is expressed in technical language by saying that the orbit of such a motion is a link-polygon (funicular polygon) for the hodograph as a vector-polygon (force-polygon), and this forms the basis of a graphical method of dealing with central accelerations.

a phase of mechanism for the ether which is only true for gross "matter," and which may indeed flow from the particular type of ether-motion which constitutes gross "matter." If the prime-atom be a vortex-ring it would be impossible to describe in general the action between two prime-atoms as a "mutual acceleration in the line joining them." On the other hand, if the prime-atom be an ether-squirt, this phrase would effectively describe the action between two prime-atoms. In both cases the statement that particles mutually accelerate each other's motion in the line joining them would flow either as an absolute or an approximate law from the particular structure of gross "matter," and would not be a mechanical truth for all corpuscles from ether-element up to particle.

There are still several points to be noticed with regard to the nature of the manner in which corpuscles spurt and shunt each other's motion. We have said that this depends on the relative position of the corpuscles—but is the mutual acceleration never influenced by the velocities of the corpuscles? Do two of our conceptual dancers influence each other solely by their relative position and never by the speed and direction with which they pass through that position? It has been supposed that the introduction of the relative velocity as a factor determining the mutual acceleration of two particles would be contrary to a well-established physical principle termed the conservation of energy. It is indeed a fact that many writers, from Helmholtz downwards, have given a mathematical *proof* of the conservation of energy which depends on mutual acceleration being a function of relative position and not of relative velocity. But if two moving bodies be placed in a fluid they will apparently accelerate each other with accelerations depending upon their velocities as well as on their relative position. The conservation of energy still holds in this case for the entire system of fluid and moving bodies, and yet to the observer unconscious of the fluid the mutual accelerations of the bodies would certainly appear to be determined by

their velocities as well as by their position.[1] Something
of this kind may well occur when we regard the action
between corpuscles of gross "matter" without regard to
the ether in which we conceive them floating. We
cannot assume that the mutual acceleration of prime-
atoms, chemical atoms, and molecules depends solely on
their relative positions; it may depend also on their
velocities relative to each other, or relative to the ether in
which we suppose them to be moving. This remark is of
special importance when we try to describe electric and
magnetic phenomena by the mutual accelerations of
particles at a distance.

It is usually assumed by physicists, however, that the
action between particles at a distance is to be considered
as taking place in the line joining them and as depending
only on relative position. There have not indeed been
wanting scientific writers who have asserted that the whole
universe could be described mechanically by aid of a
system of particles or points, the mutual accelerations of
which depended solely on their mutual distances. But
simple as such an hypothesis would be, its propounders
have hitherto failed to demonstrate its sufficiency.[2] Nevertheless it has played a great part in physical research,
and its influence may still be seen in much that is written
at the present time about the laws of motion and the conservation of energy.

The above discussion puts us in a better position for

[1] The ether being neglected, its unregarded kinetic energy appears as
potential energy of the moving bodies, and is generally expressible in terms
of the velocities of those bodies. Hence those bodies appear to have a
mutual acceleration depending not only on their relative position but on their
velocities.

[2] The impulse to this mode of describing the physical universe certainly
arose from the Newtonian law of gravitation. It was perhaps pushed as far
as it could possibly be of service in the writings of Poisson, Cauchy, and the
great French analysts at the beginning of the century. Traces of its persistency may be still found in modern writers; for example, we may cite Clausius
—one of the most distinguished of modern German physicists—who considered
that all the phenomena of nature can probably be reduced to points mutually
accelerating each other in the lines joining them with accelerations which are
functions only of their mutual distances (*Die mechanische Wärmetheorie*, Bd.
i. S. 17). Its insufficiency is evidenced, or apparently evidenced, in its
failure to describe completely various elastic body phenomena.

appreciating the statements that we may legitimately make with regard to the dance not only of two but of any number of corpuscles. In general we may assert that whether we are dealing with the continuous ether or with discontinuous atoms and molecules, then if we fix our attention on a geometrical point which symbolises an element of ether, atom, or molecule, the acceleration (*not* the velocity) of this point will depend on the position of this point or element relative to other points or elements (and possibly in certain cases on its velocities relative to those points or elements). For particles of gross " matter," on the other hand, we find it as a general (if not invariable) rule sufficient to assert that the mode in which their velocity is being spurted and shunted depends solely on their position relative to other particles. In particular, if two particles be alone in the field, their mutual accelerations will depend on their relative position and may be conceived as taking place in the line joining them, but in opposite senses.

§ 6.—*Velocity as an Epitome of Past History.   Mechanism and Materialism*

There are one or two points in these statements which deserve special notice.   If we avoid the metaphysical idea of force, and consider causation as pure antecedence in phenomena (pp. 128-131), then the cause of change of motion or acceleration must in our conceptual model of the phenomenal world be associated with *relative position*. The given velocities of a system at any time may be looked upon as the sum of the past changes of motion ; or the causes of a given motion can only be conceived as lying in the totality of all past relative positions of the system.   Thus force, as the conceptual idea of moving cause, could only be defined as the history of the relative positions of a system.   This history determines the actual velocities of the parts of the system, while actual position determines how the velocities are instantaneously changing. The " actual position," however, is the conceptual equivalent of the mode in which we perceptually distinguish coexisting sense-impressions, while "past history" is the conceptual equivalent of the perceptual sequence in sense-impressions. "Actual position" and "past history" taken in conjunction thus symbolise what we have termed the routine of perceptions (p. 101). We conclude, therefore, that if with the late Professor Tait and other metaphysical physicists we even project our conceptions into the perceptual sphere, we still shall not find in "force," as either the cause of motion, or the cause of change in motion, anything more than that routine of perceptions which we have already seen is the basis of the scientific definition of causation (p. 130).

The idea that the past history of a corpuscle is resumed in its present velocity is an important one. If we knew the actual velocities of all existing corpuscles and how their accelerations depend on relative position (or it may be also on relative velocity), then *theoretically*, by aid of the process indicated on our p. 259, or by an extension of this process to extended geometrical systems, we should be able to trace out the whole of the past, or, on the other hand, the whole of the future history of our conceptual model of the universe. The data would be sufficient to theoretically solve these problems, although our brains would be quite insufficient to manipulate the necessary analysis. Portions of it they do, however, manage. From the present velocities of earth and moon and their known accelerations relative to the sun and to each other, we calculate the eclipses of two or three thousand years ago, and rectify our chronology by determining the dates of eclipses which are recorded in the history of past human experience. Or, again, from thermal or tidal data we describe the condition of the universe as we conceive it to have been millions of years back, or as we conceive it will be millions of years hence. In all such cases we consider that because our conceptual model describes very accurately our limited perceptual experience of past and present, it will continue to do so if we apply it to describe sequences which cannot be verified as immediate sense-impressions. In this case we are clearly making inferences, but inferences which are logically justifiable (p. 60 and

Chap. XI. § 11); we assume that because our conceptual model describes very accurately our immediate perceptual experience, it would also describe the antecedents and consequents of that experience, did they exist perceptually; it is logical to infer when we see the panorama of a river, one portion of which accurately depicts all we know of the river Thames, that the rest of the panorama depicts parts of the *same* river, with which we are unacquainted. In the necessarily limited verifiable correspondence of our perceptual experience with our conceptual model lies the basis of our mechanical description of the universe. As a shorthand *résumé* of our perceptual experience, and as a co-ordination of that experience with stored sense-impresses, the only objective element of this mechanical theory is seen to lie in the similar perceptive and reasoning faculties of two human minds. Thus the sole support of that materialism which, " proceeding from the fixed relation between matter and force as an indestructible basis," finds " mechanical laws inherent in the things themselves," collapses under the slightest pressure of logical criticism.[1]

But while we sweep away materialism and allow that mechanism is no explanation, only a conceptual description of the changes we perceive in phenomena, we must not rush into the opposite extreme and underrate the surprising value of our mechanical model of the universe. Many as are its defects and failures we yet see its accuracy surely, if gradually, extending; its assertions as to what has happened in the past and its predictions as to what will happen in the future continually receive the most striking and ample verification. At times when mechanical analysis through some recondite mathematical process has enabled us to resume in a few brief statements numerous facts of perceptual experience, our reason seems lord of the universe, and we foretaste what a developed human

---

[1] The chief German representatives of this materialism are J. Moleschott and L. Büchner, and it found its warmest supporters in England among the followers of the late Mr. Bradlaugh. It is perhaps needless to add that the gifted lady, who spoke of secularists as holding the "creed of Clifford and Charles Bradlaugh," failed to see the irreconcilable divergence between the inventor of "mind-stuff" and the follower of Büchner.

intellect might achieve in foretelling the future or describing the past. To one who carried the mechanical description of the universe forward by leaps and bounds, to Laplace at the summit of his course of discovery, there appeared a vision and he wrote it down in the materialistic phrases of his age :—

"We ought then to regard the present state of the universe as the effect of its antecedent state and as the cause of the state that is to follow. An intelligence which should be acquainted with all the forces by which nature is animated and with the several positions at any given instant of all the parts thereof; if, further, its intellect were vast enough to submit these data to analysis, would include in one and the same formula the movements of the largest bodies in the universe and those of the lightest atom. Nothing would be uncertain for it, the future as well as the past would be present to its eyes. The human mind, in the perfection it has been able to give to astronomy, affords a feeble outline of such an intelligence. Its discoveries in mechanics and in geometry, joined to that of universal gravitation, have brought it within reach of comprehending in the same analytical expressions the past and future states of the systems of the world." [1]

Only those who realise the enormous strides made by applied mathematics in the age of Laplace, and have tasted, even if in a small degree, the joy of scientific discovery, can fairly judge such words. To treat them with contumely as a " Laplacean conceit," and to join with Napoleon—that waster of human intellectual power—in declaring their writer as "fit for nothing but solving problems in the infinitely little," [2] is indeed to proclaim oneself a dullard unable to appreciate some of the most marvellous products of the human mind. If our mechanical description of the universe has not progressed at the rate Laplace

---

[1] *Essai philosophique sur les probabilités*, p. 4. Paris, 1819. Laplace continues : "All its efforts in the search for truth cause it to continually approach the intelligence we have just conceived, but *from this intelligence it will ever remain infinitely distant.*" The last words are often omitted by those who cite the passage.

[2] James Ward : *Naturalism and Agnosticism*, vol. i. p. 45. London, 1899.

felt justified in hoping for, it is largely because we have had no second Laplace to deal with "the infinitely little," as the first Laplace dealt with "the infinitely large." The mechanical theory Laplace foreshadowed will never enable us to assert that such an event must of necessity have occurred in the past or must unquestionably occur in the future. But the description in terms of motion, the brief formula expressing the changes in time and space of geometrical concepts, is the whole content of natural science,[1] and we ought rather to wonder at the enormous power this conceptual model even at present gives us of understanding the recorded past and of anticipating the experiences of the future, than idly criticise the "incapacity" of one who did more than any other scientific worker of the nineteenth century to advance our conceptual notions in the mechanical field.

§ 7.—The Fourth Law of Motion

It is high time, however, that we should return to our discussion on the laws of motion, and, assuming for the present that relative position is the principal factor in the determination of mutual accelerations, we must ask what more exact laws may be postulated with regard to these accelerations. We have in the first place to investigate how far the *individuality* of the dancers is to be conceived as influencing the manner in which they spurt each other's motion. Do *any* two dancers, whatever their race and family, and under whatever surroundings they may meet, always dance in the same fashion whenever they come to the same position? Or must we consider it necessary to classify our corpuscles by some scale which may itself indeed change with a change in the field? Again, are two dancers to be conceived as dancing in the same manner whatever aspect (p. 224) they bear to each other,

---

[1] I use this word purposely, for I allow no distinction ultimately between the physical and biological branches of science. As the latter advance, mere descriptions of sequences of sense-impressions are more and more likely to be replaced by formulæ describing conceptual motions; such is, indeed, the confessed aim of those somewhat embryonic studies "cellular dynamics" and "protoplasmic mechanics."

whether they come to the same position face to face, or back to back, as it were?   Lastly, if we know how A and B influence each other's motions when they are alone in the field, and how A and C dance when alone together, shall we be able to tell how A will act in the presence of *both* B and C?   Here are a number of ideas which we must try and express in scientific language with the view of determining what answers are to be given to the problems they suggest.

In the first place we ask the question :—

Is there any relation between the mutual accelerations of two corpuscles A and B, which is independent (1) of their relative position, and (2) of their possible companions in the field?   Is there any relation, in fact, which depends on the *individualities* of the corpuscles A and B?

This problem may be termed that of the *Kinetic Scale*.[1] Let us see how we might solve this problem ideally.   We might take two corpuscles and put them at different distances in a field in which they alone exerted influence, and we might measure their mutual accelerations.   Then we might repeat this process with other corpuscles in the field,[2] and vary the field itself in every possible manner. We should thus obtain two series of numbers, the one series representing the acceleration of A due to B,[3] and the other the acceleration of B due to A.   In the sphere of conception we should then be applying the scientific method of classifying facts, and trying by careful examina-tion of these facts to discover a law or formula by aid of which they might be described.   And we should very soon find a fundamental relation between these mutual accelerations of A and B.   Returning to our Fig. 22, we

---

[1] *Kinetic* is an adjective formed from Greek κίνησις, a *dance*, a movement ; the kinetic scale signifies a scale of movement.

[2] The manner in which the part of A's acceleration due to B might be separated from that due to the other corpuscles in the same field cannot be fully discussed in this work.   In many cases it could be discriminated by aid of the parallelogram of accelerations (p. 263).

[3] By the expression "acceleration of A *due* to B," frequently used in this chapter, the reader is not to understand that B *enforces* A's change in motion. The term is solely used as shorthand for the conceptual idea that A and B, when in each other's presence, are to be considered as changing their relative motions in a certain manner.

should discover that the number of units of length in Qt (if this represents the acceleration of A due to B) was always in a constant ratio to the number of units of length in $Q't'$ (or the acceleration of B due to A). If Qt were 7 units and $Q't'$ 3 units, then whatever other corpuscles were brought into the field, or however the relative position of A and B might be altered, still Qt and $Q't'$, be they both large or both small, would always have the ratio of 7 to 3. Now here is the beginning of the answer to our first question, and we may state our immediate conclusion in the following words :—

The ratio of the acceleration of A *due to* B *to the acceleration of* B *due to* A *must always be considered to be the same whatever be the position of* A *and* B, *and whatever be the surrounding field.*

The ratio of mutual accelerations is thus seen to depend on the individual pair of dancers, and not on their relative position, or the presence and character of their neighbours.

But the reader may ask : How can science possibly have drawn such a wide-reaching conclusion as this, since even the most metaphysical of physicists has never caught one corpuscle, let alone two, and could not therefore have experimented upon them in every possible field ? The answer is of the same character as that to the problem of the gravitating particles (p. 308). Physicists have experimented on perceptual bodies in all sorts of fields ; they have electrified, magnetised, warmed, or mechanically united by strings or rods, bodies of finite dimensions ; but, whatever the nature of the field, they have found that the smaller the bodies—the more nearly they approached the conceptual limit of particle,—the more nearly they have been able to describe the sequence of their sense-impressions by aid of conceptual particles obeying the above law. They then postulated the above law as true for particles, and, inverting the process, proceeded by aid of this law to describe the motion of those aggregates of particles which are our symbols for perceptual bodies. The validity of the law was then demonstrated by the power it was found to give us of predicting the future routine of our sense-impressions with regard to perceptual bodies. Once established as a mechanical principle for particles, it was natural to investigate whether its application to the whole range of corpuscles would give results in agreement with our perceptual experience. In so far as it did so, it became recognised as a universal law of mechanism. This process of discovering and then justifying the conceptual law by aid of our perceptual experience applies to all our further statements with regard to the laws of motion, and I shall not think it necessary for my present purposes to refer in each individual case to the experimental discovery and justification.

§ 8.—*The Scientific Conception of Mass*

This fourth law of motion carries us a long way in our description of the dance of corpuscles, but I have now to ask the reader to follow me in a rather more difficult investigation. This will, however, eventually repay us by the number of new ideas to which it introduces us. As the fourth law stands at present we should have to make experiments on every possible pair of corpuscles in order to form a scale of the ratios of their mutual accelerations. In order to avoid this very laborious process we conceive a standard corpuscle taken, which we will represent by the letter Q, and we suppose a record formed of the ratio of the mutual accelerations of Q and of each of the other corpuscles with which we populate conceptual space.

By the third law of motion the acceleration of Q due to A will always be in the same ratio to the acceleration of A due to Q, whatever be the field. Now we are going to give a name to this ratio ; we shall call it the *mass* of A relative to the standard Q, or more simply the mass of A. Thus we have :—

$$\text{Mass of A} = \frac{\text{Acceleration of Q due to A}}{\text{Acceleration of A due to Q}} \quad . \quad . \quad (a).$$

And similarly, if B be a second corpuscle, we have :—

$$\text{Mass of B} = \frac{\text{Acceleration of Q due to B}}{\text{Acceleration of B due to Q}} \quad . \quad . \quad (\beta).$$

This definition leads us to two important points. We see, namely, that the mass of a corpuscle has relation to some standard corpuscle, or mass is always a *relative* quantity ; and, further, mass is a mere number representing a ratio of accelerations. We have here, then, a perfectly clear and intelligible definition ; we can grasp what velocity means, and we can understand how its change is measured by acceleration. Mass, accordingly, as the ratio of the numbers of units in two accelerations, is a conception which can easily be appreciated. It is in this manner that mass is invariably determined scientifically, yet nevertheless the reader will frequently find mass defined in text-books of physics as "the quantity of matter in a body." After our discussion of matter in Chapter VIII. the reader will easily appreciate how idle is a definition of mass in terms of matter.[1]

§ 9.—*The Fifth Law of Motion.   The Definition of Force*

We can now pass to the next stage in our investigation of the corpuscular dance. Having selected a standard corpuscle Q, we conceive the masses relative to it of many other corpuscles—A, B, C, etc.—measured. If we tabulated these masses and then compared them with the ratio of the mutual accelerations of A and B, B and C, C and A, etc., with a view of ascertaining whether there were any relation between the mutual accelerations of each pair and their masses, we should very soon discover a fifth important law of motion, namely, *that the ratio of the acceleration of A due to B to the acceleration of B due to A is exactly equal to the ratio of the mass of B to the mass of A*, or in simple algebraical notation :—

$$\frac{\text{Acceleration of A due to B}}{\text{Acceleration of B due to A}} = \frac{\text{Mass of B}}{\text{Mass of A}} \quad \cdot \quad \cdot \quad (\gamma).$$

This is expressed briefly by the statement that mutual

---

[1] *Quantity* belongs essentially to the sphere of sense-impression. We cannot consider it to have any meaning when projected beyond that sphere. It seems, therefore, illogical to apply the word quantity to the metaphysical "source" of sense-impressions.

accelerations are *inversely* as masses. The validity of this statement is demonstrated in precisely the same manner as the fourth law of motion. We note that if unity be taken as representing the mass of the standard corpuscle [1] Q, the definition of mass on p. 329 may be replaced by the formula :—

$$\frac{\text{Acceleration of Q due to A}}{\text{Acceleration of A due to Q}} = \frac{\text{Mass of A}}{\text{Mass of Q}} \quad . \quad (\delta),$$

a result in perfect accordance with the law just stated.

Now this law may be put into a slightly different form. By a well-known proposition [2] the product of the means in any proportion is equal to that of the extremes. Hence it follows that :—

Mass of A × Acceleration of A due to B
= Mass of B × Acceleration of B due to A.

We will, then, give a name to this product of mass into acceleration ; we will term the product of the mass of A into the acceleration of A due to the presence of B, the *force of* B *on* A. This force will be considered to have the direction and sense of the acceleration of A due to B, while its magnitude will be obtained by multiplying the number of units in the acceleration of A due to B by the number of units in the mass of A. Thus the proper measure of a force will be its number of units of mass-acceleration. Remembering that the accelerations of A and B are of opposite sense, we can now restate our fifth law in new language, thus :—

The force of B *on* A *is equal and opposite to the force of* A *on* B ;

Or, as it was originally stated by Newton himself :—

" *Action and Reaction are always equal and opposite* " [3] . . (ϵ).

Now it is clear that with our definition force is a certain measure of *how* a corpuscle is dancing relative to

---

[1] That is, the ratio of the mutual accelerations of Q and an absolutely identical corpuscle. These accelerations must by symmetry be exactly equal, and hence their ratio, the mass of Q, must be taken as unity.

[2] Euclid vi. 16, interpreted arithmetically.

[3] " *Actioni contrariam semper et aequalem esse reactionem.*"

a second corpuscle, this measure depending partly on the individual character of the first corpuscle (its mass) and partly on the attention it is paying to the presence of a second corpuscle (its acceleration due to the second corpuscle). That this measure is scientifically a convenient one is proven by its general use, and may be almost foreseen by comparing the simplicity of the statement (ϵ) with the complexity of (γ). The definition of force we have reached is a perfectly intelligible one; it is completely freed from any notion of matter as "the moving thing," or from any notion of a metaphysical "cause of motion." We have only to take the step which represents the acceleration of A due to B's presence and to stretch or magnify its length in the ratio of A's mass to the mass of the standard body Q, and we have a new step which represents B's force on A. Force is accordingly an arbitrary conceptual measure of motion without any perceptual equivalent.

The distinction between the definition of force thus given and that to be found in the ordinary text-books [1] may at first sight seem slight to the reader, but the writer ventures to think that the distinction makes all the difference between an intelligible and an unintelligible theory of life, between sound physical science and crude metaphysical materialism. Causation, as we have had occasion more than once to point out, is only intelligible in the perceptual sphere as antecedence in a routine of sense-impressions. In the conceptual sphere, on the other hand, the cause of change in the motion of our corpuscles lies solely in our desire to form an accurate mechanical model of the world of phenomena. For every definite configuration of the corpuscles we postulate certain mutual accelerations as a mode of bringing our mechanism into tune with our sense-impressions of change. Force as an arbitrary measure of these conceptual changes in motion is in-

---

[1] " Force is any cause which tends to alter a body's natural (*sic !*) state of rest, or of uniform motion in a straight line " (Tait's *Dynamics of a Particle*, art. 53). It is perhaps unnecessary to remark that we cannot conceive any body to be *naturally* at rest or moving in a straight line unless the word *natural* be re-defined in some novel sense, say, as *artificial*.

telligible. On the other hand, to project the cause of motion into something behind sense-impression is to dogmatically assert causation where we cannot know, to illogically infer from the like to the unlike (pp. 60, 183). The only alternative is to consider force as an antecedent group of sense-impressions ; this, however, is not only to project our purely conceptual notions of motion into the perceptual field, but it throws upon us the duty of defining the particular group of sense-impressions to which force corresponds. We have already spoken of the "muscular sensation of force" (p. 300), which, if we project conceptions into the perceptual field, is more accurately to be described as a sense-impression of mutual acceleration indissolubly linked to the fact of consciousness. It throws absolutely no light on the cause of motion in such "automata without consciousness," as we must conceive "phenomenal corpuscles" to be. Hence, whichever way we turn, the current definitions of both mass and force lead us only into metaphysical obscurity. Mass as the quantity of matter in a body, matter as that which perceptually moves, force as that which changes its motion, are solely and purely names which serve to cloak human ignorance. This ignorance is at bottom the ignorance of *why* there is routine in our sense-impressions, and with this question of routine we have already fully dealt (pp. 101-6). But science answers no *why*—it simply provides a shorthand description of the *how* of our sense-impressions ; and it therefore follows that if mass and force are to be used as scientific terms they must be symbols by aid of which we describe this *how*. It is thus that I have dealt with them ; we have seen that to briefly describe the corpuscular dance, which forms our conceptual model of the universe, the notions of mass and force as based on mutual accelerations arise naturally and with intelligible definition.

§ 10.—*Equality of Masses tested by Weighing*

Although it is impossible for us to review the whole field of mechanics, it is still necessary to indicate to the reader that our definitions of mass and force would ultimately lead us to the same conclusion as he will find in current physical text-books.   In the first place we will investigate an elementary problem which will lead us to a mode of testing the *equality of masses.*   Suppose we had two corpuscles or rather particles A and B of masses m_a and m_b in the same field, and we will suppose them placed in a horizontal line, A to the left and B to the right.   Now, owing to the presence of some system to the left of A, which we need not definitely describe, we

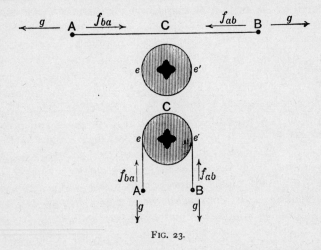

FIG. 23.

will suppose A to have an acceleration represented by g units horizontally to the *left.* Similarly B, owing to some other system, shall have a horizontal acceleration of g units to the *right.* Further, A and B will mutually accelerate each other, and we will represent B's acceleration of A from left to right by the symbol f_{ba} and A's of B by f_{ab}, which will be in the opposite sense.   We are going to choose a particular " physical field " for the acceleration of A and B ; they shall be linked together so that their distance cannot change, but the link itself shall be conceived as producing no accelerations in either A or B.   We might conceptualise this link by aid of a limit to actual perception, namely, by a fine weightless and inextensible string. Such a string would not in itself alone produce sensible accelerations in A or B. Since the string is inextensible, the whole system must move in the *same* direction, say from right to left. Then clearly the velocity of A must be at all times equal to the velocity of B, or the string would be stretched. But if the velocities of A and B are always equal, their accelerations must also be equal, or their velocities, being differently spurted, would begin to differ. Hence we conclude that the total acceleration of A towards the left must be equal to the total acceleration of B in the same direction, or in symbols :—

$$g - f_{ba} = f_{ab} - g \quad . \qquad . \qquad . \qquad . \quad \text{(i.)}.$$

But by the fifth law of motion (*i.e.* (γ), p. 303)

$$\frac{f_{ba}}{f_{ab}} = \frac{m_b}{m_a} \qquad . \qquad . \qquad . \qquad . \quad \text{(ii.)}.$$

Thus (i.) and (ii.) are two simple relations to find f_{ba} and f_{ab}. By elementary algebra we have :—

$$f_{ab} = 2 \frac{m_a}{m_a + m_b} g, \text{ and } f_{ba} = 2 \frac{m_b}{m_a + m_b} g.$$

Hence we deduce :—

Acceleration of A or B to the left $= g - f_{ba} = \dfrac{m_a - m_b}{m_a + m_b} g$ (iii.).

Further :—

Force of B on A = mass of A × acceleration of A due to B,

$$= m_a \times f_{ba},$$
$$= 2 \frac{m_a m_b}{m_a + m_b} g,$$
$$= m_b \times f_{ab}, \text{ or Force of A on B.}$$

Now this force of B on A is what we usually term the *tension in the string*. Hence we have :—

$$\text{Tension in the string} = 2 \frac{m_a m_b}{m_a + m_b} g \quad . \qquad . \quad \text{(iv.)}.$$

A further important point has now to be noticed. In order that A and B should be at rest relative to the field which produces the acceleration g, it will be necessary that their velocities should always be zero, and this involves that the changes in their velocities, or their accelerations, should always be zero. But the only way in which these accelerations can be zero is seen at once from (iii.) to arise from m_a and m_b, or the masses of A and B, being equal, for then the difference $m_a - m_b$ is zero. Thus rest will depend on the *equality of the masses* of A and B.

A further conceptual notion can now be introduced, namely, that the terminal physical effects—consequent sense-impressions—are not altered in magnitude, only in direction, by carrying a weightless inextensible string round any "perfectly smooth" body. This again is a purely conceptual limit to a very real perceptual experience. Now we will suppose our string placed round a perfectly smooth horizontal cylinder or peg inserted under it at its mid-point C, so that the portions eA, e'B of the string hang vertically downwards. We can further suppose that the particular systems, which produce the acceleration g in both A and B, are now replaced by the single system of the earth, for Galilei has demonstrated that all particles at the same place on the surface of the earth are to be conceived as having the same vertical acceleration (g) towards the surface. We conclude, therefore, that if two particles be connected by a weightless inextensible string placed over a perfectly smooth cylinder, the acceleration of one downwards and the other upwards is given by the relation (iii.) and the tension in the string by (iv.). Hence, if the particles are to be at rest, or to "balance each other," their masses must be equal. In this case, since $m_a = m_b$, the tension in the string equals $m_a \times g$, or equals the product of the mass of A into the acceleration of A due to the earth; that is, equals the *force of the earth on* A. This force is termed the *weight* of A, and since $m_a = m_b$, it follows that the weight of A is equal to the weight of B.

In this investigation, therefore, we have reached the simplest conceptual notion of a weighing-machine—an inextensible string, with the particles suspended from its extremities, placed over a smooth cylinder. If the weights of the particles are equal, their masses will also be equal, and they will balance. Thus equality of masses may be tested by *weighing*.   Another important result also flows from this discussion.   If a particle suspended by a string be at rest relative to the earth, then its weight will be equal to the tension in the string.   Hence, if the earth-acceleration g at any place be known, we have a means of measuring mass in terms of tension.   A further development of this principle forms the basis of important methods of determining the equality of masses by the equality of strains (p. 229) due to equal tensions.

§ 11.—*How far does the Mechanism of the Fourth and Fifth Laws of Motion extend?*

Before we conclude this discussion of mass, there are still several points with regard to it which must be elucidated even in an elementary work like the present. We have first to ask whether our fourth and fifth laws of motion, with the definitions of mass and force involved in them, must be conceived as holding for the whole range of corpuscles from ether-element to particle.   The same difficulty, of course, arises with regard to force as arose with regard to acceleration, if we conceive prime-atoms as possibly, and chemical atoms and molecules as almost certainly, extended bodies.   There cease to be definite points between which the mutual accelerations, and accordingly the forces, have their directions.   We are thrown back on the conception that if these laws are to be applied to atoms and molecules, it must be to the action and reaction between the elementary parts of those corpuscles and to the masses of the elementary parts that our laws refer.   From the action of these elementary parts on each other we must, then, deduce by aid of the above laws the total action between two atoms or two molecules.   This will not necessarily be measurable by a single force acting between two definite points.

Further difficulties, however, arise with regard to our conception of mass.   Is the mass of an ether-element of the same character as the mass of an atom, or a molecule, or a particle? This seems very doubtful indeed. If the ratios of the mutual accelerations of two ether-elements, of two atoms and of two particles be each in themselves constant and capable of leading us to a clear definition of mass for each type, it is still by no means certain whether the ratio of the mutual accelerations of an ether-element and a particle are inversely as the ratio of the ether-element mass to the particle mass. *Possibly we cannot conceive these masses measurable by the same standard.*

If the prime-atom consist of ether in motion, then its mass would certainly vanish with this motion; but the ether-elements which formed the prime-atom would still retain their ether-mass. Hence it seems likely that the possibility of a velocity entering into the mass of gross " matter " may hinder us from asserting that the ratio of the mutual accelerations of ether-element and particle is " inversely as their masses." Thus the idea of mechanical action and reaction between ether and gross " matter " becomes very obscure. Of the validity of postulating these laws for particles there can be small doubt; they may possibly suffice to describe the relation of ether-elements to each other, but they cannot be dogmatically asserted of the action between ether and gross " matter." I have purposely led the reader to these difficult and still unsettled points, because physicists, finding that certain laws of motion applied to particles will suffice to describe our perceptual experience of physical bodies (which they represent by systems of particles), are, I venture to think, too apt to assert that these same laws hold throughout the whole of the conceptual model by which they describe the universe.[1] They would admit that special modes of acceleration like gravitation, magnetisation, etc., probably flow from the manner in which the prime-atom and the particle are to be conceived as constituted. But there may be more than this to be admitted—the greater part of the laws of motion as we state them for particles may also flow from the

[1] See especially on this point § 4 of Chapter IX.

peculiar structure of the particle. They may largely result from the nature we postulate for the ether and from the particular types of ether-motion by aid of which we construct the various phases of gross "matter."

It is not, therefore, questioning the well-established results of modern physics when we ask whether to conceive the ether as a pure mechanism [1] is, after all, scientific. The object of science is to describe in the fewest words the widest range of phenomena, and it is quite possible that a conception of the ether may one day be formed in which the mechanism of gross "matter" itself may, to a great extent, be resumed. Indeed, it is on these points of the constitution of the ether and the structure of the prime-atom that physical theory is at present chiefly at fault. There is plenty of opportunity for careful experiments to define more narrowly the perceptual facts we want to describe scientifically; but there is still more need for a brilliant use of the scientific imagination (p. 30). There are greater conceptions yet to be formed than the law of gravitation or the evolution of species by natural selection. It is not problems that are wanting, but the inspiration to solve them; and those who shall unravel them will stand the compeers of Newton, Laplace, and Darwin.

§ 12.—*Density as the Basis of the Kinetic Scale*

If our mechanism as it is formulated in the above laws of motion can only be definitely asserted as true for particles, we have still to ask how the geometrical forms by which we symbolise perceptual bodies are to be conceived as constructed from particles, and how many different families of particles we are to postulate. Now in order to appreciate the answer to this question, we must define what we mean by *sameness of substance*. Suppose we take two portions of different bodies, or of the

---

[1] By a *pure* mechanism the writer means the reader to understand a system which is conceived to obey *all* the fundamental laws of motion as stated in mechanical treatises.

same body, and suppose we find these portions, however we test them, present to us the same groupings of physical and chemical sense-impressions, then we shall term these portions of the *same substance*.   Further, if portions of a body, taken from any part of it whatever, always appear of the same substance, so that, if we could postulate exactly the same perceptions of shape, any one portion might be mistaken for any other, then we shall say that the body is *homogeneous*.   Now although we cannot realise a particle in perception, still we conceive that if particles were to be formed by taking smaller and smaller elements from every part of such a homogeneous substance, all these particles would be of *equal mass*.[1]   We thus come to look upon our conceptual symbol for a homogeneous body as a uniform distribution of particles of equal mass throughout a geometrical surface.   Applying our laws as to the motion of particles to such a uniform distribution of particles, we construct a motion for the geometrical form which closely describes our routine of sense-impressions in the case of those perceptual bodies which approximate to the conceptual ideal of homogeneity. We then define the sum of the masses of the particles contained in any portion of our geometrical form as the mass of this portion.   From this it follows at once that : *The masses of any two portions of the same homogeneous substance are proportional to their volumes.*

This result is not a truism ;[2] it flows only from the uniform distribution of particles which we postulate for a homogeneous substance, and this distribution is a conception only justified, like the law of gravitation, by the results which it describes being in accordance with our perceptual experience.   If we take two small and equal volumes of a homogeneous substance, then the smaller they are the more nearly we can describe our perceptual experience of them by the conceptual symbols, " particles of *equal* mass."   If we take two small and equal volumes of two *different* homogeneous substances, then, the smaller

---

[1] *I.e.* of like individuality—see p. 326 and compare p. 156.
[2] It might well be described as the *sixth* fundamental law of motion.

they are, the more nearly we can describe our perceptual
experience of them by the conceptual symbols of
"particles of *different* mass." Thus in conception each
independent substance must be looked upon as indi-
vidualised for the purposes of our mechanical model of
the universe by a special mass for its fundamental
particle. If we take any homogeneous substance as a
standard substance, then if we take small and equal
volumes of any given homogeneous substance and of the
standard substance, the ratio of the masses of the particles
by which we represent conceptually these volumes as they
become smaller and smaller is termed the *density* of the
given homogeneous substance.[1] It follows, from the
above statement as to the masses of two portions of the
same homogeneous substance being proportional to their
volumes, that : *The density of a given homogeneous substance is the ratio of the masses of equal volumes of it and
of the standard substance.*

If a body be not such that two portions, anywhere
taken, present to us the same groupings of physical and
chemical sense-impressions, then the body is said to be
heterogeneous. If we take small and equal volumes of
this body from different parts, then the smaller we take
them the more nearly we find that our perceptual experience of them can be described by particles of *different*
masses. If we take small and equal volumes "from a
given point" of a heterogeneous body and from the
standard homogeneous substance, then the smaller we
take them the more nearly our perceptual experience can
be described by the mutual action of two particles. The
ratio of the mass of this particle of the heterogeneous
substance to that of the particle of the standard substance
is termed the *density* of the heterogeneous substance *at
the given point.* The density of such a substance is
therefore not, as in the case of a homogeneous substance,
the ratio of the masses of finite volumes of the given and

[1] The name adopted in the text-books is "specific gravity," but I think
this term unfortunately chosen and I prefer to use the word *density* in this
sense.

of the standard substances, it is a quantity which varies *from point to point* of the heterogeneous body.

Clearly the notion of density thus discussed affords a key to the manner in which we are to conceive the symbols for physical bodies constructed from aggregates of particles. By means of density we individualise substances and kinetically classify the particles which are the conceptual elements of bodies. Density forms the *kinetic scale* we have been in search of (p. 327); it is the fundamental means by which we measure the relative magnitude of the accelerations which we conceive the ideal elements of bodies to experience in each other's presence. It throws life into the geometrical forms by means of which we conceptualise the phenomenal universe.

The reader must, however, be careful to note that the whole of this discussion of density abounds in purely ideal notions. I have defined homogeneity; but homogeneity thus defined is a limit drawn purely in conception to a process of comparison which can be begun but not completed perceptually. No perceptual substance is accurately homogeneous. Further, I have spoken about taking "equal volumes," a process which is a geometrical conception, and never exactly realisable in perception, where continuous boundaries cannot be postulated (p. 198). Then, again, I have spoken of taking a "volume at a point," and of the "density of a heterogeneous body at a point," conceptual limits again having no exact perceptual equivalents. Lastly, I have spoken of density as equal to the ratio of the masses of "certain volumes," and of aggregates of particles as filling "geometrical forms." These indications will be sufficient to show the reader that density, like mass, is a conceptual notion, an ideal means of classifying the symbols of our conceptual model of the universe. We do, indeed, choose these densities so that our model shall describe as accurately as possible our perceptual experience, but the density itself belongs to the conceptual sphere, and is defined with regard to the geometrical forms by which we

symbolise physical bodies. It is a conceptual link between those geometrical forms and the accelerations with
which we endow them. The importance of this point
must be insisted upon, for it is this relation between
geometrical volume and mass in the case of homogeneous
substances which led physicists to the definition of mass
as the "quantity of matter in a body" (p. 330). The
geometrical form was first projected into the phenomenal
world, and then this form filled with the metaphysical
source of sense-impressions — matter. Mass as proportional to volume thus became mass as a measure of
matter, and the sluice-gate was opened for that flood of
metaphysics which at one time threatened to undermine
the solid basis of physical science.

§ 13.—*The Influence of Aspect on the Corpuscular Dance*

Hitherto I have only been dealing with the value of
the *ratio* of the mutual accelerations of two corpuscles.
The discussion of the absolute values of these mutual
accelerations for each individual field would carry us
through the whole range of modern physics ; we should
have to deal with those special laws of motion which
describe the phenomena we class under the heads of
cohesion, gravitation, capillarity, electrification, magnetisation, etc. To discuss these does not fall within the
scope of my present work, but there are one or two
general points I must notice here. I proceed, in the
first place, to state in accurate terms the second problem
suggested on p. 326. I ask : *Are the absolute magnitudes
of the mutual accelerations of two corpuscles influenced by
the aspect they present to each other ?*

Now no very decisive answer can yet be given to this
very important question of aspect influence. If we discriminate between the various types of corpuscles, there
seem no facts of our perceptual experience that would
lead us to suppose that aspect plays any part in the
mutual action of ether-elements. With regard to the
prime-atom, we can only leave the matter unsettled ; if

this atom were a vortex-ring aspect would be of importance, but if it were an ether-squirt it would not. On the
other hand, in both cases, and probably in most other
conceivable mechanisms, aspect would play a great *rôle* in
the mutual actions between chemical atoms and between
molecules. These groups, built up of comparatively few
prime-atoms, can hardly accelerate each other's motion in
the same manner however they turn towards each other.
It is to this change of mutual acceleration with change of
aspect that we have probably to look for aid in our conceptual attempts to describe such phenomena as crystal-
lisation and magnetisation. As to the particle, aspect has
probably little influence when we are dealing with particles
at distances great compared with their vanishingly small
size ; but it is still conceivable that if all the molecules in
a particle had a similar aspect, aspect might be important
in determining the action of this particle on an *adjacent*
particle. In the phenomenon of gravitation aspect does
not, however, play any part that we can perceptually
appreciate. On the whole we conclude that aspect must
be considered as a significant factor in determining the
absolute magnitudes of mutual accelerations, but the exact
influence which the " posture " of our dancers has upon
the mode in which they dance remains still one of the
obscure points of physics (see pp. 339, 353).

§ 14.—*The Hypothesis of Modified Action and the
Synthesis of Motion*

The next problem that we have to consider is one that
is of extreme importance when we are dealing with the
synthesis of motion, or the construction of the motion of
complex from simple groups of corpuscles (p. 263). It is
the problem of *modified action*. I may state it thus :—

If we have found the acceleration of A *in the presence of*
B, *will the magnitude* [1] *of this acceleration be altered when*

[1] We have already seen that the *ratio* of the mutual accelerations, or of the
masses of A and B, is not to be conceived as altered by the presence of other
corpuscles in the field ; but this leaves the question of absolute magnitudes
unsettled.

C *is introduced into the presence of* A *and* B *?*   This problem may be put a little differently, thus: Suppose we
find when A and B are alone in the field that the acceleration of A due to B is represented by the step *b*, and that
when A and C are alone in the field the acceleration of
A due to C is represented by the step *c*, then when both
B and C are in the field will these accelerations remain
the same, and consequently will the total accelerating
effect of B and C be represented, owing to the law we
have stated for combining accelerations (p. 263), by the
diagonal step *d* of the parallelogram, whose sides are *b*
and *c*?   Or, on the other hand, are we to conceive that
when B and C are both in the field the former acceleration *b* due to B is altered to *b'* and the acceleration *c* due

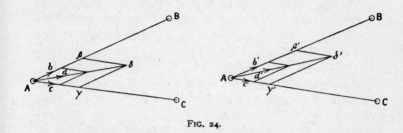

FIG. 24.

to C to *c'*, so that the total acceleration of A is now the
diagonal *d'*?   Clearly if the latter statement be correct
the synthesis of motion becomes much more complex.
It will still be true that the acceleration of A is com-
pounded of the accelerations due to B and C, but these
accelerations will depend not on the respective positions
of B and C relative to A, but on the configuration of the
entire system A, B, C.   It will thus be impossible to form
complex motions from the combination of simple ones,
until we have determined how the actions *b* and *c* of B
and C alone are modified into *b'* and *c'* by being superposed.   Now this question may also be looked at from
the standpoint of force.   If *m* be the mass of A, then
m × *b* and *m* × *c* will be the forces of B and C on A, and
will be represented by steps *m* times the steps *b* and *c* in

length (p. 331). If B and C do not modify each other's influence, then their combined action, given by the acceleration d, corresponds to a force which, measured by the product of mass and acceleration, or by $m \times d$, is m times the step d. This force is termed the *resultant force* ; and we see that, since the resultant and component forces are respectively m times the diagonal and the sides of the acceleration-parallelogram, these forces must themselves form the diagonal and sides of a parallelogram A β δ γ which is a magnified picture of the acceleration-parallelogram. This is the famous *parallelogram of forces*, and we notice that it follows at once from the parallelogram of accelerations when we assume that B and C do not modify each other's action.[1]

If they do modify each other's action there will still be a parallelogram (A β' δ' γ') of forces, namely, the resultant force $m \times a'$ will be the diagonal of the parallelogram on the sides $m \times b'$ and $m \times c'$. But if we mean, as physicists generally do, by the *force of* B *on* A the force when A and B are alone in the field, and similarly by the force of C on A the force when A and C are alone in the field, then we must assert that on the hypothesis of modified action : *The parallelogram of forces is not a synthesis by which we can truly combine forces.*

This conclusion may appear to the reader so entirely opposed to all that he has read in text-books of mechanics, that he may be led at once to reject the hypothesis of modified action. One of Newton's laws of motion distinctly excludes indeed this hypothesis, and a great simplification in our process of constructing complex from simple mechanical systems undoubtedly arises when we exclude it ; we have not to deal with every new field afresh, and to re-measure accelerations for each variation of its constituent elements : we simply analyse it, break it up into simple fields, the individual motions of which have been previously discussed. Yet it is not scientific to assert that the simplest hypothesis is necessarily correct

[1] This, for the purposes of the physics of the *particle*, might be spoken of as the *seventh* law of motion.

(Appendix, *Note III.*) ; we must ask, when we proceed to
extend it beyond the range where it has been found to
describe experience, whether it still suffices to simplify
our conceptions, or leaves undescribed certain recognised
phases of perception.   Newton's law appears perfectly
sufficient, and may therefore be said to be verified, when
we are dealing with particles of gross "matter." The
mutual accelerations, for example, of two gravitating
particles seem to be uninfluenced by the presence of a
third particle ; there is nothing, to take a still more concrete example, yet observed which would compel us to
conceive that the mutual accelerations, by which we
describe the mutual dance of sun and earth, are in the
least influenced by the presence of the moon.   Yet when
we come to extend this law of Newton's, invaluable as
it is for dealing with particles of gross "matter," to the
mutual action of molecules, atoms, and ether-elements,
there appears to be considerable reason for doubting its
accuracy.

We can conceive atomic structures—for example, the
ether-squirt—for which modified action is essentially true.
There are phenomena of cohesion which can hardly be
described without supposing the action of two molecules
A and B to be modified by the presence of a third molecule C.[1]   There are chemical facts which suggest that the
introduction of a third atom C may even reverse the sense
of the mutual accelerations of two atoms A and B.   Nay,
those who, in order to describe the radiation of light, treat
the ether as an elastic jelly (p. 290), will find that it is
very difficult to conceptualise its elastic structure, without
asserting that the hypothesis of modified action is true of
the ether-elements.   The parallelogram of forces, then, as
a synthesis of motion must be considered as applying in
the first place to particles of gross "matter" ; its extension to other corpuscles can only be made cautiously and

[1] A fuller discussion of "aspect" and "modified action" by the present
writer will be found in Todhunter and Pearson's *History of Elasticity*, vol. i.
arts. 921-31, 1527, and vol. ii. arts. 276, 304-6.   See also the *American
Journal of Mathematics*, vol. xiii. pp. 321-2, 345, 353, 361.

with continual reservation. Like so many other features of mechanism it cannot be dogmatically asserted to hold for all corpuscles, but it may in itself flow from the constitution we postulate for the ether and the structures we assume for the various types of gross " matter."

§ 15.—*Criticism of the Newtonian Laws of Motion*

Before we close our discussion of the laws of motion it is only just to the reader to state that the method adopted differs widely from the customary physical treatment ; and in deference to the authority on which that treatment is based some comparison and criticism seems called for. We have already dealt with the current definitions of force, matter, and mass, and shown reasons for rejecting them as involving metaphysical obscurity. When, therefore, we come across these terms in the statement of the laws of motion we must endeavour to interpret them in our own sense. To the reader on first examination the Newtonian statement of the laws of motion may seem much simpler than that of the present chapter. They are stated generally of *bodies*, and appear to describe the mechanism under which all bodies move, and therefore presumably describe the motion of the whole range of corpuscles from ether-element to particle. Now this loses sight of what the present writer thinks a very important possibility, namely, that not only special modes of motion, but much of the mechanism which describes the action of sensible bodies, will be found ultimately to be involved in some wide-reaching conception of ether and atom. It is not logically satisfactory to describe one mechanism by another of equal complexity ; and we must hope to ultimately conceptualise an ether from the simple structure of which several of the laws of motion postulated for particles of gross " matter " may directly flow. Remembering these points, we now turn to the usual version of the Newtonian laws given for example by Thomson and Tait.[1]

[1] *A Treatise on Natural Philosophy*, part ii. pp. 241-7. The writer will not admit that he is second to any one in his admiration for the genius of Newton,

Law I.—*Every body continues in its state of rest or of uniform motion in a straight line, except in so far as it may be compelled by force to change that state.*

Now the reader who is acquainted with treatises on dynamics will remember that one of the most difficult chapters is frequently entitled, *Motion of a Body under the Action of no Forces*. The motion described is of an extremely complex kind. For example, the body may not only be spinning about an axis, but may be, and as a general rule is, conceived as continually changing the axis about which it spins. The "state of rest or of uniform motion in a straight line" is thus *not* that which the physicist postulates to describe the motion of a body under the action of no forces. It is quite true that we conceive a certain point termed the *centre of mass* of such a body to be either at rest or moving uniformly in a straight line ; this, however, is not a conception which is itself axiomatic, but arises from an application of the principle of the equality of action and reaction to the *particles* by which we conceptually construct the body. In the first place, therefore, the use of the word *body* does not really give generality to the law, but introduces obscurity ; we ought at least to replace it by the word *particle*. In the next place, the law is very wanting in explicitness as to what we are to understand by state of rest or of uniform motion in a straight line. All motion must be *relative* to something, but Newton does not indicate with regard to what, for example, the relative path is a straight line. Force is also a relative term (p. 331), but Newton nowhere tells us what the force on the body is related to. Thus, until a second body (or a definite " frame," p. 235) be introduced (p. 314), the law remains meaningless. In the last place, what are we to understand by the words " compelled by force to change that state " ? We take force to be a certain measure of motion, namely,

or in his respect for the authors of the above classical *Treatise*. Yet he cannot believe that the two centuries which have elapsed since Newton stated his *Leges Motûs* " have not shown a necessity for any addition or modification " ! Old words grow as men are compelled to express new ideas in terms of them, and few definitions have a virile life of even a score years.

the product of mass into acceleration ; then to assert the absence of force is to assert the absence of acceleration, or the law would merely contain the platitude that without change of motion a particle moves uniformly. But Newton certainly meant something more than this, for he was thinking of force in the sense of mediæval metaphysics as " a cause of change in motion." Now the nearest approach we can get to his idea is that position relative to surrounding particles determines a given particle's acceleration, and thus the first law is seen, liberally interpreted, to amount to the statement that surrounding circumstances determine acceleration—that without the presence of other particles there is no acceleration. This is the important principle of inertia to which we have already referred (p. 313), but it certainly appears to be stated with very great obscurity in Newton's first law of motion. Further, even in this law, as I have restated it, no hint is given as to what application the principle may have to other corpuscles than particles of gross " matter " (p. 316).

Law II.—*Change of motion is proportional to force applied, and takes place in the direction of the straight line in which force acts.*

This is a veritable metaphysical somersault. How the imperceptible cause of change in motion can be applied in a straight line surpasses comprehension ; the only straight line that can be conceived, or, as some physicists would have it, *perceived*, is the direction of change of motion. We may assert that the imperceptible has this direction, but to postulate that the imperceptible will determine this direction for us seems to be pure metaphysics. We come down on our feet again, however, when we interpret this law as simply indicating that physically force is going to be taken as a measure for some change in motion (p. 331). As to the exact meaning of change of motion taking place in a straight line, all the real difficulties as to what thing we are to suppose changing its motion, and what is the presence associated with this change of motion, *i.e.* the difficulties about the line joining two corpuscles (p. 337), are concealed by talking vaguely about force as an entity

" acting in a straight line." Furthermore, if the " change of motion " is to be that of a body, not a particle, then we naturally ask which point of the body will have its motion changed in the direction of a straight line. We are thus again brought face to face with the fact that the motion of " bodies " is far more complex than is in the least indicated by this law.

Lord Kelvin and Professor Tait restated the *Second Law* in the following form :—

When any forces whatever act on a body, then, whether the body be originally at rest or moving with any velocity and in any direction, each force produces in the body the exact change of motion which it would have produced had it acted singly on the body originally at rest.

These conclusions they consider really involved in Newton's *Second Law*. The same difficulty repeats itself here with regard to the interpretation of the term " body." Further, the law thus expressed denies the possibility of " modified action " (pp. 344-347), and the likelihood that in certain cases the velocity of corpuscles may help to determine their mutual accelerations (p. 321). It thus asserts the absolute validity of that synthesis which we have termed the parallelogram of forces, and which we have ventured to suggest cannot be dogmatically asserted of corpuscles of all types.[1]

Law III.—*To every action there is always an equal and contrary reaction, or the mutual actions of any two bodies are always equal and oppositely directed.*

If we replace " bodies " by " particles "—for the mutual action of two bodies is more complex than a reader just starting his study of mechanism would imagine, if he naturally interpreted mutual action as corresponding to mutual acceleration in some one line—the above law is identical with our *Fifth Law* (p. 330), and therefore we need not repeat the qualifying discussion of our § 11. See Appendix, *Note II.*

---

[1] It is worth noting that Lord Kelvin was foremost in insisting on the multiconstant character of elasticity, a property which is certainly most readily described by this very hypothesis of modified action.

The Newtonian laws of motion form the starting-point of most modern treatises on dynamics, and it seems to me that physical science, thus started, resembles the mighty genius of an Arabian tale emerging amid metaphysical exhalations from the bottle in which for long centuries it has been corked down. When the mists have quite cleared off we shall see more clearly its proportions, and there is special need for a strong breeze to clear away our confused notions as to matter, mass, and force. The writer is far from imagining that he can accomplish this clearance, but he is convinced that a firm basis for physics will only be found when scientists recognise that mechanism is no reality of the phenomenal world—that it is solely the mode by which we conceptually mimic the routine of our perceptions. The semblance is, indeed, so striking that we are able with astonishing accuracy to predict in vast ranges of phenomena what will be the exact sequence of our future sense-impressions. If, however, the scientist projects the whole of his conceptual machinery into the perceptual world he throws himself open to the charge of being as dogmatic as either theologian or metaphysician. On the other hand, when he simply postulates the conceptual value of his symbols as a mode of describing past and predicting future perceptual experience, then his position is unassailable, for he asserts nothing as to the *why* of phenomena. But as soon as he does this, matter as that which moves, and force as the cause of change in motion, disappear into the limbo of self-contradictory notions. What moves is only a geometrical ideal, and it moves only in conception. Why things move thus becomes an idle question, and *how* things are to be *conceived* as moving the true problem of physical science.[1]

In this field we know much, but our account of the laws of motion has been specially intended to emphasise how great is the room both for further investigation and

[1] "Such demonstrations, however, only show how all these things may be ingeniously made out and disentangled, not how they may truly subsist in nature ; and indicate the apparent motions only, and a system of machinery arbitrarily devised and arranged to produce them—not the very causes and truth of things " (Bacon, *De Augmentis*, bk. iii. chap. iv.).

for the exercise of disciplined imagination.   In the vague-
ness of our conceptions of ether and atom lies the ill-
explored continent which, by clearer definition, the
Galilei and Newton of the future will annex.   But before
this annexation there is work for the unpretending pioneer
in helping to clear away the jungle of metaphysical notions
which impedes the progress of physical science.

SUMMARY

The physicist forms a conceptual model of the universe by aid of corpuscles.
These corpuscles are only symbols for the component parts of perceptual
bodies and are not to be considered as in any way resembling definite perceptual equivalents.   The corpuscles with which we have to deal are ether-
element, prime-atom, atom, molecule, and particle.   We conceive them to
move in the manner which enables us most accurately to describe the
sequences of our sense-impressions.   This manner of motion is summed up in
the so-called laws of motion.   These laws hold in the first place for particles,
but they have been frequently assumed to be true for all corpuscles.   It is
more reasonable, however, to conceive that a great part of mechanism flows
from the structure of gross " matter."

The proper measure of mass is found to be a ratio of mutual accelerations,
and force is seen to be a certain convenient measure of motion, and not its cause.
The customary definitions of mass and force, as well as the Newtonian statement of the laws of motion, are shown to abound in metaphysical obscurities.
It is also questionable whether the principles involved in the current statements
as to the superposition and combination of forces are scientifically correct when
applied to atoms and molecules.   The hope for future progress lies in clearer
conceptions of the nature of ether and of the structure of gross " matter."

LITERATURE

The views put forward in this chapter were reached when the author was
studying the laws of motion for teaching purposes in 1882, and were developed
for the purpose of college lectures in 1884 and subsequent years.   A brief
account of them was published in 1885, on pp. 267-71 of Clifford's Common
Sense of the Exact Sciences, but the only published work in which the author
has found any indication of similar opinions, or from the perusal of which he
has received any help or encouragement, and the only work he can therefore
heartily recommend to the reader, is :—

MACH, E. — Die Mechanik in ihrer Entwicklung, S. 174-228.   First
    edition, Leipzig, 1883, and many editions since.
The reader who desires to see the bearing in a wider philosophical
aspect of this idealistic view of mechanism on life may consult :—

PEARSON, K.—The Chances of Death and other Studies in Evolution, vol. i., essay on "Reaction," and Appendix.

The customary physical view of the Laws of Motion will be found in :—

CLERK-MAXWELL, J.—Matter and Motion, pp. 33-48.　London, 1876.

THOMSON, Sir W., and TAIT, P. G.—Treatise on Natural Philosophy, part i. pp. 219-24, 240-49.　Cambridge, 1879.

CHAPTER X[1]

MODERN PHYSICAL IDEAS

§ 1.—*The Present Crisis in Physical Science and its Sources*

THE foregoing chapters have to a large extent been occupied with an examination of the bases of physical science as they were usually postulated at the beginning of the last decade of the nineteenth century. It is not too much to say that at that period an epoch closed which was initiated by Copernicus. By drafting a scheme in which the sun was the centre of the universe instead of the earth, he prepared the way for dynamical science. The development of that science, first by Galilei and then by the work of Newton, Laplace, and Lagrange, consisted mainly in completing the details of Copernicus' sketch. Extensively the scheme has been elaborated to the celestial bodies as they have come within the reach of the modern telescope. Intensively it has been applied to atoms and molecules, as these concepts were developed

---

[1] I owe this chapter dealing with the ideas of modern physics to the kindness of my colleague Professor E. Cunningham. He has most valiantly endeavoured to bring those ideas into the same focus as the other sections of this work. It may be said that the time is hardly yet ripe for such an attempt, and that it is not possible at present to examine the logical foundations of the incomplete theories which have been so far developed to resume recent experimental work in physics. That opinion is probably correct, but even the slight insight that the lay reader of these pages will gain into the electron theory in the making will, I think, suffice to confirm in his mind the general thesis of this work, that science is solely occupied with the invention of a conceptual model, and that often but a rough one. The new physics have attained no more than the old mechanics to any real explanation of the perceptual universe.

in chemical and physical science. The critical examination to which the foundations were subjected in the last century marked its completion, the ideas being thereby set in logical instead of historical order.

Substantially, during four centuries, few concepts which have for any considerable time had currency have had to be surrendered owing to the advent of irreconcilable phenomena. Growth, not revision, was the characteristic of the development of science during that period. Especially firmly established was the concept of matter. The chemist introduced the idea of atoms, but they were merely the smallest portions of matter conceived to have an independent existence. They were still matter, and subject to the laws of dynamics. The nineteenth century will go down in scientific history as the era of the atomic theory of matter, but bound up with that was a material theory of atoms. It has already been pointed out that this was quite an unnecessary corollary, introduced by a craving for giving objectivity to every concept.

The end of the nineteenth century, however, marks the advent of experimental knowledge requiring an entire revision of the hypotheses and theories as to the constitution of matter. In accordance with the main thesis of this work that our conceptual universe is merely the simplest logical construct into which we can gather all known perceived phenomena, the scientific mind must be prepared, as new facts of nature are brought to light, to examine whether or no they fit into the existing scheme. If they do, then the mental picture is thereby made a little more complete. If not, modification, enlargement, or even abandonment is necessary. The object of this chapter is to describe briefly the great revision that is necessitated by an unusual influx of new physical knowledge during the last twenty years.

The present crisis lies practically in this, that whereas through the greater part of the nineteenth century, "matter" was the concept which was looked upon as fundamental in physical science, of which there was a curious accidental property called electricity, it now appears that electricity must be more fundamental than matter, in the sense that our once elementary matter must now be conceived as a manifestation of extremely complex electrical phenomena.

The way to this revolution was prepared by the growth of electrical theory on the lines indicated by Faraday, inspired by the publication of his *Experimental Researches*, and firmly established by Clerk-Maxwell. Chiefly by the work of these two men, the idea of action at a distance between one portion of matter and another became completely displaced, and a conceptual *ether* as the seat of optical and electro-magnetic activity was definitely formulated.

The idea was not a new one. An optical ether had long been a common, if somewhat vague, possibility in physical theory. M'Cullagh and others had sought to construct a mechanical representation of it in terms of the theory of elastic material media, before the discovery that light and electro-magnetic waves are propagated through space with the same velocity, made it unavoidable that these two types of phenomena should be expressed in terms of a single concept. The theory of light henceforth became in fact a part of the theory of electricity. The optical ether became none other than the medium of Faraday.

But while the nature of the light vibrations was made more definite by identification with variations in electric and magnetic forces, the nature of the medium through which they travelled thereby became more difficult to specify, inasmuch as an elastic material medium seemed inappropriate to represent the electro-magnetic phenomena. But this from our present standpoint is pure gain. The true function of the ether is merely to assist the mind to a clearer understanding of the sequences of these phenomena. Nothing more is to be predicated of it than the laws that express concisely how those sequences are unfolded. The ether of the electro-magnetic theory is to the scientist now nothing more than a vague substratum whose only properties are specified by a number of mathematical equations which will always be associated with the name of Clerk-Maxwell.

No reason has yet arisen as far as the free ether, that is, the space unoccupied by so-called matter, is concerned, why those equations should be modified, but we are by no means yet able to form a definite picture of the relations between the phenomena which we associate with the term matter.   One thing tangible does, however, seem to emerge from the experimental work of the last few years, and that is that we are compelled to assign to electricity an atomic nature instead of thinking of it as consisting of one or two continuous fluids, conceptions which have been more or less prevalent since electrical effects were first observed.   Science has now been forced to the conclusion that a continuous structureless distribution is no longer valid as a mental picture of the undefined electrical properties of matter.

§ 2.—*The Origin of the Atomic View of Electricity*

That electricity, whatever its nature, must be thought of as being transported in small parcels of definite quantity, or, in other words, that electricity is not to be thought of as indefinitely divisible, appeared first from the experiments of Faraday on electrolysis.   It was known before his time that an electric current, passing through many liquids from one metal plate to another, caused in some cases bubbles of gas to be liberated at the plates, and in other cases gave rise to a deposition on the plates of the elements contained in the fluid.   Faraday carefully examined these phenomena, and showed that in all cases in which the same gas was liberated the amount of gas produced was proportional to the amount of electricity that passed through.   He found also a similar result in the case of the deposition of metal.   Calling the mass of any substance set free by the passage of one unit of electricity the electro-chemical equivalent of the element, he showed further that for different substances the values of this equivalent were proportional to the masses of such portions of those substances as are chemically equivalent.[1]

These results may be interpreted on the atomic theory of matter by supposing that each atom, or other elementary portion of the substance set free brings with it to the plate a definite quantity of electricity. The amount, estimated from the commonly accepted mass of the hydrogen atom, is numerically about 4×10^{-10} of the electrostatic unit.[2]

This, of course, was a very slight ground on which to base the wide generalisation, that all electricity is distributed in parcels of this magnitude, and the conclusion was not generally drawn until new experimental data were forthcoming to support it. Chiefly through the work of Sir J. J. Thomson and his collaborators, new evidence has been brought to bear on the subject by phenomena of a quite different nature. It has now become common knowledge that by various means gases may be rendered capable of allowing electricity to pass through them. The suggestion that this conductivity might be due to the existence of particles within the gas carrying an electric charge led to experiments, the results of which were consistent with such a hypothesis, provided that the charge on each particle was a negative one of magnitude varying, according to different estimates, from 3×10^{-10} to 5×10^{-10} of the electrostatic unit.[3] That this charge should be so close in value to that suggested by the electrolytic effect described above may be a coincidence, but the mind, guided by the principle of economy of thought, is naturally drawn towards associating the phenomena.

The next important physical discovery was that of phenomena which seem only to be satisfactorily represented by the presence of charged particles which, if they carry the same charge as that just referred to, have a

[1] That is, as can change places in the formation of chemical compounds.

[2] The electrostatic unit of charge is commonly defined to be that charge which attracts an equal charge placed at a distance of a centimetre with a "force" equal to a dyne.

[3] The most recent experiments by Millikan seem to place the value at 4.9×10^{-10} within 1 or 2 per cent.

mass which is only one two-thousandth part of that of the hydrogen atom. It has been known for a long time that, if an electric current passes between two plates through highly rarefied air, the sides of the tube containing the air are caused to glow with a characteristic green colour. This seemed to be due to an influence radiating from the cathode, that is the plate connected to the negative pole of the battery supplying the current, and this influence thus came to be known by the name of *cathode rays*. These rays have the property of being deflected by a magnet placed near the tube, and of communicating a negative charge to bodies which they strike. Either of these properties would be explained by assuming the rays to consist of a stream of negatively electrified particles, and by ingeniously contrived experiments it has been shown that the ratio of charge to mass for these particles would have to be, as stated above, one two-thousandth of the same ratio for the hydrogen ion in electrolysis. Subsequently it was found that certain rays (β *rays*) emitted by radio-active bodies showed exactly the same properties both qualitatively and quantitatively.

One of the most notable instances of very diverse phenomena leading to the same concept is afforded by the striking agreement of this ratio of charge to mass with that obtained by Lorentz in endeavouring to explain the so-called *Zeeman effect*. If a luminous body be placed in a strong magnetic field, it is found that a given line in the spectrum of the light emitted by the body becomes divided into three or more lines. On the simple assumption that the radiation giving rise to this line in the spectrum has its origin in the periodic vibrations of a charged particle, Lorentz showed that the presence of a magnetic field would so modify the motion as to give exactly the observed effect, provided the ratio of the charge to the mass of the particle had a certain value, which proved to be in close agreement with the corresponding value for the cathode and β rays. The cumulative effect of these experiments has been to establish firmly the conception of the *electron*, that is of an elementary particle carrying a definite charge of electricity as fundamental in modern physical thought.

We have spoken above of a charged particle, but the use of these words is an example of how new conceptions arise. It was natural at first to think in terms of the older mechanics, but if the mass of these particles is to be but a very small fraction of that of the smallest atom of matter as hitherto conceived, it can certainly not be thought of as conforming to the conception of matter as built up of atoms. It has been insisted upon, earlier in this work, that the atom is no more than a part of the intellectual machinery by which phenomena are described, and it has been necessary for the chemist and physicist to postulate a number of different atoms, in order to describe different kinds of matter. The electrified particle of the new physics cannot belong to any one of these kinds of matter. Logically, if the atom is the smallest portion (in regard to mass) of a certain kind of substance that can be conceived, that which is conceived of as having a less mass cannot be said to be made of that kind of matter. The electron is no more than the atom a direct object of perception. It is a new unit in our thought, and it is far more important to science as such than it would be as a new sense-impression. It becomes a connecting link between phenomena which had hitherto seemed most diverse.

§ 3.—*On the Electro-magnetic Constitution of the Atom*

On the basis of the concept *electron*, a new theory of the constitution of matter is rapidly being built up. The conduction of heat and electricity through metals have been for some time known to be related quantitatively. Now they are related qualitatively, for they are both thought of as arising out of the motion of free electrons between the molecules. The optical behaviour of bodies under different circumstances, our knowledge of which has enormously increased of recent years, is supplied with a rationale, and has thereby become a powerful instrument of research. The greatest result perhaps of the new conception is that the atoms of the old chemistry are now no longer diverse units, but different *groupings* of the same kinds of units.

It is not yet possible to describe what exactly must be the relation of the concepts of atom and electron. This can only come when experiment has more definite evidence to offer as to the difference between the positive and negative elements of electricity. But Sir J. J. Thomson has given an indication, by a simple example, that we may expect to find that groups of positive and negative electrons would exhibit, in one very important respect, properties such as have long been known in the chemical elements. He imagines a group of like negative electrons arranged in one plane, and kept from separating from one another under their mutual repulsion by the influence of a positive charge of magnitude equal to the sum of the negative charges with sign changed from negative to positive, and examines the possible arrangements in which different numbers can rest. He finds that they will be arranged in a number of concentric rings. For instance, if there were 60 negative electrons, they would lie in five rings in which the numbers, beginning from the innermost ring, are 3, 8, 13, 16, 20 respectively. If electrons are added one by one, the compensating positive charge increasing correspondingly, the number of rings remains five for a time, though the number of charges in the rings varies. At a certain stage, however, a single charge settles in the centre of the five rings, and if more electrons are added, others join it, and start a sixth ring inside the other five. At a certain stage the number in this new ring becomes three, as it was when the number of electrons was 60 and the number of rings 5, and the arrangement in the five inner rings bears considerable similarity to the arrangement in the original five. As more electrons are added the similarity disappears. Presently a seventh ring is found in the centre, and then once more the inner rings show similarity to the original arrangement. Thus starting from any grouping, and considering the arrangements of ascending numbers of electrons, we find certain characteristics recurring at intervals in the series.

We have thus a suggestion of how, if the characteristic properties of the elements have their origin in the constitution of the atom, it may happen that, if we examine them in ascending order of atomic weight, we shall find that at certain intervals in the series elements occur which show some similarity in their properties. Such a *periodicity*, as it has been called, was actually noticed many years ago and brought into prominence by Mendeléeff.

Such an example as has been used above, though it causes Mendeléeff's law to be no longer a matter of surprise, is of course quite inadequate to explain the actual way in which this periodicity arises in properties so widely different as chemical inertness, and electrical conductivity ; but it seems to give us hope that in the future we shall be able to form a clearer mental description of the constitution of matter of different kinds from a common elementary concept. It is quite within the bounds of possibility that not many years hence most of the properties of the various elements may be expressed in terms of the number and grouping of the electrons in the atom. The result is that we are now not only willing to admit the possibility of one element being transmuted into another, but are not surprised to hear of evidence that the process has been observed. Some such result of experiment is in fact already to hand.

No more fertile and comprehensive conception than this of the *electronic theory of matter* has ever entered into scientific thought. No more powerful example could be given of progress towards a fundamental law of nature, if the tests of such a law are comprehensiveness and simplicity. When Laplace wrote " The discoveries of the human mind in mechanics and geometry, joined to that of universal gravitation, have brought it within reach of comprehending in the same analytical expressions the past and future states of the systems of the world," experimental physics was practically non-existent. The stars were the universe. The infinitely large was what the mind sought to comprehend. To-day it is otherwise. In every branch of science it is the microscopic and ultra-microscopic that is being investigated. Had our concepts not been modified, we should now be immeasurably further off from the realization of Laplace's vision than he imagined would be the case. What is now required of a comprehensive formula is that it should embrace phenomena for whose existence the scientific minds of Laplace's age were not even prepared. The laws of the mechanics of his day, it will be seen shortly, are now at best approximations to a limited class of phenomena.

But the new conception of a universe whose laws are those by which the motions of atoms of electricity are governed, brings us once again nearer the ideal that Laplace saw before him. We have a new picture of the universe. Seen from a distance it looks like the old. The details cannot be seen ; the masses are the same as a hundred years ago. But coming nearer we perceive how these mass effects are produced. We seem to see more of the detailed touches of the artist's brush.

§ 4.—*Electro-magnetic Mass*

The idea of the constitution of matter by the grouping of electrons would not have been in any respect an advance on the older theory of atoms of *different* kinds, without the assumption that the electrons were all *equal and alike*. The simplification and reduction in number of the materials of our conceptions is the most fruitful incentive to scientific research.

Once the electron theory became established, explanation was required of the experimental discovery by Kaufmann that the apparent ratio of charge to mass could not be the same for all electrons ; there was still an *individuality* (see p. 156) to be accounted for. Various writers had already noted that a charged body must possess a certain amount of inertia by virtue of the electric field set up by it, over and above the inertia it possesses in the uncharged state. Abraham made a calculation on the assumption that an electron was a small spherical distribution of electricity, and found that if the term *electro-magnetic mass* were introduced to represent this phenomenon, then this mass will depend not only on the size of the electron and its charge, but on the velocity with which it is moving. The difference between two electrons might, therefore, be sufficiently accounted for by a difference in velocity, while in other respects they were identical.

Comparison with the experiments of Kaufmann not only showed that it would be possible thus to account for the existence of variation in apparent mass, but that it would be necessary to suppose that the *entire* mass varied in the manner indicated by the formula. The conclusion was somewhat hastily formed that the whole mass of the electron was electro-magnetic, or rather that what had till then been conceived as a property of matter was in fact a property of the ether, inasmuch as it could only be calculated in terms of the electro-magnetic state in the region exterior to the electron.

The basis of Abraham's calculation lay in the description of an electron as a sphere with a distribution of electricity throughout its volume or over its surface. As will be seen below, this is an untenable conception when the electron is considered as an atom of electricity. If electricity consists of a multitude of electrons, the individual in the assemblage cannot be described in terms of the properties of the aggregate. Nevertheless the result was in accord with experiment within the limits of possible error. A second calculation was made by Lorentz [1] leading to a different result which agreed only a little less well with the same experiments, and Bucherer has stated recently that, as a result of repeated trials, the agreement is even better. Of the basis of Lorentz's argument more will be said below.

[1] See § 11 below.

The point to be noted here is that *the experimental basis* of Newtonian dynamics is now seen crumbling away. In the last chapter it was shown how, clearing away the scaffolding by which that theory had been erected, we could reach a logical construct describing mechanical phenomena. There appeared to be one hypothesis only necessary, namely, that the mass ratio of two bodies determined as the inverse ratio of their accelerations, will under all circumstances be the same. This will not fit at all with the variability of mass with velocity.[1]

Are we then to give up this hypothesis and to have no other in exchange? Our idealised conceptions of the universe are after all in essence hypotheses of the simplest nature developed to their logical conclusions, or, in other words, the hypothesis is the kernel of the concept. But without a central idea no system of the universe is possible. What is this idea now to be?

Practically we are compelled to fall back for the present on the assumption that all electrons are alike, or at any rate that all negative electrons are alike. Positive electricity is still obscure. Experiment speaks hesitatingly of it. But at any rate it would be some firm ground on which to build if we could think of a negative electron as a fundamental element in the natural order of phenomena. Then, though the Newtonian mass-number would have lost its absolute significance, there would be a new number characteristic of any material body, namely, the number of electrons combined in it. It is not here suggested that this number will play the same part that the mass-number has played, but only that the conception of a universal element for all types of matter will replace a very empirical hypothesis such as that of the constant mass-ratio.

[1] The possibility that, passing beyond gross " matter," the laws of mechanics should be found not even approximately true for atoms, prime-atoms, and ether-elements, but that their masses might be related to the velocities of their parts (see pp. 337-339) was far from being admitted generally in 1891, when the substance of the earlier chapters of this book was given in a course on the *Concepts of Modern Science* at Gresham College. The pendulum has swung considerably round since that date.—K. P.

What becomes then of the old dynamics? Has it had its day, and ceased to be? Not so. For the very lateness of the discovery of its failure is due to the rarity of the occurrence of conditions under which we become conscious of its failure. The possibility of Kaufmann's observations lay in the existence of something whose velocity was comparable with light. This had till recent years been lacking, but in the cathode and β rays this seemed to be at hand, the velocities of the electrons being estimated to reach as much as one-tenth of that of light. But even for this high velocity the apparent change of mass is only about *one half per cent.* According to theory the corresponding change for even such a velocity as that of the earth in its orbit round the sun is less than one-millionth per cent. There need not be much fear, therefore, that our older mechanics will lose their utility as a valid approximation and a simple working hypothesis in most departments of activity. Once again it may be emphasised that it is by such working hypotheses that science enlarges its boundaries, and progress is made towards a more complete and self-contained description of natural processes. Nevertheless it is sometimes more fruitful to try to explain old phenomena through new ones than to force new phenomena into old conceptions. The many attempts at a mechanical theory of the ether have produced very little result beyond preparing the way for the view that such efforts are directed towards an illogical end ; just as the growing complexity of the Ptolemaic astronomy, and the love of the human mind for simplicity, prepared the way for the revolutionary doctrine of Copernicus.

§ 5.—*A Mechanical Ether Irrational*

It will be easily seen from the above account why the desire to further conceptualise the ether, by the adaptation of an idealised material medium such as a " perfect fluid " or a " jelly," [1] has in recent years slackened. The persistence

[1] See Chapter VIII. p. 289.

of the treatment of matter as objective and fundamental had its real root in the observed fact of the constancy of the mass ratio of two material bodies under the most varied conditions attainable.   If Galilei or Newton had had an inkling of the variability of mass referred to in the last section, the structure of dynamical science would have been totally different, and in all probability we should not have progressed as far as we have in many other directions. Whatever be the changes that the new physics introduces, they will be guided by ideas culled from the old régime. If the old theory of dynamics ceases to be absolute, it causes progress by stimulating the endeavour to interpret it by means of the new theory.

As was seen in the last chapter, the basis of Newtonian dynamics is the law of the *conservation of momentum.*[1] Apart from the objection which the variability of mass raises to this law, there is a further difficulty that now we think of electrons, and therefore of matter, as being set in motion by effects propagated through the ether, and not directly by other matter.   For example, it has been shown experimentally that light falling on a reflecting body may actually cause it to move.   A beam of light emitted from the sun will to a certain extent modify the motion of the sun.   Some minutes later it may produce an effect on a terrestrial body.   In the form in which it has been stated the law of motion referred to is clearly not sufficient to describe this effect.

It has been sought to maintain it by assigning momentum and motion to the ether, and the idea has proved of value.   But it must be remembered that such an idea is merely a convenient fiction, since if the ether is a continuous medium we cannot speak of its motion as perceptually possible ; for, as has been said above, motion can only be postulated of a geometrical boundary. In a medium that is conceived as structureless and boundless it would be as meaningless to speak of following the motion of a definite point of the ether as of following

[1] This is the name which would be commonly given to what has been called above the fifth law of motion, p. 330.

that of a point of space which had nothing to distinguish it from other points, save the test of non-coincidence. In speaking of a perfect fluid or jelly whose motion is concerned in the transmission of influence from matter to matter, we should be tacitly attributing atomic structure to the medium.   This may, of course, be found one day to be necessary with the development of our physical experience, in which case the science of the ether would be analogous to our present dynamics of fluids.   For many purposes, however, a fluid may be represented by an idealised continuous construct, associated with every point of which is a directed quantity, called the velocity, but having no perceptual existence.   The Newtonian equations of motion of the constituent elements of the perceptual fluid are, by a statistical process, averaged out, and idealised laws of motion thus obtained for the conceptual fluid, which agree with the averaged perceptions which are all that our gross senses convey to us.   But such properties of material media as viscosity and elasticity are deprived of that physical significance which they have in the molecular theory of the discontinuous medium.

The mind cannot for ever rest content with an idealised concept.   It is the discontent of the scientist with having to invent a new empirical law for every new property observed that leads to progress.   It is thus that the atomic theory of matter was developed.   It is for this reason that much effort has been expended on the attempt to obtain a mechanical theory of the ether.   As long as dynamics in the old sense held undisputed sway, the attempt was reasonable.   But there are periods when it is necessary for concepts to be clarified, and then analogies may lead one astray.   Dynamics was developed without any reference to the constitution of matter, and it may be necessary for electro-dynamics to develop without inquiry as to the nature of the ether.

There is need then for a careful revision of the order of our ideas.   It cannot be helpful that matter should be explained in terms of electricity and ether, and that the properties of the ether should be expressed again in terms

of effects in matter for which the only explanation is
etherial (see p. 348).   Either ether or matter must be
placed in the more fundamental position, and there is no
doubt now that the priority must be given to the ether,
which at present occupies exactly the position once held
by matter.   We do not know what it is.   It is the most
convenient and comprehensive means of summing up
certain facts.

§ 6.—On Current Definitions of Electric Charge and Intensity at a Point

In spite of what has been said as to the insufficiency
of the mechanical view of the universe, it cannot be said
that the materials for a complete and logical alternative
are yet to hand.   Many points remain yet to be cleared
up.   Gravitation is still a phenomenon by itself.   Though
we seem to have a clear view of negative electricity as an
aggregate of like electrons, yet positive electricity is even
now puzzling our most brilliant experimental physicists.
The results of their labours may seriously change our views.

But it is at least possible to see how far the exposition
of the theory, as far as it is developed, may be made
logical in accordance with the position maintained in this
work.   We will confine our attention to two points that
seem firmly established, the electro-magnetic field and the
negative electron.

In the forefront stands an objection to current pre-
sentations of the subject.   Remembering what has been
said above about *force*, that it has been relegated to the
status of a magnitude with no direct or independent
physical significance, and determined from the motion of
material bodies for which the constancy of mass has been
assumed, let us consider how *electric charge* and *electric
intensity* have been defined.

The electric field is mapped out by imagining a small
electrified body to be placed at various places in succession
and comparing the forces upon it at those places.   Or, in
other words, the electric *intensity* at a point is defined as

the *force* which acts upon a certain standard small body placed at that point. The introduction of the term *force* implies that the material dynamics is conceived to be fundamental. Not only so, but it is clear that the definition is meaningless, unless a charged body may be conceived of as a mathematical point, and no reference is made to this possibility or assumption, save that the body is supposed *small*. This does not, of course, condemn a work which only professes to give an account of the perceptual phenomenon of electricity, but shows the necessity for refinement before a logical conceptual theory can be said to have been constructed.[1]

The atomic theory of electricity supplies us with a rational basis for the assumption of a point charge, a negative electron being, as has been stated above, itself such a concept.

Turning again to current definitions, the ratio of the *charges* of two bodies is said to be the ratio of the *forces* which act upon these bodies if placed successively in the same circumstances. Both the objections raised above apply here also, and also the further one that in this statement point charges of different intensities are contemplated, just as in material dynamics there has been used the concept of particles of different masses whose geometrical magnitude is zero. This is a difficulty which has been hinted at in earlier chapters, although not fully developed (see, however, pp. 307-8, 328). Now that the laws of motion have become simply approximations it will not be worth while dwelling on it, but we may pass at once to consider how far we may already lay down a logical order of ideas in the electron theory of matter.

§ 7.—*The Possibility of a Logical Definition of the Fundamental Quantities of the Electron Theory*

The fundamental fact of perception is that, under certain circumstances, commonly called *electrical*, bodies

---

[1] By far the most systematic development of modern electro-magnetic theory yet published is that of Abraham and Föppl, 3rd edition, 1907, Leipzig. The definitions referred to are those given in that work.

move in a manner different from that in which they would move if those circumstances were absent. On the basis of the experimental results referred to above, we venture to say that in reality all motion is associated with this phenomenon. The matter of our senses is to be conceived as a collection of points, which we call *electrons*, influencing each other's motion. Of these points we may say that there is one important class which are identical in properties. These are the so-called *negative electrons*.

We perceive that in the larger electrical phenomena the influence of one portion of matter on another is not instantaneous according to our present conception of time, but seems to move through space with a definite velocity. Hence we construct the conception that the influence of electron upon electron is propagated with the velocity of light, and proceed to further conceptualize the nature of the propagation. We speak of the ether, and the *electro-magnetic state* of the ether at a point, but the way of specifying that state is to describe the effect it would produce on one of our negative electrons situated at the point.

Experience teaches us that we must allow this effect to vary with the velocity with which the electron is already moving. An analysis of the effects produced in the case of material bodies suggests that *two* directed quantities must be assigned in order to express the way in which the acceleration varies with the velocity. We transfer this analysis to the ideal electron. To exhibit it completely would require mathematical treatment beyond the scope of this volume ; but, if we limit ourselves to velocities which are small compared with that of light, the result may be expressed by means of Fig. 25.

Let a base point O be taken and, a unit of acceleration having been chosen, O*p* drawn to represent the acceleration of the electron initially at rest at a certain point in space. Let O*q* represent the acceleration of an electron initially moving through the same point with a velocity *v* represented in the diagram by *pk*, all the conditions remaining as for the electron at rest. Then we transfer from our experience to this idealised case the assumption that the line *pq*, whatever be the magnitude and direction of *v*, lies in a certain plane through *p* (*pxy* in the figure). Further, if we draw *kn* perpendicular to this plane, *pq* is always at right angles to *pn*, and bears a ratio to it which is entirely independent of the magnitude and direction of *v*.

We thus see that by means of hypotheses, transferred and idealised from experimental observations, we have in the first place defined two directions associated with the

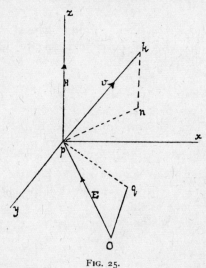

FIG. 25.

point of space that we are considering, namely, those of O*p* and of the line drawn perpendicular to the plane *pxy*. The former of these we call the direction of the *electric intensity*, the latter of the *magnetic intensity*. As to the magnitude of these two quantities, we will say that the measure of the former is the number of units of length in O*p*, and that that of the latter is equal to the ratio of *pq* to *pn* (assumed constant) multiplied by the number of units of velocity in the speed of light through space,[1] which might be conveniently taken as one.

---

[1] Students of the mathematical theory of electricity may recognise here a

The adoption of definitions of this kind would remove the mechanical terms *mass* and *force* from our development of the theory. In place of defining the *unit* of electric intensity as *that intensity under which a unit charge* (this unit being arbitrarily chosen) *is urged to move with a unit of force*, we define it as *that intensity under which our prime unit the negative electron moves with unit acceleration.*

§ 8.—*On Fluid or Space Distribution of Electricity*

The discussion in the preceding chapter of the bases of an old and highly-developed science like that of dynamics will have prepared the reader to believe that much remains to be done in the case of its infant descendant electro-dynamics, before it is possible to formulate a complete and logical account of it. Many tentative efforts will probably have to be made first. Some suggestions have been thrown out in the last section in this direction, but they cannot be considered as anything more than suggestions. For the purpose of present progress, existing treatises will probably in many respects yet prove useful, at least for some time to come.[1] It will, however, not be out of place to refer here to an outstanding difficulty in the treatment of the subject in the most recent publications.

In enunciating the fundamental relations of the electron theory Lorentz defines the distribution of electricity in space practically as follows. If the electric intensity, which for the present we assume properly defined at every point in space, be represented by imagining the space filled with a uniform incompressible fluid, whose velocity at each point is proportional to the electric

graphical expression of the common statement that the force on a moving charge is per unit charge $E + \left[\frac{v}{c}, \ H \right]$ where E is the electric and H the magnetic intensity, the charge and mass of the electron being taken as the units of charge and mass.

[1] Notably that of Abraham and Föppl, though each new edition of this work contains important additions and alterations.

intensity at that point, it may be necessary to imagine, in order to maintain the assumption of incompressibility, that fluid must be created, or destroyed at a certain rate at either a number of isolated points, or even that the process of creation or destruction is occurring everywhere. Then the amount of fluid created per unit time in any volume represents on a suitable scale the *amount of electricity* within that volume. We obtain thus the *density* of electricity " ρ " in any small volume surrounding a point, and it is distinctly stated that the charge so defined is conceived as being spread over finite volumes, and not concentrated into mathematical points. In terms of the analogy used above, the places at which the representative fluid appears or disappears are not points but finite regions. But then comes a statement which is not reconcilable with a mathematical, that is a logical, development of the theory.[1]

"As to the statement that the charges can move through the ether, the medium itself remaining at rest, if reduced to its utmost simplicity, it only means that the value of ρ which at one moment exists at a point P, will the next moment be found at another point P'." It is only necessary to try to deduce the velocity of the charge at a point within a region throughout which ρ is constant, to see that this statement really has no meaning for the purpose intended. It is in fact, to use an illustration, impossible to deduce from a knowledge of the density at every point of a given volume of a compressible fluid at two instants, the displacement of every element of the fluid during the elapsed interval.

The velocity of any physical fluid only becomes perceptible through properties which are a consequence of atomic structure. In fact it seems unavoidable that, if we are to speak of the *velocity of the electric charge*,[2] we

[1] Lorentz, *Theory of Electrons*, 1909, § 8.
[2] The only phenomena, prior to the advent of the electron theory, in which an electric charge was conceived to have a velocity whose magnitude could be stated, was that of a charged material body moving through space, the distribution of electricity on the body remaining constant. The velocity of the charge was then the velocity of the body. The laws of the effects observed in such cases have been generalised to form part of the electron

must conceive of it as distributed in discrete geometrical points. Otherwise we should be implying some property of the electric charge other than that of its relation with the electric force, by which its motion might become apparent to us.

This conclusion fits with the evidence described above as to the atomic nature of electricity. Moreover, since there is no direct necessity for ascribing to the electron any spatial extension, it is simpler to think of it as a geometrical point in the neighbourhood of which the electric intensity behaves in a certain manner.

Another reason for not ascribing any size to the electron has already been observed in the fact that only if we may speak of a point charge is it possible to determine uniquely from observed phenomena as above the electric and magnetic intensity at any point. If it were compulsory to use a charged body of finite size, the values obtained for the intensities would only be average values over a region equal to that occupied by the body, and these values might differ widely from those at individual points within that region, just as the mean density of a solid body is very different from the density estimated for a single molecule or for a portion of the space between the molecules.

It is, therefore, contended here that for a consistent basis to the electron theory it is necessary to conceive of electricity as consisting of isolated point charges, just as in the laws of motion in dynamics matter must be conceived as consisting of point masses. Experiment has in this instance given the lead, by indicating the atomic nature of electricity. The conditions by which our thought is limited require us to go further and conceive of the atoms as geometrical points. Only when further phenomena are revealed which compel us to do so, shall we really gain by giving up this conception, and speaking of the *constitution* of the electron. But this will probably not be done until a new conception

theory in its present form, on the supposition that a continuous distribution of electricity could have a velocity specified for each point of it.

more fundamental than even electricity enters into our scientific thought.

§ 9.—*On Motion Relative to the Ether in Relation to Experience*

It has been said above that the ether is in practice the frame of reference which must be postulated at the outset in the discussion of the motion of conceptual points which in our minds represent the physical universe. It is possible that this statement, without further discussion, might be held to imply that there is a *unique* frame of reference which will be common to all observers of natural phenomena.[1] Such an implication supplies the only meaning that could be given at present to the phrase *absolute motion*. But on examination it is found that the ether is far from being a *unique* frame of reference.

Since we have no direct perception of the ether, the motion of an electron relative to it can only become apparent to us through the action of the electro-magnetic field. Many experiments have been made in recent years to detect some signs of the motion of the earth through the ether. If any such motions were present, it was expected to find evidence of a difference between the velocities of light in the direction of that motion and the opposite direction. No such evidence has been forthcoming in spite of extraordinary care and accuracy in experiments of most diverse characters. The phenomenon of aberration in astronomy accords too with the conclusion that, as far as we can discover, the electromagnetic phenomena observed on the earth are consistent with the hypothesis that the earth is at rest relative to the ether.

It is not possible for us, after the wonderful progress that has followed from the Copernican setting of celestial motion, to revert to the notion of our earth being by some marvellous coincidence the one body of the whole stellar system which is at rest in the universal medium.

[1] See, however, p. 206, "atom and ether exist only in the human mind," and p. 316.—K. P.

In fact it is only the unconscious assignment of an objective existence to the ether that suggested such a thought in the first instance.[1]

If we follow the historical development of dynamics we observe that the first generalisations were in respect of motion relative to the earth ; the next step was to take the solar system as a whole, and finally to refer to the so-called fixed stars as a frame of reference. Following the same order, the laws of electro-dynamics were first formulated for phenomena as perceived by a terrestrial observer. Only when these laws fail to comprehend extra-terrestrial phenomena, is it necessary to move the base-point to some imaginary observer moving relative to the earth : this necessity has not yet become apparent. As far as we are concerned, the electro-magnetic phenomena are sufficiently well represented by a conceptual ether in which the observer is at rest. The scientist is, however, bound to recognise that he must allow every observer on the earth or any other celestial body to make the same representation. He is not sufficiently egotistic to imagine that to him alone, or to terrestrial beings alone, is the course of universal phenomena expressible in the simple form which he has accepted. There is, therefore, no ground whatever for the conception of a unique ether relative to which the motion of any point or electron can be said to have a velocity whose magnitude is in any sense characteristic of it. Velocities relative to the observer are all that can be thought of. Each mind may, if it pleases, construct its own ether, or it may, on the other hand, adopt that of any observer.

This may seem at first sight a serious blow to the value of formal electro-magnetic science, but it has to be emphasised that any such value depends only on the ability of different minds to adopt the same formulae to describe their several impressions ; and that it is the formulae rather than the conceptual embodiment of them that are

---

[1] There was nothing, Lord Kelvin once remarked, that he was more certain of than of the real existence of the ether. But twenty-five years ago most physicists would have said the same of " force " and " atom."—K. P.

the important facts. The adoption of this position requires, however, some important reflections on our *measurements* of time and space.

§ 10.—*Theory of Relativity* [1]

It has been emphasised above (Chapter V.) that time and space are merely modes of perception of the sequences of sense-impressions. Having formed in our minds the concepts of space and time, we proceed to make them metrical by the use of some standards to which we attribute a certain kind of permanency. For the purposes of physical inquiry and exact investigation of the relations between physical phenomena, we need some means of labelling any definite point of our conceptual space by a mark which shall distinguish it from all others. Our system of labelling may be any we choose to construct, and we shall naturally choose that which is most convenient for the purpose of the phenomena we are describing. When we are building up a conceptual space as a framework with respect to which physical phenomena are to be described, we construct a framework which possesses properties idealised from some of the physical phenomena which we think of as approximately permanent. The framework so formed is the *space of physics*.

Now it has been pointed out above (p. 198) that we are accustomed to speak of *rigidity* as descriptive of an ideal body of which absolute permanence of spatial extension is predicated, such an ideal body being constructed as a limit to our perceptual experience. It is this conceptual rigidity that is characteristic of the framework of physical space, relative to which all conceptual motion is described.

In the same way, as a limit to our experience of

---

[1] The ideas sketched in this section lie at the basis of the so-called *theory of relativity*, which is now being much discussed. The theory arose out of the fact referred to in the last section, that it has so far been impossible to obtain any experimental evidence of any motion of the earth relative to the frame of reference for which the usual formulae of the electro-magnetic theory are valid. The chief names associated with the theory are those of Lorentz, Einstein, and Minkowski.

regularly recurring phenomena, such as the passage of a star over the meridian, or the swing of a pendulum, we reach the conception of *physical time*.

It is thus part of the definition of our physical space that the distance between two fixed points A, B is equal to the distance between two other fixed points A′, B′, when an ideal rigid measuring-rod, which can be so placed as to extend exactly from A to B, can also be placed so as to extend exactly from A′ to B′. Similarly it is part of our definition of time that an ideally periodic phenomenon occurring on two distinct occasions occupies *equal intervals* of time.

The *metrical* space and time so defined are the space and time of the preceding chapters referring to dynamics, and it is with respect to this space and time that the fundamental laws of the electro-magnetic theory have been formulated, and with respect to which it has been discovered that light is propagated uniformly in all directions with a definite velocity.

As long as the internal constitution of matter was not considered the ideal rigid body was conceived to have exactly the same length when moving as when it was at rest ; that is, if a given rigid rod extended from a point A to a point B when at rest, then, if it were moving, without change of orientation, the instant at which one end passed through A was assumed to be simultaneous with the instant at which the other end passed through B.

But when we come to consider matter as made up of electrons, the figure of a body being maintained by means of electro-magnetic forces between them, we find that this will not be the case. It has been shown mathematically by Lorentz that, if we think of a group of electrons describing certain motions relative to one another conformably with the laws of the electron theory, and of a second group of electrons describing the same motions relative to one another, but moving relative to the first group with a uniform velocity, then the motions of the second group of electrons will *not* conform to the laws of the electron theory. This is, of course, connected with the fact that the *acceleration* of an electron in given circumstances depends on its *velocity* (see p. 372).

On the other hand, it has been shown by Lorentz that we may expect that an electro-magnetically constituted body of permanent configuration when at rest, when set in motion with velocity v, will contract in the direction of the velocity to the fraction $\sqrt{(1 - v^2/c^2)}$ of its original dimensions in that direction, distances at right angles to the velocity being unaltered. Not only so, but we may expect that the rate at which a self-contained clock of any description goes will be accelerated if it is moving with the velocity v in the ratio 1 to $\sqrt{(1 - v^2/c^2)}$. These results are quite independent of the constitution of the bodies considered from the mechanical or material point of view ; they depend solely on the fact of the configuration and internal motion of the bodies being determined by the mutual influence of electrons.

If the electro-magnetic theory of matter be accepted, it is therefore impossible to obtain as a limit to actual perceptual bodies, a rigid body whose spatial extension is permanent and independent of its velocity. Instead we arrive at the conception of a measuring-rod which shortens in the ratio $\sqrt{(1 - v^2/c^2)}$ to 1 when it moves with velocity v in the direction of its length.

Let us see now how this affects the measurement of a moving body. Let us imagine two identical bodies, and let one of these remain at rest, while the other is set in motion with a certain velocity. Imagine that an observer with an ideal measuring-rod as above described measures each of these bodies in turn. If we suppose that in order to measure the moving body, the rod has to share in its velocity, since the rod will be contracted in exactly the same manner as the moving body, the measurements in every direction will be identical with those of the fixed body measured by the same rod. The dimensions of physical objects are altered, but the scale is altered in exactly the same manner.

Exactly similar considerations apply to the measurement of time intervals between phenomena in moving bodies.

It appears, therefore, that owing to our being compelled to employ physical means for the quantitative observation of nature certain effects due to the motion of bodies through the ether, which we have constructed to embody the laws of electro-magnetic phenomena, may be entirely concealed to an observer who shares in the motion of those bodies.

The development of these ideas has led many writers to the conclusion that this concealment must be not only true in such simple phenomena as the measurement of rigid bodies, but must, in fact, extend over the whole range of phenomena which can be embraced in an electro-magnetic scheme.

The basis of this conclusion is as follows: It has been proved mathematically that, given any single description of the sequence of changes in the universe, a second construct can be built up with sequences exactly corresponding, having this property, that a sphere with fixed centre expanding or contracting with the velocity of light in the first corresponds exactly in the second to a sphere with fixed centre expanding or contracting with the velocity of light, and such that a point at rest in the first corresponds in the second to a point moving with any arbitrarily assigned uniform velocity. The mathematical expression of the correspondence is as follows: Taking axes of x, y, z, such that x is in the direction of this velocity v and taking the velocity of light to be c, let new variables be taken $t_1 = \beta\ (t - vx/c^2)$, $x_1 = \beta\ (x - vt)$, $y_1 = y$, $z_1 = z$ where $\beta^2(1 - v^2/c^2) = 1$. The motion of any point in the original system is given by the way in which its space co-ordinates vary with its time co-ordinate t. If this is given, then the new quantities x_1, y_1, z_1, t_1 are connected by a certain relation. If, therefore, a corresponding construct is built up, in which the point corresponding to the original point is given by the space-time co-ordinates x_1, y_1, z_1, t_1, the motion of this point is determined. The properties stated above follow immediately. Thus we see that it is possible so to change our scales of space and time that, while conserving the symmetry of our space for the propagation of light, we may assign to any point any velocity we choose. Further, it has been shown that the fundamental relations of the electro-magnetic theory preserve their form under this change, any one of the unlimited number of modes of description thus made possible being equally valid. It is to be expected, therefore, that, as long as we are cognizant only of phenomena which can be comprehended in the scheme of this theory, we shall be unable to say what is the velocity of any point relative to the ether. As was remarked above, every observer may construct for himself an ether in which he is himself at rest ; and yet all observers will have the same set of relations between phenomena.

It may be thought that this leaves our conceptual notions of space and time on a basis too fragile for utility, but it is to be remembered that in practice we do actually refer all motion to ourselves. The relative velocity of two points is in practice the difference of their velocities relative to ourselves. Our measurements of space and time are conditioned by our assigning to ourselves the velocity zero, and by our basing our metrical space and time on phenomena in bodies at rest relative to ourselves.

§ 11.—*Electro-magnetic Inertia according to the Theory of Relativity*

The ideas sketched in the preceding section form the basis of the treatment of the variability of the apparent mass of a body as carried out by Lorentz [1] and others.

From the standpoint of the present chapter, the phenomenon is simply that an electron will in given circumstances appear to have a different acceleration according as it is at rest relative to the observer, or in motion ; or, what is the same thing, according as the observer is at rest relative to the electron, or in motion.

Now the correspondence of two pictures of the universe sketched in the last section gives the following result, that

[1] See § 4.

if f_1 is the acceleration of an electron in the scheme in which the electron is considered to be at rest, and f_2 is the acceleration in the scheme in which it is considered to be moving with velocity v, then the ratio of f_2 to f_1 is $\sqrt{(1 - v^2/c^2)^3}$ if v is in the direction of f_1, and is $(1 - v^2/c^2)$ if v is at right angles to f_1. For other directions of v, f_2 is not in the same direction as f_1, and the ratio is intermediate between the values given above.

Proceeding from this, Lorentz makes certain assumptions about the *force* acting on the electron, and deduces the manner in which the *mass* varies.

We may note, however, that the experiments which have been brought forward to show the variability of mass have really only shown the variability of the acceleration of an electron with its velocity, and that the results agree entirely with the conclusions drawn above as far as they go.

Supposing that these experiments are borne out by others, for they are but few in number yet, what conclusion is to be drawn? Ultimately, it comes to this, that they confirm the statement in the last section that our measures of space and time are based on electro-magnetic phenomena, including the propagation of light.

Our measures of space and time, however, are in practice effected by the material machinery of rules and clocks of one sort or another. We should, therefore, have to suppose that these pieces of apparatus are also constituted on an electro-magnetic basis. This is the real foundation of our belief in the electro-magnetic theory of matter.

If we were able to communicate between one point and another, by agencies of a different nature, if, for instance, it were shown that gravitation could not be included in the electro-magnetic scheme, and could be used to measure motion, then we might be compelled to make a space-time construct in which light had not the same velocity of propagation in all directions. But so far all experiment supports the validity of the argument of the last section, and to that extent substantiates the electro-magnetic theory of matter.

§ 12.—*The Present Value of the Newtonian Dynamics*

It seems advisable, in concluding a chapter which has mainly dealt with the failure of old concepts to comprehend new facts of experience, to consider briefly the position which those concepts are likely to occupy in the science of the future. The impression may have been formed by the reader, that the foundations of all we had thought so firm are being shaken. But a very casual survey of the history of the relation of thought to practice will suffice to show that the validity of the old concepts is in important respects not the least impaired. When the earth ceased to be the centre of the universe in human thought, it did not become the less firm as a field of action, nor did man become always engaged in contemplating the " terrific " velocity with which, according to Copernican astronomy, he was being hurried through space. The very existence of Ptolemaic astronomy was evidence of the fact that in a large part of the study of the phenomena of nature the earth itself might be satisfactorily conceived as the frame of reference with respect to which those phenomena were observed. And even to-day we all go through the greater part of our thought and action as did the people of pre-Copernican days. The Ptolemaic system still holds as a valid concept in a limited range of phenomena.

So it is with our present crisis and with what lies before us. No matter how great be the extension of our electrical knowledge, the old concepts of mass will still loom largely in our everyday view of the course of nature. All that modern science will do to the dynamics of Newton and Lagrange will be to define precisely within what limits their application is .exact, or with what approximation they may be applied if exactness is not to be admitted. Their origin and growth enable us to predict that this process of definition and limitation must necessarily leave to us a very large region within which we are justified in retaining them. True perception and logical thought are not to be displaced by further perceptions. A formula which has once logically comprehended a number of accurately observed phenomena will always comprehend them. If the number of facts thereby associated be sufficiently large, it will always be convenient to retain the formula. Provided the limitations are recognised and conformed to, no misunderstanding can arise.

Nevertheless such a formula may have outlived its ability to reveal or predict the hitherto unperceived. It is rather notable that nearly all new ideas have two epochs before them. The first is one in which the main fruit which they yield consists in the discovery of new natural phenomena. The second is that of development to meet practical human needs. Dynamics has now arrived at the second stage, and will remain as a powerful agent in human activity. The development of electrodynamics in relation to the atomic nature of electricity is still in the first stage. No one can foresee the future, or predict how great its influence will be when this stage is passed. At present it is opening out new possibilities in the unifying of natural processes, giving a new impetus to experimental investigations, and especially, by requiring a revision of our concepts, compelling us to approach nature with minds free from prejudice as to the laws which will express the order of phenomena.

SUMMARY

The development of physical science during the last twenty years has revealed phenomena which illustrate clearly the principles and method of the preceding chapters. The Newtonian scheme of dynamics has been shown to be an approximation valid only for gross matter and our gross senses. There is reasonable ground for supposing that an electro-magnetic scheme of the constitution of matter will prove far more comprehensive. But there are outstanding difficulties, notably that gravitation has so far defied all efforts to bring it into line with this scheme, and that no simple concept has yet been furnished to represent the positive electricity of experiment.

The principles of conservation of energy, momentum, and mass all become meaningless without an ether which is as much and as little a reality as matter, and then mass, energy, momentum, are quantities in the same category with force.

The constancy of the mass of a body in material dynamics, which is the whole experimental basis of that science, is replaced by the conception of all electrons of the same type (negative, possibly also positive) being identical in character.

The ether is a purely conceptual medium which, as far as theory is at present developed, is structureless save that at isolated points there exist centres at which its properties are exceptional. These centres, by their mutual motion and grouping, constitute the model of the sequence of natural phenomena.

New light is thrown on our conceptions of space and time. They are interdependent and conditioned by the phenomena which they are used to describe. The phrase " motion relative to the ether " becomes meaningless. The ether is becoming more and more clearly a concept in the mind of each observer.

LITERATURE

POINCARÉ, H.—La Science et l'hypothèse (first edition, Paris, 1902) and La Valeur de la science (Paris, 1907). These treat of the logical bases of science with reference to recent developments.

LARMOR, J.—Aether and Matter. Cambridge, 1900. The historical introduction to this work is particularly interesting. A notable feature of the book is an attempt to maintain the dynamical principle of Least Action. See especially the Appendix B, on the scope of mechanical explanation.

LORENTZ, H. A.—The Theory of Electrons. Leipzig, 1909.

THOMSON, Sir J. J.—Conduction of Electricity Through Gases. Cambridge, 1903.
   Corpuscular Theory of Matter. Cambridge, 1907.

RUTHERFORD, E.—Radio-activity. Cambridge, 1904.

The two last-named works give an account of much of the experimental work which has given rise to the discussions of this chapter.

WHETHAM, W. C. D.—The Recent Development of Physical Science. Third edition. London, 1905.

This may be recommended as giving a much more complete account of the present state of experimental physical knowledge than is possible within the limits of a single chapter of this work.

APPENDIX

NOTE I

On the Principle of Inertia and "Absolute Rotation" (p. 313)

CONSIDER a very thin straight piece of material string AB, which in the conceptual limit may approach a straight line. Let C and D be two adjacent physical points of this line which in conception may approach to geometrical points. Now suppose the fact observed to be that AB remains straight and disconnected from other "matter," but that we are ignorant whether it is really in motion or not. Let us now suppose the string separated between C and D, say by

A————————C D————————B

a pair of scissors, without immediately altering the motion, if there be such. One of two things may now occur—either the pieces AC, DB continue to appear as parts of one unbroken piece of string AB, or else AC and DB begin to separate between C and D. Now the only thing of which we have destroyed the possibility is clearly a mechanical relation—a *tension* (p. 335) between the material points C and D. Hence, if the parts begin to separate after the application of the scissors, C and D must have had a tension between them, or have exerted mutual accelerations before the cutting in twain (p. 331). That is to say, D must initially have had an acceleration relative to C in the direction AB. Or we may assert, that in the limit two parts of a material line will tend after division to separate or not to separate according as its parts have a relative acceleration in the direction of its length. Now if we suppose the string or material line incapable of stretching, it is clear that D cannot initially have a velocity relative to C in the direction AB. Hence it follows that the acceleration of D relative to C must be of the nature of normal acceleration (p. 228), or the line AB must be spinning as a *whole* round some axis. On the other hand, if the parts AC and DB remain after being cut in twain in the same straight line, then no material particle C of AB has any acceleration relative to another particle D in the direction AB. In this case the line AB may have motion of translation as a whole, but has no spin.

A line, the points of which are conceived as having no relative accelerations in the direction of the line, is defined as having a *fixed direction* in space. Perceptually a material straight line, string or wire, removed from the influence of other matter, is to be represented on the conceptual model by a line "fixed in direction," provided that when it is cut in twain there is no tendency for its parts to separate, or they still appear as the parts of a continuous material straight line.

Given a perceptual body, which can be conceptually represented as rigid, how are we to ascertain whether it is to be conceived as spinning or not? For example, is the earth rotating about its axis, or is the whole vault of the heavens itself turning round—which will best enable us to describe our perceptual experience? The answer lies in determining whether a line drawn perpendicular to the axis of the earth is to be conceived as "fixed in direction" or not. Theoretically we might determine the problem of the earth's rotation in the following manner. Fix perpendicular to the axis of the earth a wire, the parts of which are not subjected to gravitation or to the resistance of the atmosphere, and observe on its being divided whether the parts remain the continuous parts of a material line or not. This experiment would of course be impossible, but it may bring to the reader's mind what Newton understands by *absolute rotation*. The effect, however, of the relative acceleration of the parts of the earth, if it exists, may be measured in other ways. For example, it would lead to an apparent lessening of gravitational acceleration at the equator, and, if the earth were not quite rigid, to a flattening at the poles. When, therefore, without rearranging any other portions of gross "matter" we can have a body in two states, in the one of which no mere division of the parts leads to discontinuity of the body as a whole, and in the other mere division does lead to discontinuity, then in the latter case we suppose that there will be, and in the former case that there will not be relative acceleration of the parts. When this relative acceleration of the parts manifests itself, although the elementary parts may have no relative velocity in the line joining them, we can describe it by aid of a spin about some axis. Since this spin does not seem to have reference to any external system, Newton termed it *absolute motion of rotation*. The name is an unfortunate one, as it suggests the possibility of an *absolute motion* (p. 233). What we have to deal with are perceptual facts which can only be conceptually described by supposing points at different distances from the earth's axis to have different velocities *relative* to the stellar system. The *fixity of direction* in a line which we have conceptually defined by absence of mutual acceleration between its parts, *appears* to coincide with fixity of direction relative to the stars, but it must be remembered that Galilei first stated the principle of inertia for bodies moving with regard to the earth, because the motion of the earth relative to the stars was insensible for most motions at its surface. It in no way follows that Newton's extension of the

APPENDIX

principle to the planetary system leads us to an absolute motion in an absolute space.

It has been asserted that Newton's rotating bucket of water and Foucault's pendulum [1] demonstrate an absolute rotation in an absolute space, but in the words of Professor Mach [2] :—

"The universe is not presented to us twice, with resting and aga n with rotating earth, but only once with its alone determinable relative motions. Accordingly we cannot say what would happen if the earth did not rotate. We can only interpret the case as it is presented to us in different ways. When we interpret it so that we are involved in a contradiction with experience, then we have interpreted it falsely. The fundamental principles of mechanics can indeed be so conceived that even for relative rotations centrifugal forces arise.

"The experiment of Newton's with the rotating bucket of water only teaches us that the rotation of the water relative to the side of the bucket gives rise to no sensible centrifugal forces, but that these forces do arise from the rotation relative to the mass of the earth and the other heavenly bodies. Nobody can say how the experiment would turn out if the sides of the bucket became thicker and more massive till they were ultimately several miles thick. There is only the one experiment, and we have to bring the same into unison with other facts known to us and not with our arbitrary imaginings."

Allowing for the difference in terminology between Professor Mach's sentences and our *Grammar*, they show, I think, how far it is safe to go in the idea of absolute direction and absolute motion. In the conceptual model we may define lines, which are conceived as having no relative acceleration of their parts, as "fixed in direction." Take two points O and P in conceptual space ; let the step OP be drawn from O, whether O be in motion or not, and let OP, after drawing, be supposed to remain "fixed in direction" ; the tops P of such steps drawn for all instants form *the path of P relative to O*. The statement that, if O and P represent particles of gross matter sufficiently far apart from each other and from other particles, this path will be a straight line, is the principle of inertia.

The perceptual equivalent for "fixity of direction" in the conceptual step was in Galilei's day [3] represented with sufficient approximation by direction fixed with regard to the earth ; since Newton we take it to sensibly coincide with direction fixed with regard to the stars. But perceptual absoluteness cannot really be asserted even in the latter case. Should the element of gross "matter," however, be ultimately conceived as a form of ether in motion, the principle of inertia will become a far more easily stated and appreciated axiom of mechanics (p. 316, and *footnote*).

---

[1] Maxwell, *Matter and Motion*, pp. 88-92.
[2] *Die Mechanik in ihrer Entwickelung*, p. 216.
[3] And even now by the writers of elementary text-books who cite bodies projected along the surface of "dry, well-swept ice" as moving in "straight lines" and illustrating Newton's first law of motion !

NOTE II

On Newton's Third Law of Motion (pp. 319, 331, 338, and 352)

WE have seen on p. 330 that one fundamental part of Newton's third law is involved in mutual accelerations being inversely as masses. This leads at once to the equality in *magnitude* of action and reaction. In the next place we conceive mutual accelerations to be parallel and opposite in sense (p. 318). This does not, however, give us completely Newton's third law as it is usually interpreted, unless we suppose these mutual accelerations to be in the *same* straight line as well as parallel. In the case of particles this straight line is usually taken to be the straight line joining them.

Now it is not at all improbable that the mutual accelerations (and therefore the mutual forces) which are ascribed to corpuscles will be ultimately found to be better described by aid of the disregarded kinetic energy of an intervening ether. For example, oscillating and pulsating bodies in a perfect fluid ether have mutual accelerations, which *may* be described by action at a distance, but are really due to the kinetic energy of the intervening ether. In the case of two small bodies moving with velocities of translation or oscillating in such an ether it by no means follows that the mutual accelerations (or the apparent action and reaction) will necessarily lie in the same straight line, and if they do, that this straight line will be the line joining the small bodies. Further, on the supposition that apparent action at a distance is due to the direct action of the ether, it does not seem likely that, if a corpuscle P be suddenly moved, the result of this motion will be immediately felt by a distant corpuscle Q, time would be required to make the change in the position of P felt at Q. The mutual actions might in this case be parallel, but it is hardly probable that they would always be in the same straight line, that is *opposite* in Newton's sense.

Thus these considerations, taken in conjunction with those referred to on p. 338 *et seq.*, suggest that greater caution is necessary than is sometimes observed in extending Newton's third law to molecules or atoms, which may really have considerable oscillatory or translatory velocities relative to the ether. For the comparatively small velocities of particles of gross "matter," the law is probably a sufficient description of our perceptual experience.

NOTE III

William of Occam's Razor (p. 92)

IN the course of our work we have frequently had occasion to notice the unscientific process of multiplying existences beyond what are really needful to describe phenomena. The canon of inference which forbids this is one of the most important in the whole field of logical thought. It has been very concisely expressed by William of Occam in the maxim : *Entia non sunt multiplicanda praeter necessitatem.* Sir William Hamilton in a valuable historical note (*Discussions on Philosophy*, 2nd edition, pp. 628-31, London, 1853) quotes the further scholastic axioms : *Principia non sunt cumulanda* and *Frustra sit per plura quod fieri potest per pauciora.* So far these axioms are valuable as canons of thought, they express no dogma but a fundamental principle of the economy of thought. When, however, Sir William Hamilton adds to them *Natura horret superfluum*, and says that they only embody Aristotle's dicta that God and Nature never operate superfluously and always through one rather than a plurality of causes, then it seems to me we are passing from the safe field of scientific thought to a region thickly strewn with the pitfalls of metaphysical dogma. Aristotle and Newton's opinion that *Natura enim simplex est* is of the same character as Euler's *Mundi universi fabrica enim perfectissima est.* They either project the notions of "simple" and "perfect" beyond the sphere of sense-impression, where alone there is any meaning to the word knowledge, or else they confuse the perceptual universe with man's scientific description of it. In the latter field only is economy of principles and causes a true canon of scientific thought. On this account the "law of parsimony," as Sir William Hamilton has termed it, seems a product of scholastic thought and not due to Aristotle. As stated by Occam, it is a far more valid axiom than in Newton's version (p. 92), and I think it might well be called after the *Venerabilis Inceptor*, who first recognised that knowledge beyond the sphere of perception was only another name for unreasoning faith.

Sir William Hamilton expresses Occam's canon in the more complete and adequate form :—

Neither more, nor more onerous, causes are to be assumed than are necessary to account for the phenomena.

NOTE IV

A. R. Wallace on Matter (p. 274)

PERHAPS a maximum of confusion between our perceptions and conceptions is reached in Dr. Alfred Russel Wallace's discussion of Matter in his *Natural Selection.* It would not be needful to refer to this singularly feeble contribution of a great naturalist to physical science, had he not recently republished it without any qualifying remarks (*Natural Selection and Tropical Nature*, pp. 207-14. London, 1891). According to Mr. Wallace, matter is not a thing-in-itself, but *is* force, and all force is probably will-force. It is unnecessary here to again remark on the illegitimate inference made in this extension of the term *will* (see our p. 58). But as force is only evidenced in change of motion, we may well ask what it is which Mr. Wallace supposes to move. If he is talking of the perceptual sphere, he fails to distinguish between our appreciation of individual groups of sense-impressions and of change in these groups, or indeed between perceptions and the routine of perception. If he is talking of the conceptual sphere he fails to distinguish between the moving ideals (geometrical bodies, points, or Boscovich's "centres of force") and the modes of their motion. As a matter of fact he uses force for sense-impression, for sequence of sense-impressions, for moving ideal, and for mode of motion. From this confusion of the perceptual and the conceptual are drawn arguments for spiritism, exactly as Aristotle, the Stoics, and Martineau have drawn them for animism (pp. 88 and 121). The chief difference between Mr. Wallace and his predecessors lies in the fact that he has polytheistic rather than monotheistic sympathies.

NOTE V

On the Reversibility of Natural Processes (pp. 82-85)

IRREVERSIBILITY of natural processes is a purely *relative* conception. History goes forward or backward according to the relative motion of the events and their observer. Conceive a colleague of Clerk-Maxwell's demon (p. 84), gifted with an immensely intensified acuteness of sight so that he could watch from enormous distances the events of our earth. Now suppose him to travel away from our earth with a velocity greater than that of light. Clearly all natural processes and all history would for him be reversed. Men would enter life by death, would grow younger and leave it finally by birth. Complex types of life would grow simpler, evolution would be reversed, and the earth, growing hotter and hotter, would at last become nebulous. Shortly, by motion to or from the earth, our demon could go forward or backward in history, or with one speed —that of light—live in an eternal *now*. This conception of historical change and of time as a problem in relative motion was suggested to me by Dr. L. N. G. Filon, and is, I think, of much interest from the standpoint of the pure relativity of all phenomena.